GIS Concepts

AND

ArcGIS Methods

4th Edition, October 2009

David M. Theobald, Ph.D.

Warner College of Natural Resources

Colorado State University

GIS Concepts and ArcGIS Methods

Copyright

Trademarks

ArcGIS, ArcMap, ArcCatalog, ArcToolbox, ArcView, ArcInfo, Spatial Analyst, Shapefile, Image Analysis, 3D Analyst, and Avenue are registered trademarks of Environmental Systems Research Institute, Inc.

Publisher

Conservation Planning Technologies, 1113 West Olive Street, Fort Collins, Colorado, 80521, USA. Phone: 970.980.1183.

For book inquiries, please visit the following website:

> http://www.consplan.com

Published in the United States of America

ISBN 0-9679208-6-8 (paper)

7

8

Single-layer analysis **329**

9   *Dual-layer analysis* **365**

10   *Spatial modeling and geoprocessing* **379**

Preface

A geographical information system (GIS) is a powerful tool to help us to understand and analyze our world. In the GIS field, as in other areas that are strongly influenced by technology, there seem to be two types of books available. First, *training* books provide a mechanical tutorial for specific software products. *Educational* textbooks, on the other hand, provide a conceptual basis and understanding for generic methods and techniques, and lend scientific rigor to the content. Students in formal GIS courses are provided general descriptions of analytical procedures through textbooks, but are left to determine which algorithm has been implemented and how it works. The result is that users frequently understand general principles but lack knowledge of specific, technical details.

A relatively recent trend GIS industry is *desktop GIS* that utilizes graphical user interface components, and ArcGIS v9 is the most recent version of software produced by Environmental Systems Research Institute (ESRI). A natural outgrowth of desktop GIS is that the user base has become broader and more diverse. One of the consequences of the broadening of the user base is that documentation has become more general and less technical, even though the software is becoming more flexible and powerful. Much of the reasoning has been lost from user manuals behind why a certain option should be selected or which algorithm should be used. There are numerous good GIS textbooks that discuss basic concepts, but increasingly many users of GIS software are not aware of this foundation.

Ten years ago I wrote the precursor to this book—*GIS Concepts and ArcView Methods*—to fill the void between textbooks and user manuals by fusing a grounded presentation of *ArcView* GIS software. Encouraged by the success of that book and stimulated by the significant changes that ArcGIS has brought, I have written the present one—*GIS Concepts and ArcGIS Methods*—in very much the same spirit, but addressing ESRI's recent flagship software, *ArcGIS*. As the book title suggests, I have attempted to organize and frame the methods and techniques used in ArcGIS within the context of GIS concepts and principles. I describe *why* you should choose a particular method or technique, in addition to how to do it—without crossing the line where the forest is lost for the trees. This fourth edition has been revised to cover ArcGIS *v9.3*.

I welcome and encourage feedback on my book, so it can be improved over time. Please write me at <u>David.Theobald@colostate.edu</u> and visit the book's website at: <u>www.consplan.com</u>.

> Cheers!
>
> Dave Theobald
> Colorado State University, Fort Collins, Colorado, USA
> October 2009

Book organization

This book is organized roughly from basic to advanced concepts, and is intended to be read roughly in the order it is presented.

- Chapter 1 defines GIS, introduces some basic geographical concepts, and describes terms and concepts specific to ArcGIS software.
- Chapter 2 describes data models and structures and provides detailed discussion about shapefiles and geodatabases.
- Chapter 3 provides a review of projections and concludes with specific projections supported in ArcGIS.
- Chapter 4 describes basic cartographic methods to produce and print a map as well as some advanced techniques to visualize geographic phenomena, including animation.
- Chapter 5 describes the numerous ways you can query map and attribute data.
- Chapter 6 provides methods both to acquire existing spatial data and to create and edit new spatial data. This includes both spatial and attribute data, as well as procedures for topological and non-topological editing.
- Chapter 7 describes raster-based analysis, modeling, and the Spatial Analyst extension.
- Chapter 8 describes how to analyze spatial data represented by a single layer of information.
- Chapter 9 details how to analyze the relationships and features between two or more layers.
- Chapter 10 describes spatial modeling, geoprocessing, the ModelBuilder window, and the basics of how to program geoprocessing objects with Python scripts.

I have tried to streamline the text to maintain readability for first-time, introductory GIS users, but you might also notice that I often provide fairly detailed information even in introductory chapters (I just am eager to enrich the learning of GIS). I conclude most sections with step-by-step instructions, rather than including them directly in the text. As a result, some of the information may be a bit detailed and seemingly out of context for first-time readers. Please simply note that "there is something more there" and refer back to it at a later reading. To spice things up a bit, I've sprinkled throughout some historical anecdotes, technical references, and editorial comments, though these are provided as footnotes.

In an effort to maintain a low-cost, high-quality textbook, and to minimize impacts on our natural resources, we have printed this edition in black and white. However, the full color versions of all figures are available digitally (and free!) on our website: www.consplan.com.

Acknowledgements

I wish to thank my students who have helped me to continue to learn over the years and my colleagues at the Natural Resource Ecology Lab for providing such a stimulating and fun environment. I also am grateful to my numerous colleagues and friends for heartfelt discussions about ways to promote sustainable living and about the important role GIS can play. Thanks to Nate Peterson, Anne Smith, and Sophia Linn who provided helpful feedback on earlier drafts, and thanks to Robyn, Steve, and Hank for sharing their Iron Horse retreat. To Pam and Charlie (and Lucy too)—although I have tested your patience and good will a third time and yet one more, you have responded with encouragement and support. I thank you for your love and understanding while I was periodically absorbed writing this book.

1 Introduction to GIS and ArcGIS

1.1 GIS defined: what is where and why

A geographical information system (GIS) is used to produce information useful in decision-making, historically in the natural resource management area, but increasingly for business, health, marketing, and other fields. A GIS is an information system that manages, manipulates, and analyzes spatial data. Although there are many definitions, a common one is that a GIS is "...an integrated collection of computer software and data used to view and manage information about geographic places, analyze spatial relationships, and model spatial processes. A GIS provides a framework for gathering and organizing spatial data and related information so that it can be displayed and analyzed."[1]

A comprehensive definition of GIS must include people—the users of GIS—and so ESRI president Jack Dangermond's three "Ws of Geography" is helpful here: *what* is where, *why* is it there, and *why* do I care. By emphasizing the interconnected grouping of data, algorithms, display, management, *and* people, GIS can be seen as a coordinated

---

1. Wade, T. and S. Sommer. 2006. *A to Z GIS: An illustrated dictionary of geographic information systems.* ESRI Press. 288 pages.

system. This system includes the combination of software, hardware, and geographic data. Visualization and analysis of geographic data is the key to transforming geographic data into powerful, useful information. GIS is typically distinguished from other systems that manipulate spatial data, such as Computer-Aided Design (CAD), by their ability to perform complex spatial operations and analyses.

There are three key characteristics that provide the "magic" of GIS: georeferenced features containing attributes and organized as layers. *Georeferencing* means that geographic features of interest are spatially aligned using a known coordinate system. Because each feature has a known location in space, *attributes* (non-spatial information) can be linked to a feature and retrieved. And geographic features can be organized into layers according to some theme (e.g., roads, land use, hydrography, etc.) and then vertically integrated or "stacked" on top of one another (graphic from ESRI Help).

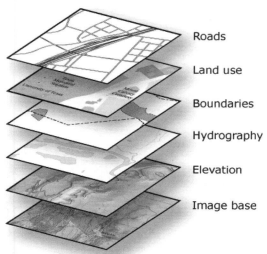

Roads

Land use

Boundaries

Hydrography

Elevation

Image base

1.1.1 Maps and more...

Geographic data are typically displayed in a map form. Indeed, the metaphor of a "smart" or electronic map is often made to describe GIS and its display of geographic data. The analogy is useful to some degree, especially to describe the electronic medium used to portray spatial data, and the "smart" moniker hints at the information that lies (virtually) behind the map. However, there are a number of ways that the metaphor breaks down, as the underlying geographic data manipulated by GIS are much more than just electronic maps.

To illustrate this point, imagine that you are interested in forests, and patches of quaking aspen in Colorado in particular—they are quite beautiful in the fall (Figure 1.1). First, because geographic data can be manipulated in a GIS, the map of quaking aspen could be viewed in a variety of ways. This provides the user with the ability to examine not just *the* map, but many possible maps by varying the way features are portrayed through different symbols, or the way the data are classified into different categories. A second difference is that typically there are many different attributes associated with spatial features. Not only can all of these be accessed, but they can also be interactively queried to answer questions like: "What vegetation type is here?" "Where are patches of aspen located?" "How many acres of patches of aspen are there?" Moreover, the spatial location of features can be compared to one another, so questions about distance and direction can be answered. That is, are aspen patches clustered together, or are they scattered throughout the landscape? Third, data can be transformed into information that fits a user's context through a rich set of analytical tools. The relationship between different attributes can be examined to investigate, for example, the spatial arrangement of aspen clones with respect to soil type, aspect, or time since disturbance. Fourth, geographic data in a GIS do not suffer, as they do in paper maps, from the fundamental trade-off between spatial detail and geographic coverage (although because most geographic data are derived from paper maps, they typically can only represent features to a certain resolution). This is because the scale of a map can change depending on user needs, yet the underlying data remains the same.

Clearly, GIS utilize maps as the primary means of graphic display, however, it is critical to understand that it is the underlying digital data that is associated with the map display that gives GIS its analytical power.

FIGURE 1.1. A map of land cover types in Colorado, USA. Patches of quaking aspen are displayed in bright yellow, and county boundaries (black lines) are shown for reference.[2] (Download color figures from www.consplan.com).

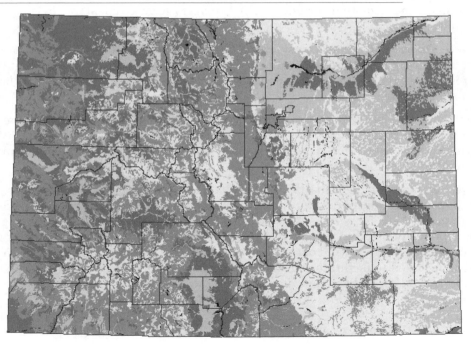

2. Data source: the Colorado Gap Analysis Project, 2000.

1.1.2 GIS functions

Generally, there are four groups of functions that GIS software and hardware provide:

- input,
- management,
- analysis, and
- output.

Geographic data are *input* into a GIS through a variety of mechanisms. A common form of data collection is through digitizing or scanning existing paper maps. For example, the US Geological Survey creates Digital Line Graphs by digitizing its topographic series to create political boundaries, roads, contour lines, etc., while Digital Raster Graphics are created by scanning topographic maps to create georeferenced images that can serve as a reference or base for other geographic data. Increasingly, data are collected by Global Positioning Systems (GPS) to create high-quality data about features such as parcel boundaries, roads, wildlife movement, fire boundaries, etc. Data are also collected through remote sensing methods that include satellite imagery (e.g., Landsat or SPOT) and aerial photography.

Once these geographic data are input into a GIS, they require *management*. There can be massive volumes of data that would quickly overwhelm users without tools to handle large geographic data sets. Data need to be stored in such a manner that they can be easily maintained and retrieved.

The heart of a GIS is *analysis*: the creation of new information from existing data. New geographic information is created by a user's queries of an individual data set, through overlaying a number of different layers of geographic data, and through complex modeling and simulation.

The most common way to visualize the results of queries and analyses is through map *output*. A map can be output via a printer or large-format plotter, included in an electronic report (e.g., in PDF format), shared with other programs such as Google Earth, or exported as an interactive map (e.g., through dynamic HTML). Graphs and summary statistics are often created and output in a report. A powerful way to use GIS is to project maps onto a screen to facilitate collection, interpretation, and decision making by groups of scientists, decision makers, and the public (Figure 1.2).

FIGURE 1.2. Scientists from the Nature Conservancy using GIS to develop a conservation plan for the Southern Rockies Ecoregion.

1.1.3 Spatial analysis

Another characteristic commonly used to describe GIS and differentiate it from other spatial technologies is that it allows users to conduct advanced spatial analysis. *Spatial analysis* is a general term to encompass the manipulation of spatial data to examine the location, attributes, and relationships of geographic features to gain information. There are three types of *spatial relations*[3]:

- proximity,
- directional, and
- topological.

3. A classic paper on spatial relations is: Freeman, J. 1975. The modeling of spatial relations. *Computer Graphics and Image Processing* 4: 156-171.

Proximity denotes how close a feature is to another feature, and proximal relations include relative measures such as near and far, and absolute such as measured distances (e.g., Lake Tahoe is about 250 kilometers from San Francisco).

Directional relations provide information about which direction a feature is from another feature, including relative relationships such as foreground/background (also known as in front of/behind), above/below, left/right; and absolute relationships such as north, south, east, west, and azimuthal (compass) bearings. Occasionally above/below is used to describe some topological relationship as well, for example, Lake Mead (formed by Hoover Dam) is above Lake Havasu (formed by Parker Dam) on the Colorado River.

Topological relations describe how a feature may overlap with another feature. That is, topologically, two or more features can be equivalent (spatially), partially equivalent (meaning that they overlap one another or cross one another), contained (one feature is wholly inside another), adjacent (two features share a common boundary or meet at a point), or separate (disjoint or not adjacent). (Also see Figure 1.3.) Most analyses are based on relationships between and among geographic features.

FIGURE 1.3. **Examples of topologic relationships:** *equivalent* **(top left, two polygons of Lake Tahoe, CA on top of one another);** *partial equivalent* **(top right, Lake Tahoe overlaps parts of 5 counties);** *contained* **(bottom left, two islands are wholly inside Lake Mono and Lake Mono is wholly within Mono County);** *adjacent* **(bottom right, Placer County is adjacent to Washoe, Carson City, Douglas, and El Dorado counties);** *separate* **(bottom right, Washoe County is disjoint from El Dorado County).**

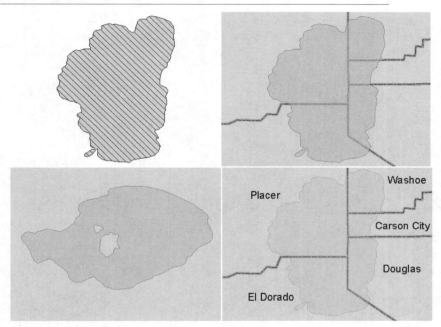

Spatial analyses range from simple to advanced and typically rely on some combination of spatial relations. For example, location analysis enables you to query "What is here?", which uses a combination of equivalent (Is this city at the same location as the user-defined location?) and containment (Which polygon is the user-defined location within?) relations. Nearest-neighbor analysis utilizes adjacency relations. It is used, for example, when all the counties adjacent to a disease outbreak need to be determined. Proximity analysis uses the concept of a buffer around an object to determine what features are within a certain distance of another feature. This assists us in answering questions like: which houses are further away than a three-mile radius of a fire station? What areas are sensitive to encroachment in parks and protected areas? (see Figure 1.4). Note that the relationships most closely associated with advanced GIS analyses—connectivity, containment, and contiguity—are all topological relationships.

FIGURE 1.4. Spatial analysis can be used to examine how parks and protected areas may be effected by non-compatible land uses in adjacent areas. Jardin Botanico outside San Miguel de Allende, Mexico.

1.1.4 A framework for Geographic Information Science

As GIS and related technologies have been found to be fundamental to integrative science, a number of educators collaborated on a *model curricula* effort to develop a framework or infrastructure for Geographic Information Science and Technology (GIS&T).[4] This effort, known as "the Body of Knowledge" (BoK), provides an framework around which GISc concepts and techniques can be organized and compared. In particular, this framework

---

4. DiBiase, D., M. DeMers, A. Johnson, K. Kemp, A. Taylor-Luck, B. Plewe, and E. Wentz. 2006. Geographic Information Science and Technology Body of Knowledge. Association of American Geographers, Washington, D.C. 162 pgs.

allows curricula and courses to be aligned with a series of clear objectives with an associated level of understanding.

To assist readers of this book to understand how the various concepts and techniques covered here relate to the GIScience knowledge domain, I provide a table below (Table 1.1) that summarizes the linkages between sections in the book and BoK knowledge areas. As the BoK is quite comprehensive, there are a number of knowledge areas and units that are not addressed in this book.

TABLE 1.1. A cross-listing of the sections of this book to GIS & T Body of Knowledge areas.

Knowledge area	Units	Sections
Analytical Methods (AM)	1. Academic and analytical origins	
	2. Query operations & query languages	5.1, 5.2, 5.4-5
	3. Geometric measures	5.3, 8.3
	4. Basic analytical operations	7.6, 8.4, 9.1-2
	5. Basic analytical methods	7.4
	6. Analysis of surfaces	7.4
	7. Spatial statistics	
	8. Geostatistics	
	9. Spatial regression & econometrics	
	10. Data mining	
	11. Network analysis	
	12. Optimization and location-allocation modeling	
Conceptual Foundations (CF)	1. Philosophical foundations	
	2. Cognitive & social foundations	1.1
	3. Domains of geographic information	
	4. Elements of geographic information	2.1
	5. Relationships	5.5
	6. Imperfections in geographic information	6.1
Cartography and Visualization (CV)	1. History & trends	4.1
	2. Data considerations	4.2
	3. Principles of map design	4.4
	4. Graphic representation techniques	4.2, 4.3
	5. Map production	4.6
	6. Map use and evaluation	

TABLE 1.1. A cross-listing of the sections of this book to GIS & T Body of Knowledge areas.

Knowledge area	Units	Sections
Design Aspects (DA)	1. Scope of GIS&T system design 2. Project definition 3. Resource planning 4. Database design 5. Analysis design 6. Application design 7. System implementation	10
Data Modeling (DM)	1. Basic storage & retrieval structures 2. Database management systems 3. Tessellation data models 4. Vector & object data models 5. Modeling 3D, uncertainty & temporal phenomena	2.2, 2.3 2.4 2.3, 7 2.2, 6.4, 6.5
Data Manipula-tion (DN)	1. Representation transformation 2. Generalization & aggregation 3. Transaction management	7.5, 8.5 7.4
Geocomputation (GC)	1. Emergence of geocomputation 2. Computational aspects & neurocomputing 3. Cellular automata (CA) 4. Heuristics 5. Genetic algorithms (GA) 6. Agent-based models 7. Simulation modeling 8. Uncertainty 9. Fuzzy sets	10

TABLE 1.1. A cross-listing of the sections of this book to GIS & T Body of Knowledge areas.

Knowledge area	Units	Sections
Geospatial Data (GD)	1. Earth geometry	3.3
	2. Land partitioning systems	
	3. Georeferencing systems	3.3
	4. Datums	3.3
	5. Map projections	3.4
	6. Data quality	3.2
	7. Land surveying & GPS	3.6
	8. Digitizing	6.4-6.8
	9. Field data collection	7.6.4
	10. Aerial imaging and photogrammetry	
	11. Satellite and shipboard remote sensing	
	12. Metadata, standards, and infrastructures	1.3
GIS&T and Society (GS)	1. Legal aspects	
	2. Economic aspects	
	3. Use of geospatial infromation in the public sector	
	4. Geospatial information as property	
	5. Dissemination of geospatial infromation	
	6. Ethical aspects	
	7. Critical GIS	
Organizational & Institutional Aspect (OI)	1. Origins of GIS & T	
	2. Managing operations & infrastructure	
	3. Organizational structures & procedures	
	4. GIS&T workforce themes	
	5. Institutional and intern-institutional aspects	
	6. Coordinating organizations	

1.2 A brief history of GIS

Geographic Information Systems (GIS) have emerged as a key technology to manipulate and analyze geographic data. Although there are many roots of GIS (and they are often intertwined), there are a few that are worth mentioning here. The term GIS was first coined in the early 1960s by Roger Tomlinson during his work with the Canada Land

Inventory (CLI). At that time, a system was needed to analyze the data collected by the CLI to support the development of land management plans for rural areas of Canada. In the United States, the Bureau of the Census developed the DIME-GBF data structure and street database in 1967 in preparation for the 1970 census, and the TIGER topological data structure in 1988. Howard Fisher established the Laboratory for Computer Graphics and Spatial Analysis at Harvard University in 1964, and work accomplished in the 1970s and early 1980s had a major influence on the development of GIS. A number of software packages were developed there: SYMAP, CALFORM, SYMVU, GRID, POLYVRT, and ODYSSEY. Jack Dangermond, a Harvard Lab graduate, founded Environmental Systems Research Institute (ESRI) in 1969. Many of the ideas used to develop ARC/INFO, first released in the early 1980s, originated from ODYSSEY.[5] And, ARC/INFO is the main package that ArcGIS is built on today.

1.2.1 Evolution of interface design

GIS have evolved dramatically since their inception in the 1960s and 1970s. In some of the pioneering GIS, there was no separation between geographic data and the tools to query and analyze them (e.g., POLYVRT[6]). After the era of computing that required punch-cards and batch processing, command-line interfaces were developed that allowed users to type in commands. To output or print maps, clever use of different characters was made to represent different shades of grey (e.g., SYMAP[7]; Figure 1.5).

---

5. See the NCGIA's Core Curriculum project, History of GIS module: http://www.geog.ubc.ca/courses/klink/gis.notes/ncgia/u23.html#UNIT23

6. Peucker, T.K. and Chrisman, N. 1975. Geographic data structures. *The American Cartographer* 2: 55-69.

7. From: Friendly, M. and D.J. Denis, Milestones in the history of thematic cartography, statistical graphics, and data visualization. Online <URL>: www.math.orku.ca/SCS/Gallery/milestone

FIGURE 1.5. A map of Connecticut produced from the SYMAP package in the late 1960s.

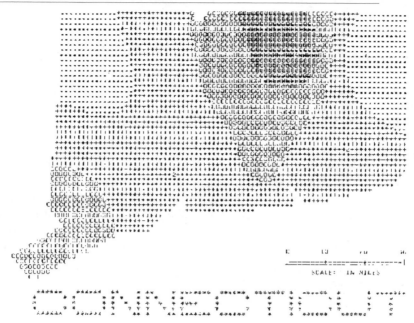

The most recent interface innovation has been a shift to what is called *desktop GIS*, which takes advantage of powerful desktop computers and graphical user interface design. ArcGIS is called a *desktop GIS* because users interact with it through a point-and-click graphical user interface (GUI). Desktop GIS simplifies user interaction by providing an easy-to-use interface and packaging common analyses that are accessible from menus and dialogs. This type of user interaction is a much different approach than a *command-line* interface (which is typically more difficult to learn, remember, and use, especially for beginning users) that is easily programmable and extendable for advanced users. ESRI's flagship product, ARC/INFO (up to v7.X) was considered to be a *toolbox GIS* and relied exclusively on a command-line interface and scripting. However, the release of ArcView (v3.x) and the recent releases of ArcGIS Desktop (v8 and v9), and its suite of applications ArcMap, ArcCatalog, and ArcToolbox, mark a significant adoption of GUI-based technology. Interestingly, the command-line interface and scripting has been revived and brought back in ArcGIS, providing users a number of ways to interact with ArcGIS.[8]

1.3 Desktop ArcGIS

1.3.1 Overview and terminology

ArcGIS is comprised of two distinct but coordinated applications or software products: *ArcMap* and *ArcCatalog*.[9] *ArcMap* is the application used primarily to examine data, query attributes, conduct spatial analysis, and design maps for output. *ArcCatalog* is the application used to browse and manage spatial data. Think of it as a specialized Microsoft® Windows® Explorer, but it can be used to search for spatial data, preview it, create and manage metadata (to describe where the data came from, its projection, attributes, scale, accuracy, etc.), and conduct basic processing of spatial data. *ArcToolbox* is a dockable window containing a set of tools that can be integrated directly into ArcMap or ArcCatalog. The tools in ArcToolbox allow data to be imported and converted into different formats and to be re-projected, and provide tools to conduct spatial analysis (see Table 1.2). The advantage of having somewhat separate but overlapping functionality in different applications is that the tool can be targeted better to the task at hand. However, the disadvantage is that you must understand which application is best for a given task.[10]

Within each application, there are three levels of functions that are provided, ranging from basic to advanced. These levels are called ArcView, ArcEditor, and ArcInfo.

---

8. Prior to the release of v3.0, ArcView had limited editing, query, and analytical functions commonly found in other industry-standard GIS. It was used mostly for map production and as a tool to query and view maps. However, v3.x of ArcView has advanced GIS capabilities. Although ArcView (v3.x) is still sold and supported by ESRI, ArcGIS (v8.x) takes advantage of Microsoft® Windows® user interface standards and a consistent programming platform to standardize all ESRI products at v8.x. ArcGIS Desktop v9 builds on the consistent platform and provides easier and more advanced ways to build models, process data, and create custom tools that can be directly integrated into the Desktop applications.

9. At v8, ArcGIS is comprised of three applications -- ArcToolbox was its own standalone application. ArcView v3 was contained all within a single application. Prior to ArcGIS, ArcView (v3.x) and ArcInfo (v7.x) were applications themselves. The names for the levels of functionality are a legacy of the past: the application ArcView (v3.x) was considered to be more of a data viewer (hence the name) and so was considered to be the "little brother" to the application ArcInfo (v7.x). So, the ArcView level of ArcGIS provides basic functionality such as making maps, querying data, and analyzing spatial relationships, with some limitation on creating and editing certain types of data. At the advanced ArcInfo level, you can also edit some additional data formats and some additional analysis tools are available as well. Also, ArcInfo Workstation (a command-line interface based on the legacy ArcInfo v7.x) is available at the ArcInfo level of ArcGIS. The level of functionality is administered by the ArcGIS license manager.

10. Another disadvantage is that you may not be able to change the properties of a dataset (i.e. that needs write-access) through one application (e.g., ArcToolbox) if it is already being accessed through another application (e.g., ArcMap).

Unfortunately, the distinction between ESRI software (ArcINFO vs. ArcView vs. ArcGIS) and the type of functions that are available within ArcGIS can be confusing.

TABLE 1.2. **Which application should you use for a given task? (++ primarily, + secondarily). *Available only at ArcInfo level.**

Task	ArcMap	ArcCatalog	ArcToolbox
Input			
- creating new layers		++	
- heads-up digitizing	++		
- importing data	+		++
Management			
- copying and moving datasets	+	++	
- setting projection information		+	++
- metadata		++	
- searching	+	++	
- re-projecting	+		++
- building topology		+	++
Analysis			
- query	++	+	
- buffering	++		++
- geoprocessing	++		++
- overlay	++		++*
- modeling	+		++
Output			
- map design and layout	++		
- export to *.e00			++*
- export to graphics	++		
- export to interactive map	++		
- export to other map formats	+	+	++
- print	++		

Although most of us are fairly familiar with maps already, there are few key terms that have very specific meanings within the context of ArcGIS that are useful to know.

- A *map* in ArcGIS is composed of one or more layers of geographic information.
- The map can be viewed in the *map display* (typically the large portion on the right). In the display, a map can be viewed either in the data view or layout view.

- The *data view* fills the map display window with the map. This is typically used during data query.

- The *layout view* displays the map but places it on a sheet of paper to see what the map would look like if it were printed.

- A *layer* contains geographic data about a single theme, such as a layer of streams or roads.

- In a map, a layer is viewed through a *data frame* that specifies the geographic extent that is shown. There can be multiple data frames in a single map, so that different parts of the world can be compared in a single map, or perhaps an "inset" (more detailed portion) can be placed within a regional map. A map layout commonly has additional elements that complement the main graphic that is composed of layers, such as a title, legend, scale, and ancillary text.

1.3.2 ArcMap basics

The main use of *ArcMap* is viewing spatial data by creating and querying a map, hence the name. The main document that ArcMap works with is called the *map document*, stored in a file with extension *.mxd.[11] After the ArcMap application has been started, you can either open an existing map document or create a new one. It is important to realize that the map document stores the layers, symbology, and layout, but does *not* store the actual datasets themselves. Rather, the map document simply "points to" the various files that are being accessed in ArcMap. This is impor-

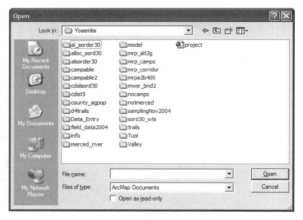

tant to new users of ArcGIS because managing the numerous, various, and large files is one of the biggest challenges to overcome early on. For example, if you would like to share a layer with someone, you need to provide both the dataset and the layer file. Also, there are two ways that ArcGIS stores that pathname to the datasets in a layer file. The default method is to use the *absolute* or *full pathname* (e.g., c:\esri\data\usa\counties.shp). This requires that those who wish to use the layer file have the data on their computers using the same folder structure. Datasets can also be referenced using *relative* pathnames (e.g, \usa\counties.shp). Because relative paths do not contain drive names, data can be moved more easily between computers.

---

11. A map document (*.mxd) essentially replaces ArcView v3.x project files (*.apr).

The interface associated with ArcMap provides a variety of ways to interact: through a map display, through menu bar, and through tools. Each map document is composed of at least two panels (Figure 1.6). The *table of contents* is shown on the left, and the *map display* (or map view) is shown on the right. The table of contents lists the layers that are contained within the map document. Each *layer* is identified by a name, which, by default, is the same as the filename (names can be changed in the table of contents by a soft-click). To the left of the name is the visibility check box—you can control the visibility (whether the layer is drawn or not) by checking or un-checking it. To the left of the visibility check box is the layer expansion box (+ or -), which you can use to control whether the symbology for a layer is displayed or not underneath the layer name. Layers are drawn in a bottom-to-top order, so that layers at the top of the table of contents list are drawn on top of lower layers. You can change the draw order by clicking on the name and dragging it up or down to the desired order. Layers can be grouped together using a *group layer*, which is particularly useful to organize a group of similar layers. Multiple layers can be selected by shift-click and/or ctrl-click. Press alt-click on a layer to draw just that layer. Context menus for each layer can be accessed by right-clicking on a layer name. Many operations that are specific to a given layer are accessed in this way (e.g., opening the attribute table, copying or deleting a layer, setting and viewing properties, etc.). You can also bring up the Properties dialog by double-clicking on the layer name.

FIGURE 1.6. A typical ArcMap map document (v9), with table of contents (left), Toolbox (center), map display (right), and command line interface (bottom). Add or remove these windows through the Windows menu.

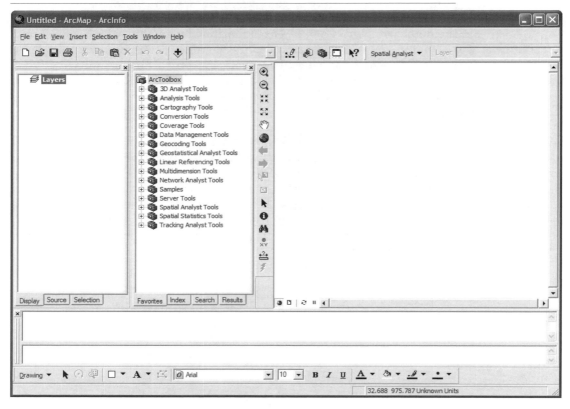

Two additional panels or windows that provide tools for users to process (manage, analyze, query, etc.) layers can be docked into the interface. The ArcToolbox window can be docked (as shown below) or allowed to float allowing easy access to a variety of tools. The command-line interface can also be docked allowing users to type in commands. These windows can be added to ArcMap either through buttons on the standard toolbar or through the Window menu.

At the bottom of the table of contents are three tabs: *display* and *source* and *selection*. The appearance of the layers in the table of contents changes with each tab. In the **Display** tab, layer names are shown in the draw order of the layers, and layers can be re-ordered only in this tab (click-and-drag). If you click on a layer's name, then the number of selected features will be listed in the lower-left corner of the map document. (If no features are selected, then the message will be blank.) In the **Source** tab, layers are organized by the source location (folder/pathname) -- but the layer name is still used. Also, clicking on a layer in the Source tab will cause the number of features to be listed below. Note that a table can be added to an ArcMap document, but can be accessed only through the *source* tab. In the **Selection** tab, layers are listed with checks if they are selectable layers. If any features are selected, then the layer is "bolded" and the number of features are provided in parentheses.

Layers are organized within a *data frame*, and they share the same coordinate system (e.g., latitude/longitude, UTM, or Albers Equal Area). The coordinate system will default to the first layer added to the data frame (though this can be changed through the data frame properties dialog). All layers within a data frame will then be on the fly projected to the same coordinate system (see Chapter 3 for more discussion about coordinate systems). Note that multiple layers in a data frame can reference the same dataset. Also, layers can be copied from one map document and pasted into another map document. The default data frame is called *Layers*. Occasionally, you may want to have multiple data frames in a map document, to create a map complete with inset or overview maps, for example. When there is more than one data frame in a map document, the active data frame is shown by the **bolded** data frame name. Data frames can also be expanded or contracted to control the complexity of the table of contents. You can switch between the views using the **View** menu item, or by using the tabs (display, source, selection) at the lower-left corner of the map display.[12]

Opening an existing map document.
1. Select File -> Open....
2. Navigate to desired folder.
3. Select *.mxd file.
4. Click Open.

---

12. Multiple data views can be used in a roughly similar fashion as views in ArcView v3.x. However, there is only one layout view in ArcMap, in contrast to the possibility of many layouts in ArcView v3.x.

The layers are shown in the map display to the right side of the map document. There are two types of displays: *data view* and *layout view*. Data view is used when you want to "browse" the data—that is, to examine and query the spatial data. Only one data frame can be visible at a time (the active one), and cartographic elements such as legends and scale bars are hidden when in data view. The layout view is used to compose a map, to complement the geographic features with other cartographic elements such as legends, scale bars, and north arrows; and usually for exporting and printing. All data frames are visible when in layout view, and multiple data frames are often used to create a complex map layout showing different aspects of the same geographic area, or perhaps to include an inset map. An additional button is located at the bottom of the data frame (to the right of the data view and layout view tabs), that *pauses drawing* so that you can make changes to the symbology of numerous layers without re-drawing. Click the button again to restart drawing.[13]

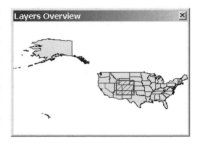

Two other ways to "view" your maps are through the overview and magnify windows. The *overview window* provides the spatial context by showing the full extent of the map with the current spatial extent outlined in red on the map. The *magnifier window* allows you to essentially move a magnifying glass over your map for closer inspection.

Opening overview & magnification windows

1. Select Window -> Overview... or Window -> Magnifier....
2. Click and drag on floating window.

Surrounding the table of contents and map display areas are a variety of menus, buttons, and tools. The *cursor coordinates* of the current location of the cursor (in the active data frame coordinate system) are displayed at the bottom of the application window, and the

---

13. Pressing F9 also pauses drawing. Press F9 again to resume drawing.

coordinate units (e.g., lat/long vs. UTM coordinates) can be changed in the properties dialog of the data frame.

Setting cursor coordinate system

1. Select View -> Data Frame Properties....
2. Click General tab.
3. Set Display: drop-down list to desired units.

There are two ways that data can be added from your computer to an existing or new map document. The first is to add data stored on your computer (also called the catalog) directly to a map document. Data are inserted into the table of contents ordered from top to bottom by point, line, polygon, and then raster.[14] A second way to add data is to locate a dataset using ArcCatalog, click on the dataset icon, and then drag it into a map document.

A *layer file* (*.lyr) stores a specific

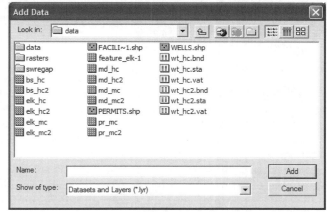

representation or symbology of a dataset (and any relates or joins), but does not store the data itself (see Table 1.3). To bundle the symbology and data together, use a *layer package* (<layername>.lpk). Packages contain the map layer, a copy of the layer's data, and an XML file with a brief description, and are especially useful to share maps with ArcGlobe and ArcGIS Explorer users.

Adding data to map document

1. Select File -> Add Data....
2. Navigate to desired folder.
3. Select dataset(s).
4. Click Add.

---

14. By default, new maps are immediately visible (drawn), but this option can be changed in ArcMap by selecting **Tools -> Options**, clicking on the Applications tab, then unchecking the New Layer Visibility box.

A wide variety of data types are supported in ArcGIS. Some of the more frequently used ones include: shapefiles, geodatabases, coverages, TINs, and GRIDs.

Although most software allows you free reign over the naming of files and folders, with ArcGIS it is wise to cultivate good working habits and follow dogmatically a few naming conventions for your files *and* your path names (the folders that your spatial datasets are stored in).

- Do not use spaces or any non-alphanumeric character—excluding the underscore ("_") character—in the filename *or* the folders that contain your files. This includes the default location for your files in "My Documents" and the like.

- Hyphens or periods in particular are a poor choice because unique field names are generated when joining one table to another by appending the <table name>"-"<field name>.

- Do not start a file name or folder with a number.

In addition, datasets that are available on the Internet can be added directly into a map document. These datasets are called *map services* or *GIS Servers* and there are five general types: *ArcGIS Server*, *ArcIMS Server*, *WCS Server*, and *WMS Server*. For example, ESRI provides ArcGIS Server that allows aerial photographs to added as a layer to ArcGIS. An ArcIMS *image service* takes snapshots of the map on the server and then sends an image over the Internet. Because a static image of a map is served, the symbology cannot be changed. Also, if the map service contains raster data, then the coordinate system of your data frame and the map service must be the same; otherwise, the raster layer will not be displayed.

An ArcIMS *feature service* streams the actual features themselves so symbology can be changed. Feature services cannot contain raster-based data, however. When datasets are added to a map document in this way (i.e. "served"), the data itself is not downloaded onto your hard-drive. Rather, you work with a "live" service over the Internet. The advantages of map services are that you do not have to store and manage the data yourself, and you are sure to be accessing the most up-to-date dataset. The disadvantage is that the layer will

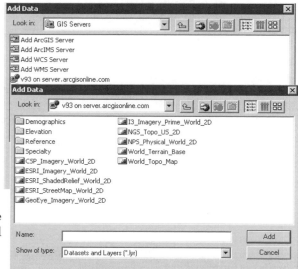

become unavailable if the service or server goes down. Also, depending on your Internet connection speed, map display and query can be slow at times.

TABLE 1.3. **Commonly used datasets, layers, and their icons.**

Name	Type	Dataset	Layer
Shapefile	point	places.shp	places.lyr
	line	Rivers.shp	rivers.lyr
	polygon	LAKES.shp	lakes.lyr
Coverage	coverage	states	states.lyr
	arc	arc	
	point	label	
	polygon	polygon	
GRID		dem30	dem30.lyr

TABLE 1.3. Commonly used datasets, layers, and their icons.

Name	Type	Dataset	Layer
TIN		tin_study	tin_stud...
Geodatabase		yellowsto...	

Once a layer has been added to a map document, a common task is to manipulate the data with a "tool." The **Tools** bar (or tool palette) contains a number of commonly used tools. The top eight tools are navigational tools, which allow you to change the view on your data. You can interactively zoom in or out, zoom in or out a predefined amount, pan (re-center), go to the full extent, and go back to the previous extent or forward to the next extent. Note that you can also use a *spatial bookmark*, which allows you to name and store spatial extents, and to quickly navigate to particular parts of a map. Bookmarks are stored within the *.mxd file, but can also be saved outside (to a *.dat file) so that bookmarks can be shared between map documents (and users)

Setting a spatial bookmark

1. Navigate to a desired spatial extent.
2. Select **Bookmarks -> Create....**
3. Type in a name.
4. Click **OK**.

The bottom tools allow you to interact with the features and their attributes in various ways.

- You can select specific features using the *Selection* tool ( ).

- You can select and move graphics using the plain arrow tool.

- The *Identify* tool ( ) allows you to click on a feature and get various attributes about it.

- The *Find* tool ( ) allows you to quickly search for text in the attribute table.

- The *Measure* tool (⊞) can be used to measure distances on the map by interactively defining straight-line segments (double-click to end).

- The *Hyperlink* tool (⚡) can be used to access hyperlinks that are attached to features, for instance, to bring up an picture taken at a certain location.

1.3.3 ArcCatalog basics

ArcCatalog is used to manage your data: to find particular datasets on your hard-drive, to copy and move datasets around your system, and to document your geographic datasets with metadata. ArcCatalog can be best thought of as a specialized Microsoft® Windows® Explorer-like application designed especially to handle geographic data. Not surprisingly then, the Arc-Catalog application looks familiar, with the *catalog tree* to the left and the *catalog display* to the right (Figure 1.7). One of the most useful aspects of this application is that because a single geographic dataset is often composed of multiple files in multiple folders (e.g., a coverage or a GRID), copying and deleting them cannot be done using the standard Windows Explorer. Rather, ArcCatalog can deal with these complex data structures properly.

FIGURE 1.7. **A typical ArcCatalog dialog, with the catalog tree (left) and catalog display (right).**

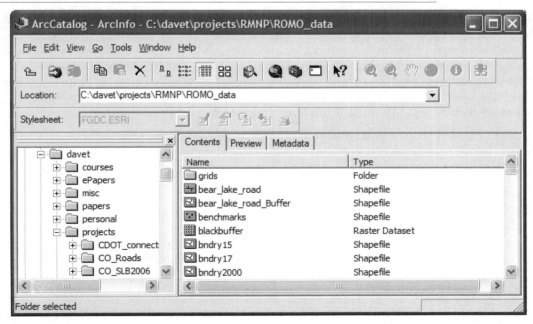

Use the catalog tree to navigate your hard-drive or
network to find a folder where your desired data reside.
There are three tabs of the catalog display. The *contents
tab* shows the recognized datasets available, and you
can show them with icons, as a list with icons and types,
or as thumbnails. Again, you can bring up a context
menu by right-clicking on a dataset to bring up a
number of actions specific to a given dataset. One of
these actions is to open the properties dialog (double-
clicking will also show this), which is where you can see
and change a number of parameters. General properties
such as a dataset's name are described here. In the
fields tab, you can find out the data types and size of
each of your fields. By selecting the shape field, you can
either examine the *coordinate system* of a dataset or
specify it by clicking on the button to the right of the
spatial reference row (and then saving it to a *.prj) file. In the *index tab*, you can also
examine or create an index file associated with a specific attribute to speed up queries and
display. (Note that if the fields are greyed out, then it is likely that your data set is read-
only.)

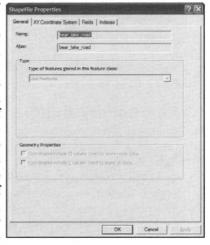

You can also create a *folder connection* to streamline the catalog so that it only includes
folders where you have spatial datasets located. For example, if you only have data on
c:\data, then create a folder connection to this folder, then remove the **c:** folder connection
to make adding data faster. If you have data in multiple folders, you can create multiple
folder connections and add them to the top level of the Catalog so that your most
frequently used data locations are convenient to access. A folder connection is similar to a
working directory, but allows multiple directories to be rapidly accessible.

The *preview view* allows you to browse a map or the attribute table of a selected layer
(Figure 1.8). The *metadata view* allows you to examine metadata that describes various
factors about your dataset.

FIGURE 1.8. **ArcCatalog with the preview tab showing in the catalog display (right). Note that the navigation (zoom in, zoom out, pan, full extent) and identify tools at the center-right are now available to use, so that you can zoom into an area of interest and then query for an attribute value.**

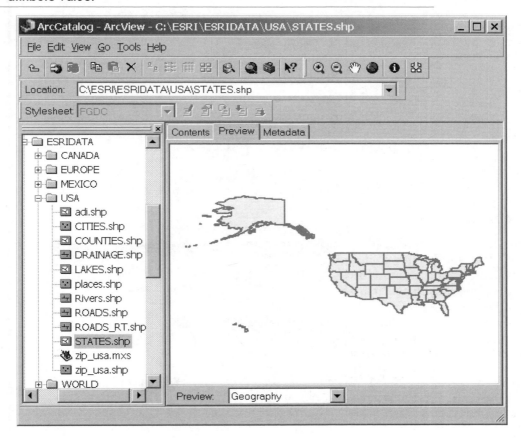

An interesting and useful function available in ArcCatalog is the *search tool* (Figure 1.9), which allows datasets to be located by specifying the name, geographic location, date created/modified, or keywords in metadata. Once you have located a dataset(s) that you would like to work with, you can "drag and drop" it directly from ArcCatalog into ArcMap.

FIGURE 1.9. The ArcCatalog search tool dialog.

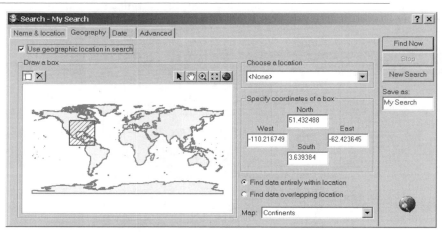

1.3.4 Metadata

Metadata is often described as "data about data". That is, it is additional documentation about a spatial dataset that describes things such as its coordinate system, spatial extent, descriptions of attributes, how and when the data were created, and who to contact for further information. ArcCatalog provides tools to maintain metadata.

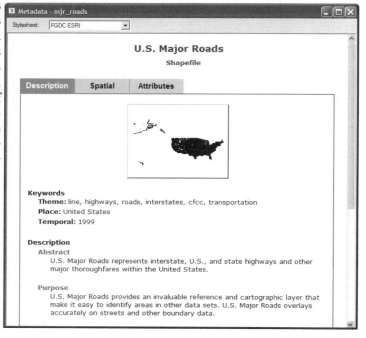

ArcCatalog automatically maintains the technical metadata such as coordinate system and spatial extent. It falls to your shoulders to enter other metadata, such as a general description of the dataset, why you created it, and what are proper (and potentially improper) uses. This may seem to be a heavy responsibility, but hard-won words of advice (a.k.a. the *documentation mantra*) about metadata are:

- document *early*,
- document *frequently,* and
- document *thoroughly*.

Taking two minutes to document now will prevent two days of angst later. Really, it's true!

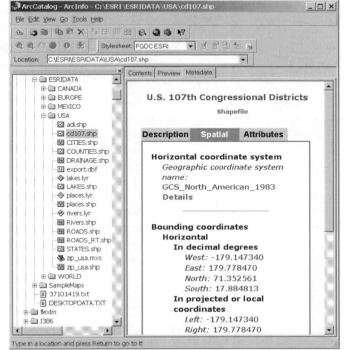

Editing metadata

1. In ArcCatalog, navigate to the desired folder.
2. Select the dataset of interest.
3. Click on the **Metadata** tab.
4. If the metadata toolbar is not displayed ("Stylesheet"... above), then click **View -> Toolbars -> Metadata**.
5. Click on the edit metadata button ( ). (Note: if it is greyed out, check to see if the file is read-only.)
6. Modify metadata.
7. Click **OK**.

1.3.5 ArcToolbox and geoprocessing

Geoprocessing is defined as the processing of geographic information through an operation that generates desired information, typically in the form of a new spatial dataset but also as a simple statistical value or a table. In addition, a series of multiple operations can also be conducted. In this chapter geoprocessing is introduced; Chapter 10 provides a more detailed discussion of geoprocessing within the context of spatial modelling.

In ArcGIS, a variety of interfaces are provided that allow access to geoprocessing (here listed loosely in novice to expert). First, a tool can be located and run from the ArcToolbox window. Each tool has a dialog associated with it to provide information about how the tool should be used, what inputs are required (or optional), and what outputs are generated. Note that these dialogs are non-modal (meaning that you are not required to close the dialog before continuing to work with other windows), so that you can continue work while the tool is running. When starting a tool from ArcMap, the selected set of features is respected. Also, most of the Wizards that were common in v8 have been removed and replaced by dialogs. Second, a tool can be run from the command-line interface. The name of a tool can be typed interactively, complete with an excellent "in-line-completion", or whole strings can be cut and paste. Third, a model can be created in ModelBuilder that represents and runs a sequence of tools. Fourth, a script or program can be written that runs a variety of geoprocessing tools.

Each operation or process is called a *command* or a tool, and ArcGIS provides numerous commands and tools through the native interface. The most common way to access these tools is through *ArcToolbox*, which organizes tools within toolsets and toolboxes. A *toolset* can contain tools, other toolsets, scripts, and models. A *toolbox* is similar to a toolset in that it can contain tools, other toolsets, scripts, and models—but a toolbox cannot contain other toolboxes. In addition, users can create their own operations by writing a *script*, which is a set of instructions stored in a file and typically interpreted (but can be compiled) at run time. A script can be as simple as calling a single tool, but typically it automates a more complex series of operations. Another way to group tools is by creating a model. In ArcGIS, a *model* is composed of one or more commands or tools that are strung together in a specific way through a new application within ArcGIS called *ModelBuilder*.

ArcToolbox provides access to a wide variety of tools. At the ArcView (basic) level, there are analysis tools, conversion tools (both import and export), data management tools, geocoding tools, linear referencing tools, and spatial statistics tools. Additional tools may be available for each extension.

At the ArcInfo level, the same basic set of toolboxes are available, but a much richer set of tools, particularly analytical, are available as well.[15]

The command-line interface is typically used to start an operation when you are familiar with a tool and its parameters. There are two sections to the command-line interface. In the top portion, commands can be typed in (with Intelli-sense). Note that the full list of tools available and their required parameters (including user-created tools) can be accessed here by simply typing commands in the command line.

There are three ways to easily find out what commands to use and the types of information (parameters) each command requires. First, when you use a tool interactively through its dialogs, the progress of the tool is listed out in the bottom part of the command-line dialog box (assuming the command dialog has been added to ArcMap; do this through the Window menu item). This is a useful way to learn the commands and to understand how a tool operates. Second, you can begin typing in the few beginning letters of a command and the "intellisense" will offer you a list of commands (see graphics below). Third, visit the help dialog of each tool for a listing of the command syntax.

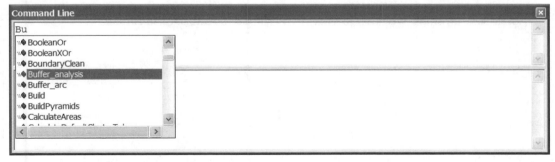

---

15. An easy way to see which tools are available (or not) is to toggle the visibility of tools in the ArcToolbox window (right-click --> Hide Locked Tools).

```
Buffer_analysis <in_features> <out_feature_class> <buffer_distance_or_field> {line_side} {line_end_type} {dissolve_option}
{dissolve_field;dissolve_field...}
```

```
Buffer_analysis |
```

1.3.6 Extensions

In addition to the two ArcGIS applications, a number of *extension* products provide additional capabilities (Table 1.4), such as ArcGlobe. Typically, extensions require an additional license. If you have a license for an extension, remember that it is a two-step process to get the extension working in ArcMap:

1. add the extension (Tools -> Extensions),

2. add the toolbar (View -> Tool-bars,...).

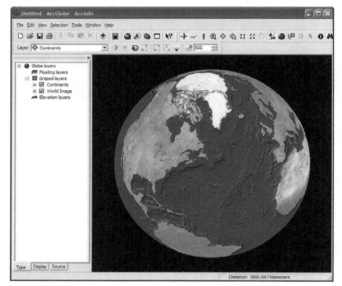

TABLE 1.4. Extensions available to provide additional capabilities to ArcGIS.

Name	Functionality
3D Analyst	Allows three-dimensional displays, fly-throughs, visualization and analysis.
ArcGlobe	Visualize spatial data on a globe.
ArcReader	Provides browsing of maps (created by ArcGIS Publisher) through a free application.
Data Interoperability	Integrate a variety of spatial data formats by directly using, import-ing, and exporting numerous feature-based data formats, as well as modeling new customized spatial data formats.

TABLE 1.4. Extensions available to provide additional capabilities to ArcGIS.

Name	Functionality
Geostatistical Analyst	Allows advanced interpolation and geostatistical analysis of surfaces, including kriging.
Maplex	Sophisticated map labeling for cartographic products.
Network Analyst	Allows routing and planning with networks. Available post v8.2.
Publisher	Allows you to convert a map document into an interactive map readable by ArcReader (a free plug-in).
Schematics	Allows you to represent the connectivity of linear and network data through schematic diagrams.
Spatial Analyst	Allows manipulation, analysis, and modeling of raster-based (GRID) data.
StreetMap (USA and Europe)	Provides street mapping and geocoding dataset.
Tracking Analyst	Provides tracking and analysis of temporal data.

1.4 Chapter review

- A quick definition of GIS is *what is where* and *why*.
- Three key characteristics of GIS are: *layers* of *georeferenced* features with *attributes*.
- Four functions of a GIS are input, management, analysis, and output of geographic information.
- ArcGIS is composed of two (or possibly three) applications: ArcMap (viewing and analyzing maps) and ArcCatalog (managing and organizing data). ArcToolbox can be used in either ArcMap or ArcCatalog.
- A map document in ArcMap stores the layers, symbology, and layout, but does *not* store the actual datasets themselves. Saving your work is a two-step process: 1) save the *.mxd; 2) save your spatial datasets (i.e. shapefiles, etc.).
- Name your spatial datasets and pathnames to files only with a-z, A-Z, and "_" characters (no spaces or other characters).
- During a work session with ArcGIS, open a word processor document to record your notes. The results from your tool processing are provided in the Command Line window, which can be copy and pasted into the processor (try *.rtf format).

- Spend a couple of minutes each work session documenting your datasets through metadata tools.

2 Geographic data

2.1 Representing geography

Geographic information systems are concerned with representing geographic features or phenomena: those that occur at or near Earth's surface. Because we are challenged to deal with the complexity of the world, we have developed ways to simplify it. The key, like all modeling efforts, is to identify the salient characteristics, the essential features—to know what to represent. Then, the task becomes one of how to best represent them.

2.1.1 Where, what, and when?

Three aspects are central to understanding the nature of geographic data. Typically, we need to know *where*, or at what place, a geographic phenomena of interest is located. We also need to know specifically *what* we are interested in. There can be many attributes of a place, such as the elevation, the soil type, the amount of annual precipitation, the population density, who owns the land or mineral rights, etc. And although many aspects of a place change very slowly, such as elevation, others change rapidly. So, *when* a particular feature was recorded at a given location, usually specified by date or time, is important as well.

2.1.2 Discrete or continuous geographic features

Humans typically view space in two different ways. The first way we view space is as a continuous field of Cartesian coordinates, so that for any given location a value can be described. This view is typically used when thinking about continuous phenomena that vary smoothly over space, such as elevation, temperature, or precipitation. A second view of space is that we typically enumerate various entities or features, such as houses, lakes, roads, or forests. Representing geographic phenomena as entities assumes that they are discrete, clearly bounded objects.

Viewing space as either continuous or discrete is helpful, but to get any practical work done, we need to move beyond simply conceptualizing reality as either entities or fields (see Table 2.1). The next step is to formalize our conceptual model of reality as a *data model*. There are two common data models: *vector* (also called object, entity, or feature) and *raster* (also called field).[1] Vector data models represent geographic features as points, lines, areas, or networks. The raster data model represents geographic phenomenon as a matrix or grid of cells (or pixels), typically at equal spaced locations across a surface. Although in the past there was lengthy debate about which approach was better,[2] a more useful perspective is to understand the advantages and disadvantages to both approaches (Table 2.2) as routines to convert between the two are available.[3]

TABLE 2.1. Geography and geographic features can be conceptualized as existing in either discrete (vector) or continuous (raster) space.

	Discrete	*Continuous*
Reality	Lakes, houses, roads	Watersheds
Data model	Vector (feature)	Raster (field)
Data structure	Coverage, shapefile, geodatabase, DLG, etc.	GRID, image, DEM, etc.

---

1. Goodchild, M.F. 1992. Geographical data modeling. *Computers & Geosciences* 18(4): 401-408.
2. One adage that developed in the 1980s was: "Raster is faster but vector is corrector".

TABLE 2.2. **Advantages and disadvantages of representing geographic features using vector or raster.**

Model	Advantages	Disadvantages
Vector	Represent discrete entities (e.g., point, line, polygon) Compact representation of a feature Easy coordinate transformation	Complex data structure Geometric intersection (overlay) of features is computationally expensive Display/drawing of features is time-consuming Spatial modeling more difficult
Raster	Represent continuous phenomena Simple data structure Topological relationships implicit in column/row data structure Simplifies spatial analysis and modeling	Must compromise between resolution and data size Crude raster maps of poor cartographic quality

Finally, there are numerous *data structures* that implement each data model. A data structure is a specific implementation of a data model that specifies the way electronic data is organized or formatted in a computer. Indeed, much of the pioneering efforts in the GIS field were spent working out different ways to implement data models as data structures, and work on these data structures have been hailed as some of the most important contributions to GIScience.[4] This is because the ease or difficulty of different types of display, queries, and spatial analyses hinges on the data structure used to store the geographic features. And, in practice, data are commonly converted from one data model to another to ease modeling or analysis, and from one data structure to another. Moreover, some data structures, in particular the Geodatabase, can contain both vector and raster data (more on this below).

Typically, data models and data structures are discussed separately, but below I discuss them together to highlight the nested or hierarchical relationship. A detailed description of common data structures used in ArcGIS (i.e. coverages, shapefiles, geodatabases, GRIDs, and TINs) is provided within the context of data models.

---

3. More recently, there has been increasing recognition that these conceptualizations are not mutually exclusive, that "at some level... fields [raster] and objects [vector] can coexist." Worboys, M.F. 1995. *GIS: a computing perspective.* London: Taylor & Francis. Also, object fields have been developed to allow a many-to-many relationship between geographic objects and every location in the field. See: Cova, T.J. and M.F. Goodchild. 2002. Extending geographical representation to include fields of spatial objects. *International Journal of Geographical Information Science* 16(6):509-532.

4. Goodchild, M.F. 1992. Geographical Information Science. *International Journal of Geographical Information Systems* 6(1):31-45.

2.2 Vector

Vector data represent geographic phenomena as discrete entities. There are a number of fundamental *geographical primitives,* or feature types, in the vector data model: points, lines, areas, networks, and surfaces (some consider volume to be a sixth type). Each of these feature types is represented by different types of data structures: geometric, topologic, network, and surface.

A geometric data structure simply represents the geographical primitives, but not the spatial relationships between the features. Generally, topology is defined as the spatial relationships between connecting or adjacent features. A *topological data structure* then *explicitly* stores topological relations in a data file. Historically it was thought that one of the defining features of GIS was the ability to manipulate topologic data, which was thought to mean that topology needed to be stored explicitly (i.e. in a topological data structure). But, as you shall read about below, this is not so true anymore.

A relatively recent advance in GIS has been the *object-oriented* data structure. Rather than simplifying complex geographic features as either points, lines, or areas, object-oriented approaches attempt to better represent the complexity of real-world features. In particular, object-oriented techniques allow not only the *state* of a feature (i.e. what it is), but also the *behavior* of a feature (i.e. what it does) to be captured. Similar geographic features are grouped together as a class, and in addition to defining intra-class relationships, inter-class relationships can be defined as well.[5] Imagine that you have a database that contains building objects and parcel objects. It would make little sense for two buildings to overlap or be located within the same parcel, so behavioral rules could prohibit placing buildings so that they overlap. Also, it does not make sense that a building can be located in a street or right-of-way parcel, and so this situation could also be prohibited through establishing a spatial relationship between features.

5. Zeiler, M. 1999. *Modeling our world: The ESRI guide to geodatabase design.* Redlands, California: ESRI Press.

GIS Concepts and ArcGIS Methods

2.2.1 Geometric (non-topological) data structure

Geometric (sometimes called cartographic) data structures represent point, line, and areal features. *Point* features are represented as a single geographic location using *x, y* coordinate pairs. For example, cities are often represented as points, especially in broad-scale, national or regional maps. Imagine that you are on US Interstate 25, driving north from Sante Fe, NM to Denver, CO. Eventually you will likely consider whether you have enough fuel to reach your destination, and in this case, your mental representation of Denver is likely to be as a point.

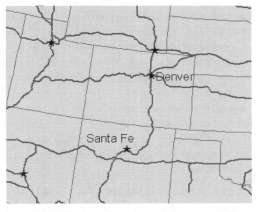

A *line* feature is recorded as an ordered series of connected line segments, where each line segment has two *x, y* coordinates, or *vertices*. Lines are used to represent features such as rivers, powerlines, and roads, such as I-25 between Santa Fe and Denver.

An *areal* feature, such as a lake, forest, or state is represented as a polygon, an ordered series of a minimum of three connected line segments, but the starting and ending vertices are at the same location. Polygons cannot have self-intersecting boundaries. Even though earlier we considered Denver and Santa Fe to be points, we could also think of them as polygons. For example, as you approach Denver from the south on I-25 (assuming you did have enough fuel), you see the different parts of the city and you may think about how the city has grown and expanded.

Lines and polygons can represent *simple features* or *complex features*. Simple features have one contiguous feature, such as the polygon that represents the State of Colorado. Complex features are often represented by polygons with perforations. For example, if we were interested in the land area of each state, we might want to exclude the Great Salt Lake in Utah, which is a noticeable perforation even from outer space. In this case, Utah would be represented by both an exterior polygon showing the state boundaries, and an interior polygon delimiting the Great Salt Lake.

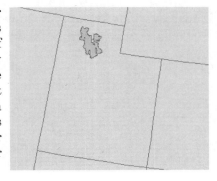

Complex features also can be comprised of multiple polygons (or lines) that are discontinuous (but usually nearby), which are known as *multi-part* features. For example, while Hawaii is a single state, it is comprised of seven islands (actually there are many additional, smaller islands). Within coverages, these discontinuous, multiple polygon features are known as *regions*. Line features can also be comprised of multiple, discontinuous features. For example, sometimes a stream appears to be discontinuous, being interrupted by geologic strata 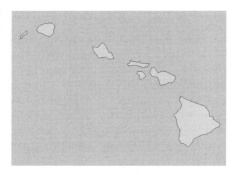 where the water disappears into the ground, and later resurfaces (e.g., Lost Creek in Colorado).

One particular instance of a geometric data structure is the so-called *"spaghetti"* model or structure.[6] This analogy refers to the messy representation of geographic features by a heap of tangled lines that twist, curl, and cross one another—no more structured "than a plate of spaghetti." Representing geographic features using a spaghetti data structure poses four distinct problems. First, the lines have little or no relationship to the geographic features they represent. For example, in Figure 2.1 (and Table 2.3), line 1 represents portions of polygons 1 and 2, but there is no direct relationship between the lines and the polygonal features. Another example is that a feature like a lake may be represented by a single line, many lines that run end-to-end, or by a small part of a line (and many lakes may be represented by a single line). Second, the relationships between adjacent features are not explicitly stored, and so advanced analyses are more difficult to conduct. Third, the boundaries of polygons must be represented twice, and so there is data redundancy. Fourth, inconsistencies in the boundaries between adjacent polygons can cause overlaps or gaps. However, although the geometric data structure is commonly considered to be the same as the "spaghetti" model, this is not the case.

6. Dangermond, J. 1982. A classification of software components commonly used in Geographic Information Systems. *In Proceedings of the US-Australia Workshop on the Design and Implementation of Computer-Based Geographic Information Systems*, Honolulu, HI. Pgs. 70-91.

FIGURE 2.1. An example of geographic features stored in a spaghetti data structure. The entire outside boundary was digitized first (line 1), then the bisecting line (line 2), then the island polygon (line 3).

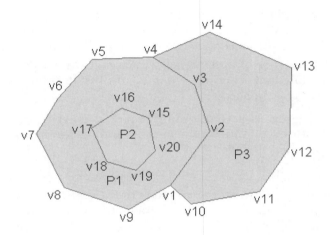

TABLE 2.3. Lines and vertices from Figure 2.1.

Line	Vertices
1	v1, v10, v11, v12, v13, v14, v4, v5, v6, v7, v8, v9, v1
2	v1, v2, v3, v4
3	v15, v20, v19, v18, v17, v16, v15

However, it is important to make a distinction between the spaghetti and geometric data structure. The geometric data structure shares all but the first characteristic with the spaghetti structure. That is, in a geometric data structure there *is* a strong and direct relationship between the feature being represented and the primitive type that represents it, while for the spaghetti data structure this is not necessarily so. For example, a lake (as an areal feature) is represented in a geometric data structure as a polygon, not a tangle of lines. Historically, numerous data structures that were developed for cartography were simply spaghetti data structures, and making a clear distinction between these and ones that represented topological features was important in defining the newly emergent GIS field. However, contemporary claims that non-topologic data structures are not useful in GIS ignores this important distinction, and is central to understanding the difference between non-topological and topological data structures, and especially the utility of shapefiles and KML files.[7]

2.2.1.1 Shapefiles

A *shapefile* is a geometric data structure that ESRI developed originally for ArcView v1 (see Figure 2.2 and Table 2.4), but has found much wider application and acceptance and can be used by ArcGIS. In fact, some have recently called shapefiles the *de facto* standard for GIS data.[8] Indeed, because of its simplicity and open standards many applications, ranging from GIS to global positioning systems (GPS) to desktop publishing to globe viewers (e.g., Google Earth), support it.

The shapefile data structure is actually composed of at least three files (*.shp, *.shx, *.dbf). These are *not* stored in a directory format so they *can* be copied around using system-level copy. These files include:

.shp - the shape file, which stores feature geometry (required).

.shx - the shape index, which stores an index to the feature geometry, because each feature may have a different number of coordinates. This means that the *.shp file is a variable-length record. The *.shx file then indexes the *.shp file for faster access.

.dbf - dBASE file that stores the attribute information of features.

.sbn (spatial bin) and *.sbx* (spatial bin index) - store the *spatial index* of the features. When you index on the shape field, ArcGIS partitions the geographic features in spatial *bins* or rectangular areas. The record number of each feature then is stored into a bin. If you create an index on a theme's shape field, you will create a spatial index. A spatial index improves performance on identify, all drawing operations, spatial joins, and select by location operations.[9]

.ain and *.aih* - *.ain* stores the attribute index of the active fields in a table or a theme's attribute table. This index improves the speed of joining and linking and simple queries. The *.aih* file is the attribute header file, which contains the name of each field that has been indexed. These files exist only if an index on an attribute field has been created.

7. Theobald, D.M. 2001. Topology revisited: Representing spatial relations. *International Journal of Geographical Information Science* 15(8): 689-705. Also, as Tor Bernhardsen explains: "...the problems related to spaghetti and topology have changed somewhat during recent years with the advent of new GIS software which treats polygons as independent objects that may overlap and need not fill the plane, and with systems permitting shapes." Bernhardsen, T. 1999. *Geographic Information Systems: An Introduction.* John Wiley & Sons.

8. Strand, E. 1999. Shapefiles shape GIS data transfer standards. *GeoWorld* (April), pgs 12-13.

9. Ormsby, T. and J. Alvi. 1999. *Extending ArcView GIS.* ESRI Press, Appendix C.

*.fbn and *.fbx - these store the spatial index of features for shapefiles that are read-only.

*.atx - this stores an attribute index for the .dbf in the form of <shapefile>.<attribute name>.atx.

the attribute index of the active fields in a table or a theme's attribute table. This index improves the speed of joining and linking and simple queries. The *.aih file is the attribute header file, which contains the name of each field that has been indexed. These files exist only if an index on an attribute field has been created.

The spatial coordinates of shapefiles are stored with *double precision*. That is, the *x* and *y* locations for vertices that represent geometric features are stored using 2 words (64 bits). But shapefiles will contain only *single precision* level data (accurate to 4 bytes or 32 bits) if the source document was a single-precision coverage (such as a PC ARC/INFO coverage). The spatial coordinates for a coverage stored in single-precision are stored to seven significant digits, so that a precision of one unit can be maintained for a theme whose extent is 10,000,000 units wide. Coordinates in a double-precision coverage are stored to 15 significant digits. Of course double-precision coverages require additional storage space, but file sizes are generally smaller than twice the size of a single-precision file. Shapefiles also support some extended feature types for *measured* and *3D* shapes. In addition to storing *x, y* coordinates for each vertex in a shapefile, you can store a measure and/or an elevation value at each vertex. These are called the *m* value and *z* value, respectively. This is useful, for example, to store the distances from a starting point along a transect or the elevation of each point.

FIGURE 2.2. An example of geographic features represented in a shapefile data structure showing the polygon feature type. There are 20 vertices (e.g., v1 to v20) and three polygons (e.g., P1, P2, and P3).

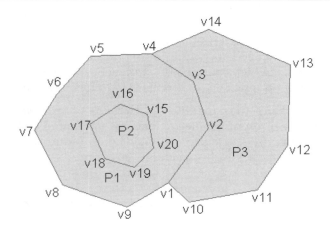

TABLE 2.4. The three features shown in Figure 2.2 are comprised of three polygons, formed by the list of vertices detailed below.

Polygon	Part (ring)	Vertices
P1	1	v1, v9, v8, v7, v6, v4, v3, v2, v1
	2	v15, v16, v17, v18, v19, v20, v15
P2	1	v15, v20, v19, v18, v17, v16, v15
P3	1	v1, v2, v3, v4, v14, v13, v12, v11, v10, v1

There is a lot of confusion in the GIS world regarding topology in the shapefile data structure.[10] To clear up this confusion, it is helpful to know about two aspects of topology: adjacency and planar enforcement. A topological data structure stores topological (adjacency) relationships explicitly in a file, in addition to the geometry (spatial coordinates) and attribute data. In this sense, other GIS data formats such as coverages "have topology," while shapefiles do not. Many people assume that typical GIS analyses, such as adjacency analysis (i.e. find the neighbors adjacent to a particular feature) cannot be accomplished using geometric (non-topological) data structures. And because shapefiles

10. Theobald, D.M. 2001. Understanding topology and shapefiles. *ArcUser* (Spring): 24-26. www.esri.com/news/arcuser/0401/topo.html.

do not store topology, it is assumed, therefore, that these types of analyses cannot be achieved with shapefile data.

This reasoning is incorrect! Topology can be generated *on the fly,* rather than being explicitly stored. For example, two polygons can be determined to be adjacent by finding a common vertex (or vertices).[11] In fact, one has to remember that the topological data files themselves must be created somehow in the first place! Beginning with ArcGIS v8.3, geodatabases employ rules that are applied dynamically, rather than explicitly storing spatial relationships (see section 2.2.5.1). Moreover, computationally efficient overlay selections rely on spatial indexing, not topology.

Although ESRI shapefiles are a non-topological data structure, they are more accurately classified as a geometric, rather than a spaghetti data structure. There is a direct relationship between geographic features and their object, or "shape" representation. Also, complex polygons can be represented because shapefiles store rings (e.g., polygon 1 is represented by two rings in Figure 2.2) with their vertices in clockwise order. This allows shapefiles to know what is "inside" and what is "outside" a polygon.[12] The bottom line is that ArcGIS and shapefiles *do* support most analyses that require adjacency information and with reasonable performance. However, for very large files and certain functions (e.g., dissolving adjacent polygons with similar attribute values), storage of explicit adjacency is necessary.

The second important aspect of topology to consider is whether the spatial data have had planar topology enforced during their creation and subsequent editing. A consequence of planar enforcement is that there is one and only one geographical feature at any x, y location. This means that lines that cross one another cross at a node, and that polygons are space-filling and exhaustive. One important and useful consequence of a planar-enforced theme is that the sum of the area of the individual polygons equals the area of the extent of all polygons (not including the universe polygon). If polygons overlap or if there are gaps between them, summations may be erroneous. A topologically-correct polygon coverage has no overlapping polygons, nor does it have areas surrounded by polygons without a polygon in the middle–commonly called a *gap.* Also, maps created from data with slight gaps and overlaps are not pleasing to the eye.

Most shapefiles are topologically correct in this planar graph sense because shapefiles are commonly derived directly from coverages. However, because shapefiles can be edited in ArcView v3.x and ArcGIS, which do not *require* topology to be enforced, you need to be careful when assuming that a shapefile is topologically correct. However, ArcGIS *does*

---

11. Worboys, M.F. 1995. *GIS: A computing perspective.* Taylor & Francis.
12. ESRI, 1998. *ESRI shapefile technical description.* ArcView White Paper Series.

provide powerful editing tools that make it easy to maintain planar topology and update attribute information about the geometry of features (e.g., area/perimeter and length).

Even though the vast majority of geographic data sets are planar enforced, for some situations it can be useful to break the restrictions of planar topology. For example, some geographic features overlap, such as winter range and severe winter range for elk. That is, a single location may be considered to have both winter range and severe winter range. Some geographic features are represented as discontinuous polygons, but are still considered the same feature—think back to the seven islands of Hawaii. Also, a single land ownership parcel is often literally split by a road right-of-way, creating non-contiguous polygons. Whether the two polygons represent a single parcel or two parcels is a very important issue, because development rights are conferred typically on a per-parcel basis.

2.2.1.2 Geodatabases

Geographic databases, or *geodatabases*, build on the shapefile and coverage data structures by providing a number of advanced capabilities. A geodatabase is a container that holds a collection of datasets, and there are three types of geodatabases.

- *Personal geodatabases* store datasets within a Microsoft Access data file, which is limited to 2.1 GB in size.

- *File geodatabases* store datasets as folders in a file system, and can be as large as 1 TB[13]. This is the preferred option over personal geodatabases, because they are optimized to be smaller file sizes (about 1/3 of shapefiles and personal geodatabases), has faster query performance, and operates across operating systems (i.e. beyond Microsoft Windows).

- *ArcSDE geodatabases* store datasets in a relational database (e.g., Oracle, SQL Server) that are typical set up for multi-user and enterprise efforts.

Geodatabases can store both vector and raster data, but here I will focus on the vector capabilities. Geodatabases store geographic information inside a database management system (DBMS) following the relational data model where an object and its attributes are stored as a row in a table. The power of storing objects in a geodatabase is the ability to represent and emulate real-world features and behavior—to put the behavior in with the data, rather than building behavior in through an application. Referring back to the parcel example, while a polygon shapefile can represent the geometry of a land ownership parcel (and some attributes as well), a geodatabase can also represent relationships between parcels and other features so that a parcel cannot overlap with another and only one building can occur in a parcel. Although at first blush geodatabases can appear to be quite

---

13. Yep, that's a tera-byte (1,000 GB). This is new to v9.2.

complex (and indeed the innards often are), there are three primary advantages to geodatabases.

First, all types of data can be stored together in a geodatabase, including feature, CAD, raster, attributes, addresses, annotation, etc. This makes sharing data straightforward (just one file to locate!), and these data can be managed seamlessly. Also, because these comprehensive datasets are stored and managed within a commercial, off-the-shelf database management system, multiple and iterative editing sessions can be long (up to months!) and different versions can be tracked.

Second, "smart" features, rules, and relationships can be implemented. Vector features can have two (x, y), three (x, y, z), or four dimensions (x, y, z, m); line segments can be represented by true curves (circular, elliptical, Bezier); and networks can be implemented. Rules that define spatial relationships between features can be established, including methods to enforce planar topology, as well as rules to specify relationships between attribute objects.

Third, *ArcGIS data models* (please don't confuse this with the broader conceptual definition of a data model) that are specific to different industries or applications have been developed (and additional ones can be created). This provides an easy way for industry-wide standards to be incorporated into a framework to capture the behavior of real-world objects.[14] Currently, a number of data models are available, including: forestry, geology, hydrology[15], land use parcels, petroleum, pipelines, etc.

Geodatabases are organized as a hierarchical collection of datasets, feature classes, object classes, and relationship classes (Table 2.5). There are three types of datasets: feature, raster, and TIN. A *feature dataset* shares a common coordinate system (also called *XY domain* or spatial extent) and contains feature classes (i.e. point, line, area, network). Although feature classes can exist outside of a feature dataset, using topological constraints between features can be done only within a feature dataset (because they must share the same coordinate system). A *feature class* is a collection of features that share the same type of geometry (roughly comparable to point, polyline, and polygon shapefiles). An *object class* is a table that stores descriptive information about a particular type of feature (e.g., parcels) rather than to an individual instance of a feature (e.g., a particular parcel)

---

14. For example, the ArcGIS Land Parcel data model, described in ArcNews 24(3): 6-9. http://www.esri.com/news/arcnews/fall02articles/tofc-fall02.html. Also, ESRI's ArcGIS data models provide a number of templates for different industries and applications: http://www.esri.com/software/arcgisdatamodels/index.html.

15. See: Maidment, D. 2002. ArcHydro: GIS for water resources. ESRI Press. Also, see: Maidment, D. and D. Djokic (eds.). 2000. Hydrologic and hydraulic modeling support with Geographic Information Systems. ESRI Press.

as an attribute table does. A *relationship class* stores relationships between features or objects so that dependencies between features and behavior can be modeled.

TABLE 2.5. A comparison of the organizational structure of vector data models.

	Shapefile	Coverage	Geodatabase
Collections of datasets	Folder of shape-files	ArcInfo Work-space	Geodatabase
Datasets	One feature class	Coverage	Collection of classes
Collections of features	Feature class	Feature class	Features of same type
Features	Point, Multi-point Polyline Polygon	Primary: Point or label, arc and node Secondary: poly-gon, tic, link, section, annota-tion Compound: region and route	Point, multi-point Polyline Polygon Network Annotation

Feature types in geodatabases implement a full range of geometry types. In addition to point and multi-point features, *network junctions* (where two or more *network edges* meet) are available. Single- and multi-part polylines can be implemented, and in addition to straight-line segments, circular, elliptical, and Bezier curves are available, as well as edges that form a one-dimensional *geometric network*. Polygons are formed from one or more rings. A *ring* is a closed, non-intersecting *path*. A path is a simple, connected series of polylines.

Rather than building topology based on arc-node relationships (as in the coverage model), geodatabases[16] employ spatial relationship and integrity rules established between feature geometry. Specifying topology directly on feature types allows multiple layers (feature classes) to be coincident with one another, a wider-range of spatial relationships to be enforced, direct control over which layers will have topology or which will not, and increased display and editing performance.[17] Topological relationships can be best considered to be spatial constraints or a set of integrity rules. These rules build on the basic spatial relations between two features: equals (spatially equivalent, where all

16. Actually, topology is fully implemented in ArcGIS v8.3.
17. For a good overview article, see: ArcNews Summer 2002 issue: http://www.esri.com/news/arcnews/summer02articles/arcgis83-brings.html.

constituent vertices are the identical), contains (a feature is wholly within another), within (inside, but can touch), crosses (e.g., two lines intersect), overlaps, disjoint (spatially separate), or touches (boundaries intersect). Using these basic relationships, rules can be specified, such as: *polygons must not overlap* or *lines must not have dangles.* Note that instead of the coverage model where geometry is a collection of arcs, nodes, and label points, each feature in a geodatabase is represented by a single shape (or geometry) and can exist on its own. For example, a parcel is represented as a polygon, not as a combination of arcs and nodes. This allows more rapid display, query, and editing of features.

In addition to constraints for features, attribute values can be constrained through *attribute domains* to minimize data-entry errors and to ensure data integrity. A *range domain* can be specified for numeric fields that represent quantitative data, which prescribe the minimum and maximum values.[18] A *coded domain* can be specified for non-numeric fields that represent qualitative data (e.g., nominal classes), which prescribe a set of valid values. For example, a field representing the number of housing units in a county could be constrained using a range domain of 0 to 1,000,000, while a field representing land use types could be constrained using a coded domain of valid classes such as: commercial, residential, agricultural, transportation, forested, mining, etc.

2.2.2 Topological data structure

Generally, topology is defined as the spatial relationships between connecting or adjacent features. A *topological data structure* then *explicitly* stores topological relations in a data file (Figure 2.3 and Table 2.6).

Topological data structures were developed to allow a mathematically robust means of verifying data entry and to increase computational efficiency of complex queries that involved adjacency or containment. A full review of the various data structures that have been developed over the past 30 years is beyond the scope of this book, but a useful comparison of four main topological data structures including POLYVRT, CANSIS, and TIGER is provided in Bonham-Carter's book.[19]

Spatial relations are typically stored as adjacent polygons in a Polygon Topology Table or an Arc Attribute Table, or as connected lines. Also note that the boundaries between polygons are stored only once. In contrast, a *geometric data structure* such as a shapefile simply stores the geometry of features, rather than both the geometry and topology of features. Shapefiles store the common boundaries between adjacent polygons twice.

---

18. At v8.2, range domains must be validated in a step after data entry.
19. Bonham-Carter, G.F. 1996. *Geographic Information Systems for Geoscientists: Modelling with GIS.* Ontario, Canada: Pergamon Press. Also, see Peucker, T.K. and Chrisman, N. 1975. Geographic data structures. *The American Cartographer* 2: 55-69.

The most common implementation of a topological data structure uses some form of *arc-node* topology. The biggest difference between topological and geometric data structures is the extension of the concept of a line to a chain terminated by nodes. The first vertex is called the *start node* (or from node) and the last vertex is called the *end node* (or to node). Chains are linked to

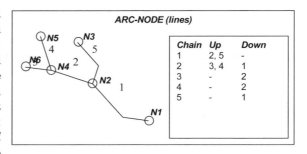

other chains through nodes. Because the vertices of a chain are ordered (which allows the computer to know about the start and end node), the direction of a network can be determined. This allows, for instance, a network of lines representing streams to "flow downhill." For example, chain 1 runs from node N1 to node N2, allowing us to determine that chains 2 and 5 are upstream of chain 1.

Chains are also linked together through nodes in the case of the polygon feature type. Again, because there is a direction to a chain, the left and right adjacent polygons can be determined. For example, in the diagram and table on the following page, you can determine that polygon 1 is adjacent to polygon 2, while polygon 3 is adjacent to only polygon 2.

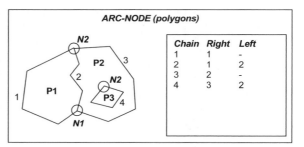

FIGURE 2.3. An example of geographic features represented in a topological data structure. Nodes are shown with red points (download color figures from www.consplan.com).

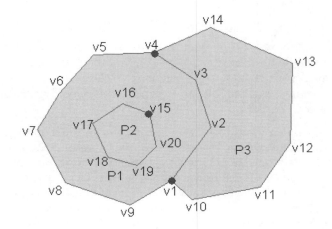

TABLE 2.6. Topology tables for Figure 2.3. The top table below stores the vertices that comprise the individual arcs, and the associated left and right adjacent polygons. The bottom table shows the Polygon Attribute Table.

Arc	Vertices	Left polygon	Right polygon
A1	v15, v16, v17, v18, v19, v20, v15	P2	P1
A2	v4, v5, v6, v7, v8, v9, v1	P1	-
A3	v1, v2, v3, v4	P1	P3
A4	v1, v10, v11, v12, v13, v14, v4	P3	-

Polygon	Adjacent polygon
P1	P2, P3
P2	P1
P3	P2

In addition to explicitly storing adjacent polygons, topological data structures utilize planar graph[20] theory, which requires that polygons are space filling and exhaustive. This means that interior polygons such as P2 in Figure 2.3 are represented as a polygon, not a hole. Also, it means that there are no overlaps among adjacent polygons or gaps between adjacent polygons.

2.2.2.1 Coverage

A *coverage* is a spatial data structure developed by ESRI over two decades ago for use primarily in ArcInfo. Coverages store geographic data in a topological data structure.[21] A coverage can store multiple feature types (e.g., points, labels, lines, polygons, regions, etc.) simultaneously. The coverage feature types that ArcGIS recognizes are: *points, arcs, labelpoint, polygons, routes, regions*, and *annotation*. Only one feature class at a time can be recognized per layer in ArcMap.

A coverage is actually not a single file, but is a collection of files organized within two directories or folders. The first directory (the "arc" part), named the same as the coverage name, contains files that store the geometry, projection, and log information. A second directory, always named "INFO," holds files for the attribute and topological files (basically all tables) for the coverage, and all other coverages at that same level in the directory structure. Because the attribute data for a coverage is stored in a separate directory (the info directory), you cannot copy or move these files using system-level copy commands (e.g., `copy <f1> <f2>`). Instead, you need to use the ArcCatalog (or copy the entire parent directory, with all the other sibling coverages, of the coverage directory). You can also import ArcInfo export format files (*.e00) using the Import to Coverage utility available through ArcToolbox.[22] However, you cannot export layers to the export (*.e00) format without the ArcInfo version of ArcGIS. Also, you can use ArcCatalog (ArcEditor or ArcInfo version) to clean and build a coverage to enforce topology.

---

20. In topological data structures, the geometric feature types (points, lines, areas) are referred to as 0, 1, and 2 cells. These cells correspond to their respective dimension — that is, points are considered 0 dimensional, lines are 1 dimensional, and polygons are 2 dimensional objects. Another source of potential confusion is the wide variety of terms often used formally in spatial data standards, and informally by GIS users, such as *chains, arcs,* and *rings.* See: Corbett, J.P. 1979. *Topological principles in cartography.* Technical Paper 48. US Department of Commerce, Bureau of the Census. Washington, D.C. 50 pgs. In a planar graph, the node and link or chain objects of the graph are represented as though they occur upon a planar surface. Only one node may exist at any given point on the surface, and links or chains intersect only at nodes.

21. Morehouse, S. 1992. The ARC/INFO geographic information system. *Computers & Geosciences* 18: 435-441.

22. GRIDs in *.e00 files can also be imported using this tool.

TABLE 2.7. Definitions of point vector data structures (sub-classes are distinguished by italics below).

Geodatabase & Shapefile	Coverage
Point - a single location specified by x, y	Points - a single location specified by x, y
Label point - used to display map and chart text (e.g., annotation)	Labelpoints - a point that identifies a features center for labeling, which are guaranteed to fall within polygons, unlike true centroid.
PointM (measured point) - an x, y point that stores a third variable (m), and is used to represent time, distance, or any other measure (such as events).	
PointZ (3D point) - an x, y point that stores a z (elevation) value	Tics - points that are used to help georeference a coverage
Multipoint - represents a set of points	Nodes - points where two lines are coincident
MultipointM	
MultipointZ	

TABLE 2.8. Definitions of line vector data structures (sub-classes are distinguished by italics below).

Geodatabase & Shapefile	Coverage
Line - a single geometric line segment defined by two points. Lines may intersect other lines.	Segment - straight line connecting two points
Polyline - a set of one or more parts. Each part contains one or more contiguous lines. Parts are discontinuous. Polylines may intersect other polylines.	Arcs - Arcs represent linear features such as streams, streets and contours. Note this term is NOT consistent with SDTS terms. ARC/INFO arcs are similar to chains.
PolylineM (dynamic segmentation) - a measured polyline contains measures used to locate data that describe parts along a route	Routes - are linear features composed of one or more arcs or parts of an arc.
Arc - a curve defined by mathematical functions	Chain - a directed, non branching sequence of non-crossing line segments and/or arcs bounded by nodes
Circle - a geometric circle	*Complete chain* - references left and right polygons and start and end nodes
Oval - a geometric ellipse	*Area chain* - references left and right polygons but not the start and end nodes
Rectangle - a geometric rectangle	*Network chain* - references start and end nodes but not left and right polygons

TABLE 2.9. Definitions of polygon vector data structures (sub-classes are distinguished by italics below).

Geodatabase & Shapefile	Coverage
<u>Polygon</u> - an area that consists of a set of *directed* rings. Each ring is a set of non- self-intersecting polylines that close back to the first vertex. A polygon can be made up of several disjunct polygons -- similar to a region (e.g., the Hawaiian Islands would be one feature). Because clockwise-ordered rings are used, "inside" and "outside" can be determined (as you walk along the ring the inside is to the right). *PolygonM* *PolygonZ*	<u>GT-polygon</u> - the boundary of a GT-polygon may be defined by GT-rings created from its bounding chains. A GT-polygon may also be associated with its chains (either the bounding set, or the complete set) by direct reference to these chains. The complete set of chains associated with a GT-polygon may also be found by examining the polygon references on the chains. <u>Universe polygon</u> - the part of the universe that is outside the perimeter of the area covered by other GT-polygons. This polygon completes the adjacency relationships of the perimeter polygons.

2.2.2.2 Network

Certain applications, such as transportation services, route planning, hydrological analysis, and utility management, require a special type of topologic data structure, called the *network data model*. Networks are built from nodes and lines, or more precisely chains (often called "edges" in graph theory), and explicitly represent how lines intersect one another (Figure 2.4 and Table 2.10). For example, transportation systems, with their interconnected network of interstates, highways, and local roads are represented as a network. Another example of geographic system that is typically represented as a network is a *hydrologic network* that shows the location of streams and rivers, as well as the flow direction. Flow direction is represented using "from-to" topology, so that a stream reach is represented by a single chain (or edge), which is oriented to run upstream (from node being lower than to node), ending at a confluence(s) or at a headwater. Thus, a confluence can be defined as a node where two from nodes and one to node are collocated. Areal features such as lakes and ponds, however, cannot be explicitly represented. Instead, special line segments called *artificial paths* are often used.[23] Note that although the third dimension (elevation) profoundly influences the behavior of hydrologic systems, to date it has not been fully incorporated into spatial network models.

---

23. For example, see the USGS National Hydrography Dataset's data model: http://nhd.usgs.gov

FIGURE 2.4. Example of a network data structure. Nodes are labeled by letters, and edges are labeled by numbers. Note that the table could have a fourth column to represent the weight or cost to traverse each edge and that the arcs are directed upstream.

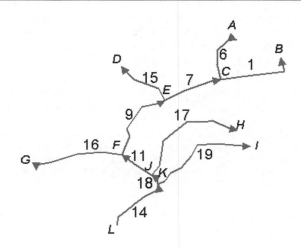

TABLE 2.10. The edge table for Figure 2.4.

Edge	From Node	To Node
1	C	B
6	C	A
7	E	C
9	F	E
11	J	F
14	L	K
15	E	D
16	F	G
17	J	H
18	K	J
19	K	I

In ArcGIS, the geodatabase model (described on the next page) provides for a special type of geodatabase called a *geometric network*. Networks are represented as two-dimensional non-planar graphs. These data structures are called geometric networks because connectivity is based on geometric coincidence. Networks are composed of *edges* and *junctions* (nodes). A simple edge always has one junction at each end. For example, a stream reach is represented as an edge, ending at a junction (confluence) at each end. A complex edge may have an additional junction feature somewhere between the end junctions. Flow direction along an edge is calculated by distinguishing sources and sinks. Water flows from a source to a sink in a hydrologic network. You can also attribute edges with a weight, which can be used to calculate the cost of traversing a network feature. For example, this can be used to differentiate the lengths of different stream reaches. You can then conduct a number of trace analyses, for example, to find all the upstream features from a particular point on a hydrologic network (Figure 2.5). (Please see the discussion on geodatabases later in this chapter for further description of geometric networks.)

FIGURE 2.5. Example of geometric network analysis using hydrology data. The stream is flowing from top right to bottom left (shown by arrows). Upstream reaches of the dam (red triangle) are selected (cyan) using upstream tracing (left). Downstream reaches selected using downstream tracing (right) (download color figures from www.consplan.com).

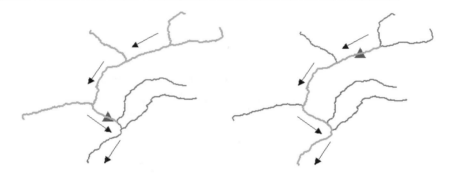

2.2.2.3 Surfaces

A *surface data structure* represents a surface as a 2.5D structure, where each location has one and only one z-value (e.g., elevation). This contrasts with a true 3D data structure where each location can have multiple z-values. Probably the most commonly used data structure for surfaces is the Digital Elevation Model (DEM) data structure which is based on a raster data model (discussed later in this chapter).

TINs (Triangulated Irregular Networks) use a vector data model to represent surfaces. TINs represent surfaces using a network of irregularly shaped triangles that are contiguous and non-overlapping (Figure 2.6). TINs are typically based on point-based elevation values. The actual sample points serve as the nodes of the triangles, and planar surfaces fit through the triangle. Because triangles are very fast to draw using computer graphic rendering technology, TINs are used for draping attributes onto surfaces to enable oblique perspectives and "fly-by" animations. You will need to have the 3D Analyst extension to create and analyze these data (though you can view an existing TIN in ArcMap).

FIGURE 2.6. Example of a TIN data structure representing the elevation surface near Yellowstone National. Park, Wyoming.

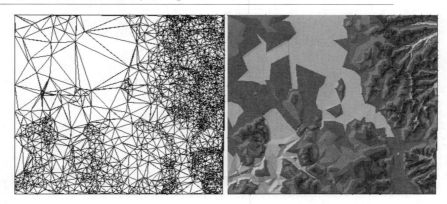

2.2.2.4 Other structures

In addition to shapefiles, coverages, and geodatabases, a number of other spatial data formats are directly supported by ArcGIS. That is, these do not need to be imported or converted somehow to be usable. Table 2.11 summarizes the vector data structures that are supported in

ArcGIS.

TABLE 2.11. Supported vector data formats.

Name	Description
ArcIMS Feature Service, ArcIMS Map Service	ArcIMS Feature Service streams features over the Internet, so a Feature Service layer works the same as any other feature layer.
Coverages	Both Workstation and PC ArcINFO coverages.
DGN	MicroStation design file, supported to v8.
DWG	AutoCAD drawing file. Note that a CAD layer can be georeferenced by using the Transformation tab in the Properties dialog (through v2006).
DXF	CAD interchange files. Note that ASCII, binary, and partial drawing interchange files that comply with DXF are supported.

TABLE 2.11. Supported vector data formats.

Geodatabases	Discussed above.
Geography network	Adds data from ESRI's geography network.
OLE DB	Allows access to OLE DB providers.
PMF	ESRI's published map format (*.pmf), which can be created using ArcGIS Publisher extension and read with ArcReader.
SDC	Smart Data Compression dataset is an encrypted and compressed format used by ESRI to provide StreetMap data.
SDE layer	ArcSDE (spatial database engine) layers are treated as geodatabase feature classes and tables. Not available with ArcView functionality.
Shapefiles	Discussed above.
Text files	Tabular data that contain x, y coordinates can be added as a point layer. The table can be in comma-delimited files (*.asc, *.csv, *.txt) or tab-delimited (*.tab).
TIN	Described above.
VPF	The Vector Product Format (VPF) can be read in ArcCatalog. For more information, visit: http://www.nima.mil/vpf-proto/

2.2.3 Spatial indexing

Although *spatial indexing* is not a data structure *per se*, it is key to providing adequate performance for spatial queries and analysis of data stored in a feature data structure. Spatial indexing increases the speed of graphical display, spatial queries, and analyses. For example, if you have zoomed into a small portion of a map, then ArcGIS uses the spatial index to find the features that fall within that display area *before* they are drawn.

How do spatial indexes work? Imagine you have just opened a new, 100-piece puzzle and you set out to complete it as fast as possible. What are your strategies? If you are like most puzzlers, you might use shape (border pieces first) and color and pattern to group (visually or literally) pieces to reduce the number of possible combinations that need to be carefully compared (i.e., picked up and tried with another). As the puzzle comes together, notice that the rate which pieces are added increases dramatically as the number of pieces declines--that is, it is slow going in the beginning punctuated by a flurry of activity at the end. Why is this? With 100 pieces, there are nearly 5,000 possible combinations to compare all pieces. But if the puzzle was separated into even just 4 groups (e.g., the border pieces and the red, black, and white pieces), there would be about 1,200 possible combinations—nearly a five-fold reduction! And if the puzzle could be separated further into 10 groups of 10, there would be only 495 possible combinations—the puzzle would be a piece o' cake at this point.

Although there are a variety of approaches to index space, generally spatial indexing works by reducing the number of possible combinations to compare by separating features into groups, just like a puzzle. Geographic features are grouped or partitioned into spatial *bins* or rectangular areas (also known as grids—not to be confused with GRID, a raster data structure).[24] A list of the geographic features that fall within each bin is then recorded. Often, *minimum bounding rectangles* are used as an approximation of the more detailed geographic features to further reduce the time it takes to find adjacent features. When the features need to be accessed, first the bins that are needed are found, then the features in those bins are accessed.

Creating a spatial index

1. Open ArcCatalog.
2. Navigate to find the desired dataset and select it.
2. Select **File** -> **Properties...**
3. Select the **Index** tab.
4. Click **Add**. (Note: If this button is greyed-out, then Arc-Catalog cannot establish a "write-lock." Remove the database from ArcMap or ArcToolbox and/or remove the read-only lock in Windows Explorer).
5. Click **OK**.
- OR -
1. Open ArcToolbox.
2. Open the **Data Management Tools**, then **Indexes**.
3. Double-click on **Add Spatial Index**.

2.3 Raster

Geographic phenomena that varies continuously through space, such as elevation, are usually represented using the *raster* data model and implemented using a raster data structure.[25] A raster contains a matrix or mesh of *cells* (or *pixels)* that contain a particular

---

24. Rigaux, P., M. Scholl, and A. Voisard. 2002. *Spatial databases with application to GIS*. Morgan Kaufmann Publishers.

numeric value, such as a brightness value or a land cover type. A cell typically is square, and all cells in a raster are the same size. In addition, information that places a raster within a geographic coordinate system is needed. That is, a spatial reference is needed that specifies the geographic coordinate of, typically, the top-left cell.

Conceptually, there are three ways to store data at each cell. First, if the attribute of interest is either there or not there (present/absent), then this layer can be represented using a single layer of binary values. For example, the public/private land ownership pattern could be represented as private and not private by simply setting a binary flag for presence/absence. A second approach also represents just a single layer of interest but allows a number of values to occur at each cell. For example, land use categories could be represented with integer values (e.g., 1=grassland, 2=forest, 3=urban, etc.), or elevation could be represented with real values (e.g., Pikes Peak, Colorado is at 4301.2 meters). Finally, one could represent multiple themes at each cell, so cells could be stacked one upon another (like "crowning" in checkers). For example, a cell could have a 1 because it is private, and in the second level, 2 because it is forest. An advantage of the first (single-layer-binary-value) approach is that data can be stored in a very storage-efficient manner. However, it can become quite cumbersome when many layers are needed to represent seemingly related items (e.g., grassland/not grassland, forest/not forest, urban/not urban, etc.). The second approach, called single-layer integer/ratio value, is commonly used in commercial systems such as ArcGIS because of its versatility and the direct association between a file and a layer. The third approach, the stacking-layer approach, is an efficient storage model but lacks versatility during analysis.

A raster can contain a single *band* (a single matrix or layer of cells) or multiple bands that contain multiple layers of matrices representing the same area. For example, since there is only one elevation value at any location on Earth, then a single band raster can adequately represent elevation. Most satellite or aerial photo imagery is composed of three (or more) bands, such as the red, green, and blue bands, and typically is held in a multi-band dataset.

Each raster band stores a matrix of cells or pixels, which can contain either integer or floating point values. Integer values are whole numbers (e.g., 0, 29, 248) while floating points contain real numbers with a decimal point (e.g., 0.01, 3.14, 1000.0). This is known as the raster *data type*.

Each cell stores a value, and the range of values that can be stored depends on the *data depth* (also known as the pixel or bit depth) of the raster dataset, which is based on binary math (2^n, where n is the bit depth). So, a bit depth of 1 can represent values from 0 to 1,

---

25. For a thorough introduction to raster data structures, see: Holroyd, F. and S.B.M. Bell. 1992. Raster GIS: Models of raster encoding. *Computers & Geosciences* 18(4): 419-426.

and a bit depth of signed 32 bit can represent values between positive and negative 2.14 x 10^9.

The file size for a raster dataset can be very large because it increases exponentially as the cell size decreases. Consequently, numerous ways have been developed to compress a file to reduce its size. One common method is called *run-length encoding*[26], which compresses data on a row-by-row basis, storing both the value and the number of times that a value occurs in successive columns. Adjacent pixels on a row that share the same value are represented as a pair of numbers. The more homogeneous (across columns) the data are, the better this compression scheme works. Note that run-length encoding works only on data represented as integer values, not real values.

There are numerous additional modifications to the standard raster data structure that attempt to address one or more limitations. For example, the *block code* data model is an extension of run-length encoding to two dimensions. Block codes store four numbers: the value, the origin x, the origin y, and the length of the square block. Essentially, space is partitioned into a set of space-filling, nested squares of varying sizes. This compression scheme works best for simple, homogenous shapes that result in large average-square size. Block codes are the basis for compression schemes commonly used by facsimile machines.[27] Another common raster data model is the *quad-tree*, which provides a compact representation of space by successively (recursively) dividing space into finer and finer hierarchical tiles. There are numerous data structures used to implement the raster data model; indeed, a number of books have been written on this topic.[28]

In an integer raster, all cells that have the same value belong to the same *zone*. There is one attribute record per zone in the attribute table. A zone can be comprised of contiguous cells that have the same value, disjoint cells that are at some distance away, or both. For example, a number of disjoint patches of aspen would be represented by a single value (e.g., 1) for each cell that occurs within the patches. In contrast, when patches of aspen are represented as polygons (feature data model), the individual patches of aspen are each represented by a unique polygon (and therefore have a record in the polygon attribute table). In the raster representation of the patches of aspen, all patches are represented by the same zone with a value of 1 (Figure 2.7).

26. Rutovitz, D. 1968. Data structures for operations on digital images. *Pictorial Pattern Recognition*, Cheng, G.C. et al. (eds). Thompson Book Co. p. 105-133.
27. Burrough, P.A. and R.A. McDonnell, 1998. *Principles of Geographical Informational Systems*. Oxford University Press. Page 54.
28. Samet, H. 1990. *The Design and Analysis of Spatial Data Structures*. Addison-Wesley, Reading, MA.

FIGURE 2.7. *Three patches of aspen embedded in sagebrush illustrate the difference between raster and feature attribute tables, and zones and polygons.*

Type	Map	Attribute Table
Polygon	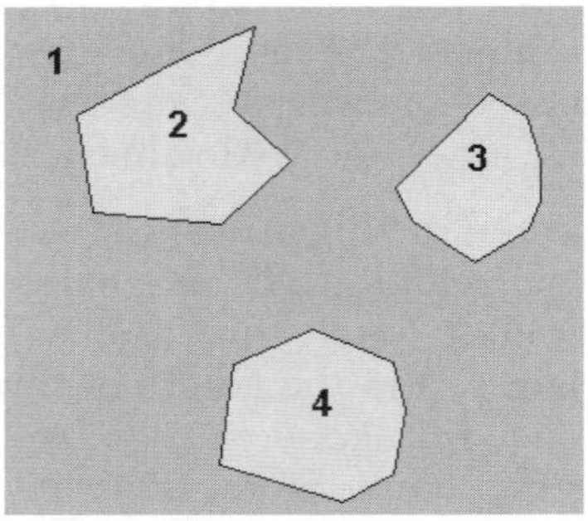	**ID Type** 1 Sage 2 Aspen 3 Aspen 4 Aspen
raster (zone)	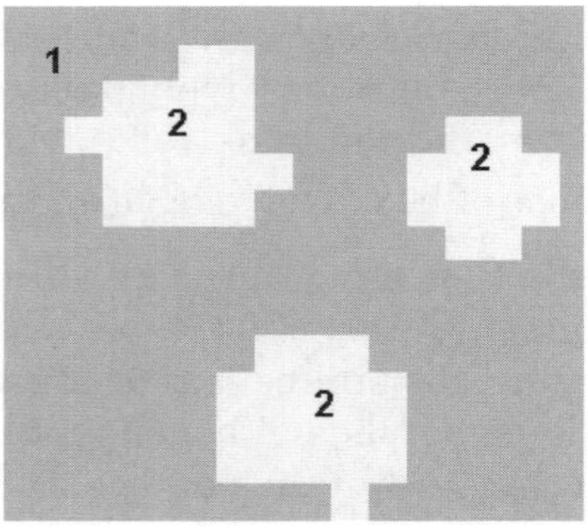	**Value Type** 1 Sage 2 Aspen
raster (after region grouping)	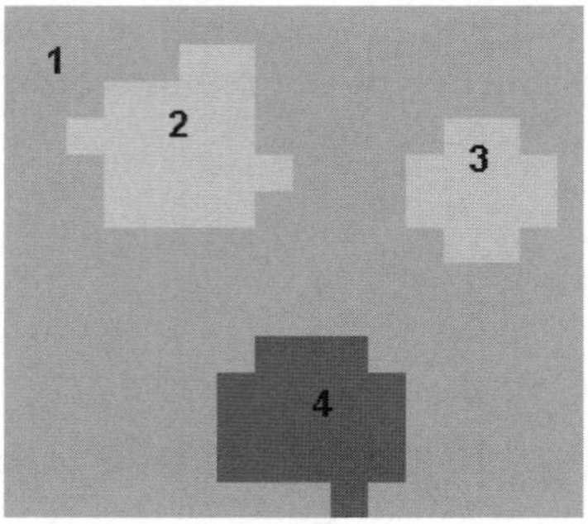	**Value Type** 1 Sage 2 Aspen 3 Aspen 4 Aspen

In order to distinguish the unique patches of aspen in the raster, contiguous regions of same- valued cells must be identified. A *region* is a zone of contiguous cells that have the same, unique value. That is, a cell is grouped with neighboring cells, using either the four adjacent (rook's or von Neumann's case) or eight adjacent and diagonal (queen's or Moore's case) cells that share the same value. The result of this region grouping process is a raster that has zones with unique values. The use of the term *regions* in this context requires adjacency, while (unfortunately the same term is used) a region in a coverage (feature data structure) is able to store disjoint polygons as a single feature (remember the example of the seven islands of Hawaii).

The *spatial extent* of a raster is defined by the number of columns (m) and rows (n) and the cell size or resolution, totaling C cells in the entire spatial extent (Figure 2.8). Note that the spatial extent of a raster is always rectangular in shape. Within the spatial extent, the *NoData* value is used in a raster to signify that the phenomenon of interest does not occur at that location, is outside the study boundary, or that data is missing at that location. Do not confuse NoData with the value 0.0, as 0.0 is valid in raster. NoData values are ignored when computing statistics, and attribute data cannot be associated with them. You can control how different functions behave when they encounter NoData values so that NoData is returned, NoData is ignored and available values are used, or the value is estimated. Locations outside of the extent are considered to have NoData.

FIGURE 2.8. **Analysis properties in Spatial Analyst. A GRID with 5 columns (*m*) and 5 rows (*n*), and total number of cells (C) equals *m* x *n* = C=25. Note that there are 4 NoData (*nd*) values (lighter grey), and the valued cells (darker grey) constitute the analysis mask, which contains C_{nd}=(*m* x *n*)-*nd* cells.**

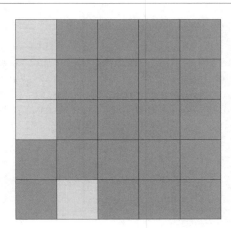

The Source tab on the Layer Properties dialog (shown at right) provides a number of characteristics about a raster. The raster type, directory location, name, status (permanent or temporary), and coordinate system are provided in the Data Source box. Note that the Data Source can be changed to another raster dataset (using the Set Data Source button). In the middle of the dialog are listings for the number of rows and columns (10 each in the

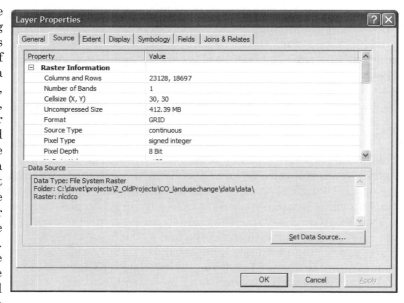

example), the number of bands (typically 1 for regular rasters, but remotely sensed images often have multiple bands), the x and y cell size (meaning the width and height in map units, not area!), the data type (integer or real), and whether pyramids have been created or not. At the bottom, a number of statistics are provided, including: minimum, maximum, mean, and standard deviation. Also note that the *sum* of all raster values is displayed in the classification dialog (from the Symbology tab).

A raster attribute table (a.k.a. the Value Attribute Table) contains, at a minimum, two fields: *value* and *count*. The value field contains the values of a raster cell, and the count field stores the number of cells in a raster that have that value (see the example below, which shows the VAT for the raster in Figure 2.9). A raster will not have an attribute table if the raster is a floating-point type or if it was created from a 1-bit image theme.

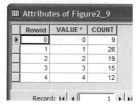

FIGURE 2.9. Raster data represented as a flat ASCII file (upper left), run-length encoded (upper-right), and graphic (lower). NoData values are value -9 (and shown in black).

Flat ASCII	Run-length
-9 -9 1 1 0 1 0 1 -9 -9	2 -9 2 1 1 0 1 1 1 0 1 1 2 -9
-9 -9 1 1 2 2 2 1 1 -9	2 -9 2 1 3 2 2 1 1 -9
-9 1 1 1 2 2 2 2 3 3	4 1 4 2 2 3
1 1 1 1 2 2 2 2 3 3	4 1 4 2 2 3
0 1 1 1 1 2 3 3 3 3	1 0 4 1 1 2 4 3
0 0 0 1 1 1 1 1 1 1	3 0 7 1
0 2 2 3 3 3 -9 4 4 4	1 0 2 2 3 3 1 -9 3 4
0 2 2 3 3 3 3 4 4 4	1 0 2 2 4 3 3 4
0 2 2 2 4 4 4 4 4 4	1 0 3 2 6 4

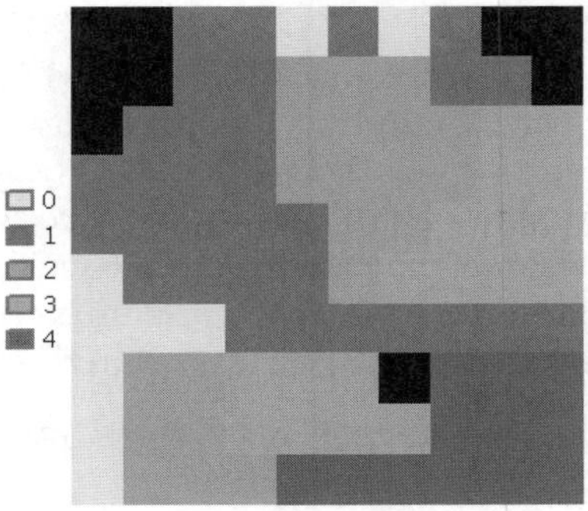

2.3.1 GRID

A GRID is an implementation of a raster data structure developed by ESRI. GRIDs are implementations of the single-layer, multiple value method. GRIDs have m columns and n rows of cells, and are ordered starting from the origin in the upper-left corner. There are two types of GRIDs: *integer GRIDs* and *real GRIDs*. Integer values are used to represent nominal, ordinal, and ratio data and cells that have the same integer values have the same attributes. Integer GRIDs can also be used to represent continuous phenomena. Note that the *Spatial Analyst* extension is needed to conduct analyses on GRIDs, though GRIDs can be displayed and queried in ArcMap without Spatial Analyst.

Run-length encoding is used to compress GRIDs. For example, a GRID comprised of 1,000 columns and 1,000 rows containing all 1s requires about 30KB, but a checkerboard of alternating 0s and 1s (also 1000x1000) requires 358K, about 11 times as much disk space, because there is no row-wise correlation and therefore no compression! Floating-point values are used to represent truly continuous phenomena, but require much more disk space because they cannot be run-length encoded.

One way to reduce the size of a GRID that represents continuous phenomena with floating-point values is to multiply values by an increment of 10 to convert the GRID to an integer GRID. For instance, you could represent the value 10.123 by multiplying the value by 1000, resulting in a GRID value of 10,123 (of course you'll need to remember to divide the value in subsequent analyses by 1,000). The maximum value an integer GRID can represent is 2,147,483,648 (a 4-byte, 32-bit integer) and floating-point GRIDs can store values from -3.4^{38} to 3.4^{38}. The location of pixels and the extent of a GRID is stored using 8-byte floating point numbers (double precision). Previous to ArcGIS v9, the maximum size (m x n) of a GRID was limited by the maximum file size of 2.147 GB (a 32-bit system constraint), which limits an integer GRID to roughly 125,000 x 125,000 and a floating point GRID to roughly 23,000 x 23,000. Raster datasets can be of unlimited size as of v9.

2.3.2 Geodatabase raster

Raster datasets can also be stored directly in geodatabases. There are a number of advantages of using this data structure, including managing a large number of datasets within a single geodatabase, larger (up to 1 TB) file sizes, and faster display and processing. Often multiple rasters are organized using a *raster catalog*, which is a collection of datasets defined in a table format where each record in the table represents an individual raster dataset. Catalogs are often used to manage and display tiled or adjacent datasets, such as a collection of topographic quadrangles for your study area.

Chapter 7 provides a detailed discussion of raster datasets and analysis, in particular raster datasets, raster dataset bands, and raster catalogs.

2.3.3 Images

Image data, which are also stored inside a raster dataset, include remotely sensed satellite images, scanned aerial photographs, and Digital Raster Graphics (digital topographic quads) (Figure 2.10). *Georeferenced images* have an associated header or world file that tells software where to place the image in space. For example, Digital Raster Graphics (scanned, georeferenced images of topographic maps) are typically used as background maps, with spatial data drawn on top of them. Images do not contain attribute data about the features they show, so you cannot query them as you can GRID data. Most common image formats are supported in ArcGIS, such as TIFF, JPEG, and GIF.

FIGURE 2.10. A remotely-sensed image taken mid-morning on April 1, 2004 of the Picnic Rock fire west of Fort Collins, Colorado (image from NASA Earth Observatory website).

2.4 Attribute (non-spatial) data

Recall that one of the key features of GIS is the explicit linkage between a geographic feature at a place and its *attributes*, or information about that feature at that location. A collection of attributes for the features in a given dataset are stored in an *attribute table*, which is implemented using a relational database structure. Data in a *table* are stored as ordered rows, or records. Each record represents a geographic feature, and each record has the same number of columns, or attribute *fields*, associated with it. Each field represents a single attribute. Returning to the earlier example of a map of aspen patches in Chapter 1, the table for the dataset might have, for each patch, attributes such as ID, name, condition, age class, tree size, acres, and aspect.

2.4.1 Data types

It is important to understand the types of attribute data that can be stored, managed, analyzed, and displayed in attribute tables. Generally, attribute data is either qualitative or quantitative. *Qualitative* information tells you what things exist, while *quantitative* information measures the magnitude of things. There are five data types (one qualitative and four quantitative): nominal, ordinal, interval, ratio, and cyclic. The data types that are used most commonly are nominal and ratio.

The *nominal* data type is used for qualitative data: that is, data that indicate the kind of a thing at a location, but not the quantity. This type is also associated with class or categorical data. In the example of the aspen map (Figure 1.2), name and ID (e.g., "Routt-1") would be considered nominal data types. Land cover and land use data are also typical examples of nominal data. Usually nominal data are stored using a text field (e.g., "forest," "wetland," "tundra"). However, nominal data are occasionally stored as integer values (e.g., 1=forest, 2=wetland, 3=tundra). Do not confuse the field data type (string vs. number) with the measurement level (nominal vs. ratio) it represents. Even though nominal data can be (and often are) stored in a numerical field, it is still nominal data. Dividing 3 by 2 (i.e. tundra divided by wetland) when using nominal data is nonsensical. This is sometimes difficult to remember when nominal data are stored in a numerical field, especially when using an integer GRID to represent nominal data.

The *ordinal* data type is used to partition features along some continuum. It is also called rank data. The aspen condition field, with classes of poor, good, and excellent is an example of ordinal data. Also, population density classes such as low, medium, and high, and wildfire hazard ratings of low, medium, high, and extreme are other examples of ordinal data. Again, mathematical operations (e.g., low divided by high) and statistical summaries (e.g., the average) on these data make no sense, though the median class (where an equal number of attributes are higher ranked and lower ranked) is a useful surrogate for the central value.

The *interval* data type is also used to organize features along a continuum, and the intervals between groups have meaning—but the numbers do not have an absolute scale. Temperature is a good example of the interval data type. Because the 0 value for temperature is arbitrary, it does not make sense to say that 60°F is twice as hot as 30°F.

The *ratio* data type is used to organize values along a continuum where the values *do* have an absolute meaning. The number of acres in the aspen patch is a good example of ratio data. Another example is the number of people per county. With ratio data, it does make sense to conduct computations such as "county A has 2.7 times the population of county B", and statistical summaries such as "the average population by county in the US in 2000 is 87,630.5."

The *cyclic* data type is used to characterize directional attributes, such as aspect, degrees on a compass, etc. The reason why this data type is different from ratio is that, although it does make sense to compute and average aspect, you cannot simply average values. For example, although the average of 178° and 182° is 180° (south), the average aspect of 350° and 10° is 180°, but it should be 0° (north). Another example of cyclic data occurs when months in the year are represented as the integers 1 through 12. That is, the colder months (for the northern hemisphere) are typically considered to be 11, 12, 1, and 2 (November through February). These are discontinuous as ratio data, but are actually cyclical where 1 (January) follows 12 (December).

2.4.2 Tables in ArcGIS

In ArcGIS, you can work with tables in both ArcCatalog and ArcMap. ArcCatalog is used primarily to access the properties of fields of attribute tables and to view other existing tables, but tables can also (and only) be created in ArcCatalog. ArcMap is used primarily to work with existing tables, especially to view and edit data (Figure 2.11). Tables that are not associated with a layer are accessed through the Source tab of the table of contents (and again, through its context menu).[29] Tables are stored as database files, such as INFO, dBase, Access, and Oracle, text files (e.g., CSV or tab-delimited), or Microsoft Excel spreadsheets.

---

29. If you are having trouble opening a table that has another table related to it, make sure that filenames conform to the file and path naming conventions—only alphanumeric and underscore are allowed (no spaces).

FIGURE 2.11. Example of a feature attribute table for a polygon shapefile of all the counties in the United States.

ObjectID*	Shape	NAME	STATE_NAME	STATE_FIPS	CNTY_FIPS	FIPS	POP2000	POP2005	POP00_SQMI	POP05_SQMI	WHITE
0	Polygon	Lake of the Woods	Minnesota	27	077	27077	4522	4489	2.5	2.5	4396
1	Polygon	Ferry	Washington	53	019	53019	7260	7347	3.2	3.3	5480
2	Polygon	Stevens	Washington	53	065	53065	40066	41007	15.8	16.1	36078
3	Polygon	Okanogan	Washington	53	047	53047	39564	39942	7.4	7.5	29799
4	Polygon	Pend Oreille	Washington	53	051	53051	11732	12255	8.2	8.6	10973
5	Polygon	Boundary	Idaho	16	021	16021	9871	9933	7.7	7.8	9401
6	Polygon	Lincoln	Montana	30	053	30053	18837	19066	5.1	5.2	18100
7	Polygon	Flathead	Montana	30	029	30029	74471	79196	14.2	15.1	71689
8	Polygon	Glacier	Montana	30	035	30035	13247	12950	4.4	4.3	4693
9	Polygon	Toole	Montana	30	101	30101	5267	5347	2.7	2.7	4945
10	Polygon	Liberty	Montana	30	051	30051	2158	2073	1.5	1.4	2141
11	Polygon	Hill	Montana	30	041	30041	16673	16317	5.7	5.6	13263
12	Polygon	Sheridan	Montana	30	091	30091	4105	3691	2.4	2.2	3982
13	Polygon	Divide	North Dakota	38	023	38023	2283	2090	1.8	1.6	2260
14	Polygon	Burke	North Dakota	38	013	38013	2242	2008	2	1.8	2225
15	Polygon	Renville	North Dakota	38	075	38075	2610	2429	2.9	2.7	2551
16	Polygon	Bottineau	North Dakota	38	009	38009	7149	6509	4.2	3.8	6950
17	Polygon	Rolette	North Dakota	38	079	38079	13674	13642	14.6	14.5	3435
18	Polygon	Towner	North Dakota	38	095	38095	2876	2627	2.8	2.5	2799
19	Polygon	Cavalier	North Dakota	38	019	38019	4831	4257	3.2	2.8	4739
20	Polygon	Pembina	North Dakota	38	067	38067	8585	8007	7.7	7.1	8198
21	Polygon	Kittson	Minnesota	27	069	27069	5285	4994	4.8	4.5	5184
22	Polygon	Roseau	Minnesota	27	135	27135	16338	16781	9.7	10	15671
23	Polygon	Blaine	Montana	30	005	30005	7009	6743	1.7	1.6	3685
24	Polygon	Phillips	Montana	30	071	30071	4601	4404	0.9	0.8	4115

Record: 1 of Records (0 out of 3141 Selected)

Opening an attribute table

1. Open ArcMap.
2. Right-click on the name of the layer in the Table of Contents.
3. Select **Open Attribute Table**.

Previewing an attribute table

1. Open ArcCatalog.
2. Navigate to a desired location and select a dataset.
3. Select the **Preview** tab.
4. Select the Table type from the "Preview:" drop-down list.

2.4.3 Attribute fields

There are seven *field types* that can be used to store data on numerical values, text, dates, and BLOBs (binary large objects). These field types include:

- *short integer*, which can store whole numbers from -32,768 to 32,768 (it uses 2 bytes or 16 bits).
- *long integer*, which can store numbers ranging from -2,147,483,648 to 2,147,483,648 (using 4 bytes).
- *float* (i.e. short real), which can store a value up to 7 significant digits (using 4 bytes).
- *double* (i.e. long real), which can store a value up to 15 significant digits (using 8 bytes).
- *text*, which stores a series of alphanumeric characters (text string) of up to 255 characters in length.
- *date*, which stores dates and times in a particular format, usually: mm/dd/yyyy hh:mm:ss.
- *BLOB* (binary large object) can store a variety of items in a Geodatabase as a long sequence of binary numbers, such as images or multimedia.

To store numbers with values to the right of the decimal place (fractions or real numbers), you need to use either float or double field types. For integer fields (short and long), specify the *precision*, which is the total number of digits stored in a field. For real numerical fields (float and double), specify both the precision and the *scale*, which is the total number of decimal places stored in a field. Be sure to set the fields large enough to hold the desired values, otherwise numbers may be rounded or values changed without any notice. Note that ArcGIS will attempt to change the type of field if the precision and/or scale exceeds the limits of a particular numeric type.

The attribute tables associated with geodatabases offer the ability to apply *attribute domains*, which can be used to constrain the allowable values for a field. There are two types of domains: range and coded. *Range domains* can be applied to quantitative data to specify a minimum and maximum value. *Coded domains* can be applied to any type of data, though they most commonly are applied to nominal data types where there are a limited number possible values. The type of domain is specified in ArcCatalog during the creation of the geodatabase.

An attribute table has a record for each geographic feature showing its associated attributes. There is a column for each field, and the field name is displayed at the top of the column. If a field is indexed, then the name has an asterisk (*) to the right of it. A column can be widened or narrowed by clicking on the vertical black bar to the right of the column name, then dragging to the desired location. A column can also be moved to a different location as well, by clicking on the name and dragging it to the desired location. To keep a column in view when scrolling across a table, *freeze* the column by right-clicking on the header and select **Freeze/Unfreeze Column**. You can move a field to be adjacent to another one (rather than in the default order) by selecting the field, then dragging it to the desired location. You can get more information about the

details of a field through the *Field Properties* dialog (right-click on the desired field and select Field Properties).

Another useful but under-appreciated feature is the ability to modify the display of numbers in the table. That is, you can change the *number format* to make the display of the number more specific to the values represented in the table. This allows you to represent percentages, add thousand's separators (i.e. commas), change the rounding, specify fractions or angles, etc.

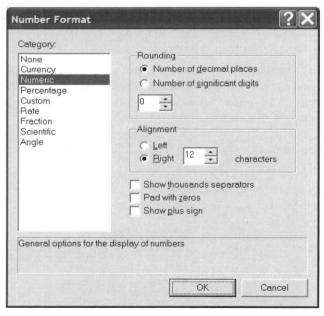

Deleting an existing field

1. With a table open, right-click on field to delete.
2. Select **Delete Field**.

Adding a field

1. With a table open, click on the **Options** button.
2. Select **Add Field...**.

Also, you can *sort* (ascending or descending) a column (or multiple columns) through a field's context menu (by double-clicking on a field name). A very useful technique to explore, understand, and check the values in a field is to sort ascending, examine the values, then sort descending and re-examine the values. Through the Fields tab of the Layers Properties dialog, you can set a number of additional properties of fields (Figure 2.12). Aliases can be provided to change the field name to something more meaningful and fields can be completely hidden from view -- but not removed from the dataset -- by setting their visibility off. The *primary display field* can also be set, which is used to organize the results of an Identify query, to label features on a map, and for *map tips*. From the "Options" menu on a table, you can also bring up the Appearance dialog, which allows you to change the font, size, and of the text in a table, the selection color, and the highlighting color.Also, the context menu is opened by clicking on the "Options" button. Through this menu, the table can be exported and a field can be added[30], among other things. Existing fields cannot be modified, however, so it is best to delete a field, then add a new field to replace it.

Sorting on multiple fields

1. Right-click on field name and select **Advanced Sorting**.
2. Select the field to first sort by and select Ascending or Descending.
3. Continue with additional fields (up to 4 total).
5. Select **OK.**

---

30. A field can also be added using ArcCatalog through the Fields tab of the Properties dialog.

FIGURE 2.12. Aliases, visibility, and the look of a field can be specified in the Fields tab of the Layer Properties dialog.

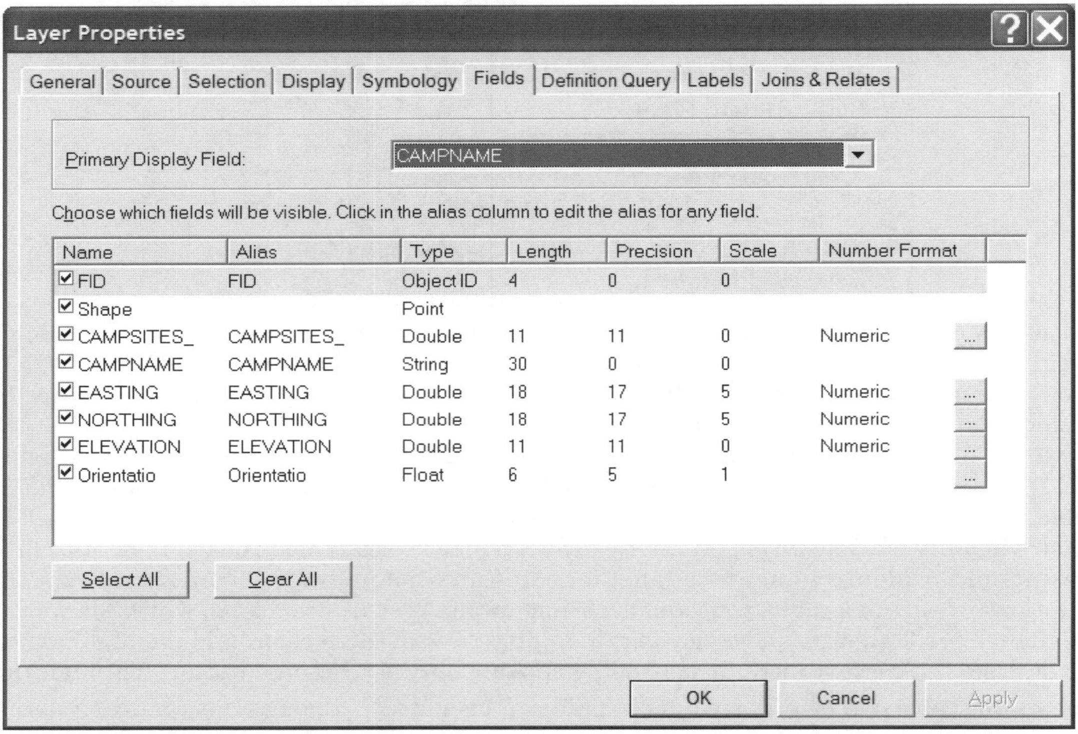

2.4.4 Selections and the selection set

An important concept is the idea of *selections*, or the *selection set*. A selection is a subset of rows in an attribute table and/or a subset of features in a feature class. Knowing what features or rows are selected (and which are not) is important because ArcGIS can perform different operations to a feature or row depending whether it is in the selection set or not. The number of selected and total records is displayed at the bottom of an attribute table, and you can go directly to a specific record number by entering it into the box in the lower-left corner of the attribute table. The "All" and "Selected" buttons allow you to display all the records or just the selected records. The *Selection tab* will also allow you to see how many features are selected in each layer. By clicking on the check box to the left of the layer name, you can specify whether a layer is selectable, so that when you do interactive selection queries on a map, a given layer will respond if designated to do so.

2.4.5 Editing a table

In order to edit attribute data, an editing session needs to be started. Edits can then be made directly to a table (click in a table cell and change it to the desired value). To add a record to a table, scroll all the way to the bottom of the table, and then type into the cells in the blank row at the end. Records can be copied and pasted. To delete a record, select the record (ctrl-click to select multiple records) and then press the Delete key. You can also undo edits during your edit session using Edit->Undo. In order to save edits, the edit session must be closed. Fields cannot be added or deleted during an edit session.

Starting/stopping an edit session

1. Make sure Editor toolbox is opened (if not, select **View -> Toolbars -> Editor**).
2. Select **Editor** (button) **-> Start Editing** (or **Stop Editing**).

2.4.6 Joining and relating tables

Relational tables are useful because they organize attributes in a straightforward way, and data from another table can be related using a relational join. *Joining* and *relating* allow you to associate any two tables to access additional data about geographic features. Typically, tables are joined to display additional data that is not currently in a layer's attribute table. The key to relating tables is that they must have a *common field*. For example, typically, an attribute table contains a unique ID field, such as a name (e.g., Larimer County), but more commonly a number (e.g., a county FIPS code: 8069). If a separate table with additional attribute data (e.g., 2000 Census data) also has the unique ID field, then the two can be related. In ArcGIS, you can either *join* or *relate* two tables. Joining brings the two tables together "virtually," so they appear as one but remain two separate files. The map document saves the virtual join and re-establishes the join when you open it. To permanently join two tables, use the Join Field tool.

Relating, however, establishes a linkage between two tables, but they remain separate.[31] There are four types of relates: one-to-one, many-to-one, one-to-many, and many-to-many (Table 2.12). In ArcGIS, the common fields do not need to have the same name, but the two fields do need to be the same *type* (e.g., string or number).[32] You can join numbers to numbers, strings to strings (case sensitive), Boolean to Boolean, and dates to dates. The table name is inserted in front of the field names in the resulting joined table, so that in

---

31. This is like *link* in ArcView v3.x.
32. Previous releases of ArcInfo (commands JOINITEM or RELATE) required common names as well.

the joined table the new name will be <TableName>.<FieldName>. Properties of joined fields are also provided.

Joining and relating tables

1. In ArcMap, right-click on the name of the desired layer (in the Table of Contents).
2. Select **Joins and Relates** -> **Join...** (or Relate...).
3. Choose the common field in Step 1.
4. Choose the table to join in Step 2.
5. Select the common field for the joined table in Step 3.
4. Click **OK**.

Permanently joining tables

1. In ArcToolbox, open **Data Management Tools** -> **Joins** -> **Join Field**.
2. Select the input dataset (table) to join a table to.
3. Choose the field in the input dataset to join on.
4. Choose the table to join.
5. Select the common field for the joined table.
4. Click **OK**.

Joins may fail if fields are improperly named. Field names should not any characters that are not alphanumeric or an underscore (but do not start the field name with a number or underscore). The maximum length of a field name is 10 for shapefiles (and .dbf), 16 for INFO tables, and 52 for Geodatabase. Lastly, field names should not include "reserved words", more common reserved words include: avg, count, counter, currency, date, day, description, end, group, index, key, left, max, min, mod, month, name, note, parameter, PERCENT, PRIMARY, RIGHT, sum, time, union, value, values, year, zone..

TABLE 2.12. Relate types. Tables can be joined for one-to-one and many-to-one types. Tables can be related for one-to-many and many-to-one types.

Type	Table A		Table B		Result		
One-to-one	Value A1		Value B1		Value A1 B1		
	1	a	1	A	1	a	A
	2	b	2	B	2	b	B
	3	c	3	C	3	c	C
	4	d	4	D	4	d	D
	5	e	5	E	5	e	E
Many-to-one	Value A1		Value B1		Value A1 B1		
	1	a	1	A	1	a	A
	1	b	2	B	1	b	A
	2	c	3	C	2	c	B
	4	d	4	D	4	d	D
	4	e	5	E	4	e	D
One-to-many	Value A1		Value B1				
	1	a	1	A			
	2	b	1	B			
	3	c	3	C			
	4	d	3	D			
	5	e	3	E			
Many-to-many	Value A1		Value B1				
	1	a	1	A			
	1	b	1	B			
	2	c	1	C			
	3	d	2	D			
	3	e	2	E			

2.4.7 Importing and exporting tables

Occasionally you will need to bring tabular data into ArcGIS that is not currently in a database format such as dBASE or INFO. ArcGIS automatically recognizes *.txt, *.csv, and *.asc files as comma delimited, and *.tab files as tab-delimited tables. Note that you cannot edit these text file tables in ArcGIS, however. To gain access to these data, simply add the tables to the map document just as you would a coverage or shapefile. Be sure to close the text file (e.g., if you created the file in Microsoft® Excel) before trying to add the data to ArcGIS. Alternatively, you can convert a text file into a dBASE file, and an easy way to convert a spreadsheet is to save it to dBASE IV format. Be sure to double-check your data, however, as some spreadsheet conversion routines (especially MS Excel 97) have some idiosyncrasies.

The first line in the text file must contain the field names for the table, and strings can be either quoted or unquoted. Fields with values containing any non-numeric characters are treated as string fields. Fields with values containing only numbers are treated as numeric fields. (If you want to read numeric values in as strings, enclose the numbers in quotes). Spaces and underscores are the only non-alphanumeric characters that should be used. Although ArcGIS will read *.txt files with field names that contain spaces and are longer than 11 characters, due to dBASE limitations you should keep field names to 10 characters or less and without spaces, brackets, and hyphens.

Occasionally you may want to add tabular data that have x, y data, also known as point event data.[33] For example, output files from GPS typically create tabular files with x, y coordinates, such as latitude/longitude, and this provides an easy method to add tabular data as a map layer. Tables can be exported to a variety of data formats, including: text (comma-delimited), dBASE, INFO, geodatabase, and SDE.

Adding x, y data from a table

1. In ArcMap, select **Tools -> Add XY Data...**
2. Browse to find desired file.
3. Specify the fields that contain the x and y data.
4. Click **OK**.

Exporting a table

1. In ArcMap, open the table (right-click, **Open Attribute Table...**).
2. Click on **Options** button.
3. Select **Export...**
4. Click on the Browse button and specify the table type and name.
5. Click **Save**.

---

33. In ArcView v3.x, this was called an event theme.

A complete list of supported formats is provided in Table 2.13.

TABLE 2.13. Feature data formats that can be imported into ArcGIS (with ArcINFO license).

Name	Description
AGF	Atlas Geo Files. Import AGF files in ArcToolbox, Conversion Tools, Import to Shapefile.
DFAD	National Imagery and Mapping Agency's format, and Digital Feature Analysis Data (DFAD) levels 1, 2, 1-c, and 3-c are supported. VPF has replaced DFAD.
DIME	US Census Bureau's Dual Independent Map Encoding (DIME) files, created for the 1980 census, and replaced in 1990 with TIGER/Line files.
DLG	US Geological Survey's Digital Line Graph (DLG), providing data on transportation, hydrography, contours, and public land boundaries. See: http://mapping.usgs.gov/standards/
E00	ESRI's ArcINFO export interchange file (*.e00). Available in ArcToolbox. Only coverages and GRIDs can be imported and exported to an e00 file.
ETAK	Etak, Inc.'s format ETAK stores street networks.
GIRAS	The US Geological Survey's Geographic Information Retrieval Analysis System (GIRAS) provides land use and land cover data. See: http://edc.usgs.gov/glis/hyper/guide/1_250_lulc
IGDS	MicroStation's Interactive Graphic Design Software (IGDS) is a CAD export format.
IGES	Initial Graphics Exchange Standard (IGES) is a neutral format for CAD/CAM data (*.iges, *.igs).
MIF	MapInfo's Map Interchange File (MIF) stores graphic data in (*.mif) and tabular data in (*.mid) files. Import MIFs in ArcToolbox, Conversion Tools, Import to Shapefile. For more information on the MIF format, see: http://www.mapinfo.com/community/free/library/interchange_file.pdf
MOSS	US Department of Interior's Mapping Overlay Statistical System (MOSS), implemented by the BLM in 1977. The exchange files. mif, dpf, dpw
S-57	International Maritime Organization format, defined by the International Hydrographic Organization Special Publication 57 (hence the name). A hierarchical collection of oceanographic features.
SDTS	US Geological Survey's Spatial Data Transfer Standard (STDS). Note that only point type data can be imported with an ArcView license. Import STDS using ArcToolbox, Conversion Tools, Import to Coverage, SDTS.Point to Coverage.

TABLE 2.13. Feature data formats that can be imported into ArcGIS (with ArcINFO license).

SLF	USF National Mapping and Imagery Agency's Standard Linear Format (SLF).
TIGER	US Bureau of Census's Topologically Integrated Geographic Encoding and Referencing system (TIGER/Line). See: http://www.census.gov/geo/www/tiger/index.html

2.5 Chapter review

- Three aspects are central to understanding the nature of geographic data: *where* a geographic phenomena of interest is located; *what* attributes of a place we are interested in; and *when* it has occurred in time.

- The two common data models are *vector* and *raster*. The vector data model represents geographic features as points, lines, areas, or networks. The raster data model represents geographic phenomenon as a matrix of cells (or pixels).

- Topology is defined as the spatial relationships between connecting or adjacent features. A *topological data structure* explicitly stores topological relations in a data file.

- Geodatabases, shapefiles, and coverages are all specific data structures implementing the vector data model.

- A GRID is a specific data structure that implements the raster data model.

- A key characteristic of GIS is the explicit linkage between a location and its attributes.

- There are five main types of attribute data: nominal (class), ordinal, interval, ratio, and cyclic. Note that these are different than the field data type (e.g., land use classes could be represented by 1, 2, 3 etc. and stored in a double numeric field type, but they still represent nominal data).

- A selection is a subset of rows in an attribute table and/or a subset of features in a feature class, which is important because ArcGIS performs different operations to a feature or row depending whether it is selected or not.

3 *Scale, coordinate systems, and projections*

3.1 Location, location, location...

Location is *the* essential feature of maps in general, and geographic information systems in particular. Humans have mapped geographic phenomena for tens of thousands of years, and numerous ways to locate geographic features have been developed.

One of these is to simply name a place. *Place names* are commonly used to reference locations, such as Timbuktu, San Francisco, Meade's Ranch[1], and the "A" overlooking the City of Fort Collins. But place names do not always remain constant through time, so trying to locate Constantinople on a World Atlas now would likely produce much frustration, unless you knew its more current name of Istanbul. (Why the name change? "...that's nobody's business but the Turks!") Moreover, the spatial resolution of places names varies greatly—picture the area covered by the following place names: Asia, Nepal, Mt. Everest, and the summit of Mt. Everest. Another method to locate places are *postal addresses*, which are used across the globe to locate residences and businesses. They, of course, work remarkably well for the delivery of

---

1. Meade's Ranch is very close to the geodetic center of North America, in Osborne County, Kansas.

mail, but they are problematic for other uses, such as identifying the response location during an emergency call (i.e. 9-1-1). Also, natural features such as mountains, rivers, and prairies cannot be addressed well. (We will return to postal addressing and geocoding later in this chapter.) As a result, we have devised ways to more systematically locate geographic features to reference any location on Earth with fine detail through the use of geographic coordinate systems.

A useful way to reference features on Earth is using a globe because mapping on one entails minimal distortion. Distance, direction, shape, area, and proximity can be measured relatively accurately. Locations on a globe are defined by a *geographical coordinate system*, namely latitude and longitude. Latitude and longitude are actually angular measurements using spherical polar coordinates. Globes are bulky and are not very functional for mapping detailed features, and distance and area computations on a globe are more complex because they require spherical geometry. But a fundamental challenge is to take a globe or sphere and flatten it out. For example, try this exercise: imagine you were holding a large orange in your hand and that you drew with a black felt-tip pen the outlines of the continents onto the orange. Notice that of course you can see only half the continents at any one time. Now try to peel the orange to create a map of the whole world, visible at once, on your desk. How'd you do?

Because of these sticky difficulties, projections were developed to transform spherical coordinates to planar (Cartesian) coordinates, to create what is called a *projected coordinate system*. A coordinate system is a reference system that allows geographic features to be represented in a coherent, comprehensive, and common geographic framework. Each coordinate system is defined by a measurement system (either geographic or projected), a unit of measurement (e.g., degrees, meters, or feet), and spheroid, datum, and projection parameters.

But before we move on, how about a concrete example? Notice the "A" in the lower-left corner of the picture to the right? That's the "A" that overlooks Colorado State University (and Hughes Stadium). What's its location? This depends on which coordinate system we want to use! Even though the location on Earth's surface is the same, its location can be described in numerous

ways. It so happens to be located at latitude 40°33'40.24373" (N) and longitude 105°09'05.97681" (W) (in NAD83). In UTM coordinates, it is at 486,993.56 (E), 4,480,125.32 (N), UTM Zone 13 N, NAD83 (meters). And in SPC coordinates, it is at 3,096,785.31 (E), 1,447,468.7 (N), SPC Colorado North, NAD83 (Feet).

3.2 Scale

Geographic features are reduced in size to enable them to be represented and displayed on a globe or map. Representing features is necessary, as Lewis Carroll makes obvious:

> *"What a useful thing a pocket-map is!" I remarked. "That's another thing we've learned from your Nation," said Mein Herr, "map-making. But we've carried it much further than you. What do you consider the largest map that would be really useful?" "About six inches to the mile." "Only six inches!" exclaimed Mein Herr. "We very soon got to six yards to the mile. Then we tried a hundred yards to the mile. And then came the grandest idea of all! We actually made a map of the country, on the scale of a mile to the mile!" "Have you used it much?" I enquired. "It has never been spread out, yet," said Mein Herr: "the farmers objected: they said it would cover the whole country, and shut out the sunlight! So we now use the country itself, as its own map, and I assure you it does nearly as well."*

> *-- Lewis Carroll -- from Silvio and Bruno Concluded, 1893.*

The amount of reduction is called the map scale. There are four common ways of expressing map scale, which are described in detail below. But it is important to understand that discussing scale in this way is very much an artifact of historical and current reliance on paper maps and the inherent limitations of them. Because much digital data are still derived from paper maps, the concepts of scale, resolution, and detection remain important for digital GIS, however.

The *scale* of a map is the *ratio* of a distance on the map to a distance on Earth. This is the first way to express map scale—as a ratio or representative fraction. For example, a baseball-sized (3.5") globe (a scale model of Earth) would be at a scale of 1:125,000,000, while a 24" globe would be at 1:20,000,000 scale. To draw a typical US highway map (1:1,000,000) would require a 41' diameter globe, while a 1,750' diameter globe would be required to map at a scale of 1:24,000 (USGS 7.5' Topographic map). On a paper map, if the length of a city block is 1 cm and on the ground it is 1 km (100,000 cm), then the map scale is 1:100,000. Notice that map scale is unitless.

Geographers (and occasionally others) are trained to refer to maps as "large" or "small" scale maps. So-called large-scale maps have relatively large ratios, such as 1:50,000, whereas small-scale maps have relatively smaller ratios, such as 1:1,000,000. Unfortunately—at least for the geographers—other disciplines and the general public tend to refer to the scale of maps in the opposite way. That is, to the broader public, large-scale maps depict broad spatial extents (e.g., 1:1,000,000, while small-scale maps show smaller extents (e.g., 1:50,000). To reduce potential confusion when discussing map scale, the terms *fine-scale* (i.e. 1:50,000) and *broad-scale* (1:1,000,000) are preferred.

A second way to describe scale is simply to use words, such as "1 inch equals 1 mile" (which corresponds to 1:63,360). A final method to describe scale is to use a graphic scale. A conventional way to show a graphic scale is in the form of a line drawn on a map that contains subdivisions of units appropriate to the scale of the map. Although this method is not as mathematically precise, it has the advantage that the scale changes size in proportion to changes in map size. That is, if you make a reduced (or enlarged) photocopy of a map, the graphic scale also is reduced and thus is still accurate, whereas the representative fraction scale (based on the original map) for the photocopied map is incorrect.

The ability to resolve features on a map depends largely on the scale of the map. Because the finest mark on a paper that can be readily reproduced is typically 0.5 mm, then the *resolution,* or ability to distinguish individual parts of a geographic object, is equal to the map scale times 0.5 mm.[2] For example, if you had a 1:24,000 scale map, the smallest feature you can represent on it is 12 meters (see Table 3.1). And to *detect* a feature requires twice the resolution, so the smallest object that can be detected on a 1:24,000 scale map is 24 m wide. It is important to know the scale of the map you are working with and to understand the associated resolution and detection levels. For one thing, determining polygons that have areas smaller than the area of the smallest detectable size feature will help you understand what features can be represented (and to set a benchmark limit to define spurious polygons).

TABLE 3.1. Sample resolution, detection, and area amounts assuming the minimum line on a map is 0.5 mm.

Scale	Resolution	Detection	Area
1:10,000	5 m	10 m	100 m^2
1:24,000	12 m	24 m	576 m^2
1:50,000	25 m	50 m	2,500 m^2
1:100,000	50 m	100 m	10,000 m^2
1:250,000	125 m	250 m	62,500 m^2
1:1,000,000	500 m	1,000 m	1,000,000 m^2

Another important concept for computer-based mapping is the precision with which spatial coordinates are stored. For example, if someone provides you with latitude and longitude coordinates that are specified to the nearest second, then what is the precision of the location that was specified? Assuming 111,195 m per degree of latitude (at the

2. Tobler, W. 1988. Resolution, resampling, and all that. In: *Building databases for Global Science*, Mounsey, H. (ed.) Taylor and Francis. Pgs 129-137.

equator), then specifying location to the nearest second is precise to within ± 30.8 m (Table 3.2).

TABLE 3.2. Precision of latitude and longitude measurements.

Precision	Distance (m)
Degree (1°)	111,195
Minute (1')	1,853
Second (1")	30.8
Decimal degree (1.0°)	11,119.5
Decimal degree (1.00°)	1,111.9
Decimal degree (1.000°)	111.1
Decimal degree (1.0000°)	11.1
Decimal degree (1.00000°)	1.1

Another related concept is the idea of the *minimum mapping unit* (MMU). The MMU is a measure of the detail (resolution) of which discrete features are represented—features on a map must be at least as large as the MMU. For example, the standard MMU for mapping land cover polygons for the USGS National Gap Program is 100 ha—smaller patches of land cover are not typically mapped. The MMU concept, however, needs to also include the shape of features in addition to area. Linear-shaped patches such as riparian areas alongside a stream are often quite large in area (and greater than the MMU), but are often not mapped because they are long and thin.[3]

3.2.1 Scale in a digital world

As was discussed earlier, traditional concepts about scale are rooted in the paper map (or analog representation), which imposes some limitations when using GIS because geographic features can now be represented and analyzed digitally. Scale in a digital world has some important differences.[4] First, with digital data, the idea of a representative fraction is no longer a definitive characteristic. That is, there is no longer a requirement for the trade-off between geographic coverage (a.k.a. spatial extent) and the resolution (or grain) of a map. Instead, it is theoretically possible to create an electronic dataset that has all 1:24,000 quads for the US (all 53,911 of them) tiled together into a single, seamless (and very large) dataset that would cover roughly four international-size

---

3. Theobald, D.M. 2000. Correcting linear and perimeter measurement errors in raster-based data. *Cartography and Geographic Information Science* 27(2): 111-116.
4. Quattrochi, D.A. and M.F. Goodchild (eds.). 1996. *Scale in Remote Sensing and GIS*. Boca Raton, Florida: Lewis Publishers.

soccer fields. In this case, the resolution or grain of the data would be based on 1:24,000 scale, but the coverage would be for the whole US. So, describing this map as a national-scale map would belie the detail of features. Second, it is possible for geographic features to be represented in a way (e.g., through object-oriented data structures like the geodatabase) so that the feature changes depending on the context of the display or analysis. For example, it would be best to use point features to represent cities if you are computing a city-to-city mileage table for a gazetteer (e.g., to determine the number of miles from Santa Fe to Denver). However, it would be best to represent cities as areal features if you wanted to estimate the amount of urban land cover, and perhaps how that has changed (i.e. the city that has sprawled most: Atlanta? Los Angeles?) in the past decade. In these examples the domain of the question (the whole US) has not changed, but the feature abstraction (point vs. area) has changed. Representing geographic features as objects offers the ability to address this complexity during display as well as analysis. Third, the detail with which features can be represented on paper maps is constant throughout the map. However, often the sampling resolution of collection varies from location to location, and digital maps can fully represent this variability. For example, census blocks (a subdivision of the more familiar census tract) are the fundamental unit for counting population in the US and for possible re-arrangement of political districts. Blocks vary widely in size depending mostly on housing density—they can be as small as a city block in an urban area, as large as a whole neighborhood in a suburban areas, or encompass tens of thousands of acres in rural areas. The sampling intensity varies tremendously, but this is not typically taken into account during analysis. As more and more datasets are created digitally and rely less and less on paper maps, the differences between digital and paper scale will become paramount. An important "take home" message of this discussion is that because extent and grain are independent properties of a digital map, one needs to specify both the spatial extent (broad or local) and grain (coarse or fine) when describing a map.

3.3 Geographic coordinate systems

Thinking of Earth as a sphere is convenient, and provides the basis for the idea of a globe. A *geographic coordinate system* uses latitude and longitude to define locations on the surface of a globe. Geographical coordinates are typically portrayed by drawing a systematic grid of latitude and longitudinal lines, called a *graticule*. A graticule is a set of meridians and parallels that represent the locations of latitude and longitude. Because Earth rotates, the rotational axis forms a useful reference point. A *parallel* is a line on Earth's surface formed by the intersection of a plane that is normal (perpendicular) to the rotational axis, or a line drawn through both poles. The *equator* is a parallel that intersects the center of the sphere, and so is found at 0° latitude. Parallels are identified by their latitude from 0° to 90°north or south of the equator.

A *meridian* is a line on Earth formed by the intersection of a plane passing through both poles. Meridians and parallels intersect at right angles on a globe. Because there is no natural reference point for meridians, the starting point for longitude, or *prime meridian* (0° longitude), has been arbitrarily defined to pass through the Royal Observatory in Greenwich, England.[5] As a result, the eastern hemisphere runs from east of this line through the International Date Line at 180°, while the western hemisphere lies to the west of the prime meridian. Geographic locations are then described in terms of degrees, minutes (there are 60 minutes in a degree), and seconds (there are 60 seconds in a minute) away

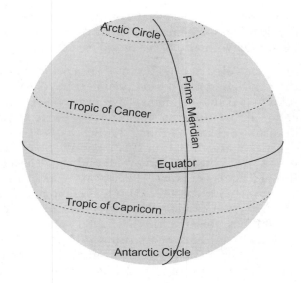

from the prime meridian (east or west longitude) and from the equator (north or south latitude).

To more easily represent geographic coordinates in a computer, degrees, minutes, and seconds are converted to decimal degrees, with the western hemisphere in negative longitude and the southern hemisphere in negative latitude. Typically meridian and parallel lines are drawn at 30° to form a graticule for world projections, but can be smaller for maps that cover a smaller area (finer-scale maps).

3.3.1 Spheroids and datums

Well, the idea that Earth is a perfect sphere is nice and makes the mathematics easier, but it turns out (pun intended) that Earth's shape is not a perfect sphere. Rather, it bulges slightly at the equator due to the force of rotation, creating what is called an *oblate spheroid*. Ellipsoids are used to represent the oblate spheroid, with the amount of flattening defined as the reduction of the minor axis relative to the major axis. Also, there

---

5. Why in Greenwich, England? Actually, numerous countries developed maps with their own prime meridians: France on Paris, US on Washington, D.C., and Brazil on Rio de Janeiro. In 1884, delegates from 25 nations convened in Washington at the International Meridian Conference, where it was decided that the world standard was to be in England, largely because England was the world naval power at this time.

are some other irregularities in the shape due to the geological composition of Earth's surface that are important for projections when high precision is required. So, cartographers and surveyors have developed a number of *spheroids* to more accurately approximate the true shape of Earth. Different spheriods have been developed to fit more accurately a particular region of Earth. For this reason, simply reporting a latitude and longitude (without noting the spheroid and datum) is inadequate.

Spheroids are used as the basis for a set of control points called a *datum*. A datum defines the position of a spheriod (usually) in relation to the center of Earth and establishes a reference frame for measuring locations on the surface. Different representations of the spheroid are required for different parts of Earth. As a result, there are a variety of different datums (Table 3.3) such as NAD27 (North American Datum 1927), NAD83 (North American Datum 1983), and WGS84 (World Geodetic System of 1984). The NAD27 uses the Clarke1866 spheroid, and the origin of the datum is a location called Meade's Ranch, Kansas. Since 1927, a number of technologies have enabled more accurate measurements, so the NAD83 was created. It uses the GRS1980 spheroid, and its origin is Earth's center of mass. The corrections to NAD27 caused shifts in North America as much as 500 feet. Because the GRS1980 spheroid is very similar to the WGS1984 spheroid, NAD1983 data are compatible with GPS data that are collected using the WGS1984 datum. Currently, the HARN (High Accuracy Reference Network) effort is re-adjusting the NAD1983 datum to a yet higher level of accuracy. There are also *vertical datums*, such as the North American Vertical Datum of 1988 (NAVD88).

TABLE 3.3. Common datums used in North America.

Datum	Description
North American Datum 1927 (NAD1927)	NAD1927 used the Clarke 1866 spheroid and yielded adjusted lat/longs for roughly 26,000 survey stations
North American Datum 1983 (NAD1983)	NAD1983 used the GRS80 ellipsoid (which is Earth-centered) and yielded adjusted lat/longs for roughly 250,000 survey stations
World Geodetic System of 1984 (WGS84)	Developed by the US Department of Defense, it has been updated by satellite measurements and uses the WGS84 ellipsoid.

Note that when you are projecting data into a coordinate system based on a different spheroid, you will also have to specify the *geographic transformation* to convert between datums. For example, if you are converting between NAD27 and NAD83 datums, then typically you will use the NADCON conversion method that is based on the National Geodetic Survey's CONUS grid that specifies the transformations for the contiguous 48 states and results in sub-meter accuracy.

3.4 Projected coordinate systems

A *projection* is a systematic rendering of geographic coordinates that allows a sphere to be transformed to a planar surface with Cartesian coordinates. A projection essentially allows you to peel your orange and stretch it out flat in a systematic, or known way, because it is impossible to flatten a spherical surface without some sort of distortion.

One reason to project geographic coordinates is that degrees of latitude and longitude do not have a standard length; that is, distance and area on the surface of Earth decline systematically as you move towards the poles away from the equator. As a result, distances (if they involve any east-west orientation) and area are systematically biased. The greater the range of latitude values, and the further the latitudes are away from the equator, the more distortion is involved[6] (Table 3.4).

TABLE 3.4. Change in east-west distance as a function of latitude.

Latitude(+/-)	Proportion	Distance (km) of 1° of longitude
0°	1.000	111.32
10°	0.985	109.63
20°	0.940	104.61
30°	0.866	96.41
40°	0.766	85.28
50°	0.643	71.56
60°	0.500	55.66
70°	0.342	38.07
80°	0.174	19.33

This approaches the computation of distance and area from a Cartesian perspective that uses planimetric computations in 2D space. Although it has become commonplace to compute geometric properties (distance, area, etc.) with projected coordinates (Professor Waldo Tobler calls this the "flat earth" syndrome[7]), there is no reason that spherical coordinates (latitude/longitude) cannot be used—it's just that spherical geometry is required to compute distance and area (i.e. a different formula). With increasing emphasis

---

6. These are rough approximations, more detailed estimates depend on the spheroid assumed.
7. Tobler, W. 2002. Global spatial analysis. www.geog.ucsb.edu/~tobler/publications/pdf_docs/geog_analysis/GloblAnalys.pdf.

in environmental science on analyzing global patterns, it makes sense to keep data in geographic coordinates and conduct analyses using spherical geometry. Another common work-around is to develop approximations using an equal-area latitude/longitude grid with cells of 1° or 2° on a side.[8]

3.4.1 Properties and characteristics

All projections have distortions in distance, direction, shape, area, or proximity. Most projections are the result of some useful compromise in one or more of these properties. *Conformality* means "correct form or shape." Conformal projections show the shapes of small features correctly (large features may have some distortion). The latitude-longitude graticule intersects at right angles in conformal projections.

Equal-area projections have the property that a unit area is equivalent in any location. So, a coin placed on one part of a map covers exactly the same area as any other part of the map. Scale changes that occur in one direction must be offset by changes in the opposite direction, and so this compensation causes some distortion, such as compaction or elongation of features. Lines of latitude and longitude do not intersect at right angles. A map cannot be simultaneously conformal and equal area.

Equi-distant projections have the property that distance from one point to others, but not all points to all other points, can be measured accurately. The most common equi-distant projection is the azimuthal equidistant projection.

Equi-azimuthal projections preserve angles (or direction), where the azimuth is defined by the angle formed at the starting point of a straight line in relation to a meridian.

All projections have discontinuities, where the globe needs to be "torn" along an edge. Most commonly for world projections this is done at the poles and at 180° longitude.

3.4.2 Projection types

A useful way to understand the patterns of distortion for a projection is to understand projection surfaces and projection light sources. That is, imagine that you were able to move a light bulb around a transparent, plastic globe with black lines showing the graticule. The amount and type of distortion that will result depends on where the light source is placed and the shape of the surface on which the globe is being projected.

3.4.2.1 Geometric

There are three geometric projection surfaces: the plane, cylinder, and cone (Figure 3.1). Typical planar projections work by simply laying a plane on top of the globe, touching at only one point. Conceptually, cylindrical projections work by wrapping a piece of paper around the globe, then unrolling it to make a map. Conical projections work by making a "hat" (cone) and

---

8. For example, Miller, R.I. .1994. *Mapping the diversity of nature.* London: Chapman & Hall.

placing it on the globe. The cylinder and cone then can be "developed" or unrolled to make a planar surface. Notice that both the cone and cylinder touch (or are tangent to) the globe along a line, rather than just at a single point.

FIGURE 3.1. **Different geometric projections: planar (polar orthographic—top left); conical (Albers equal area—top right); and cylindrical (Mercator—bottom).**

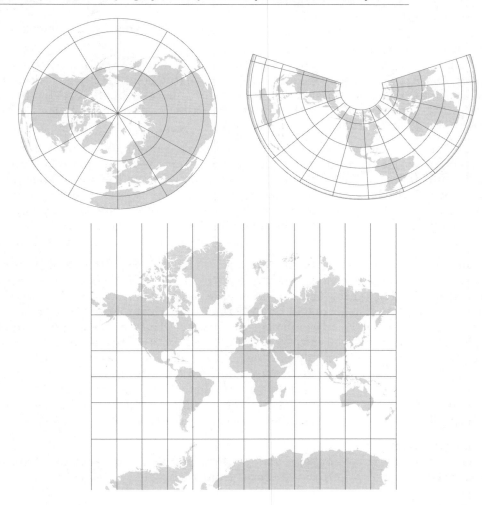

Projection characteristics can be classified by the *light source location*. Again, there are three: gnomonic, stereographic, and orthographic. A *gnomonic* light source is located at the center of the globe. This means that any *great circle*—the shortest distance between two points on a globe—is a straight line on a

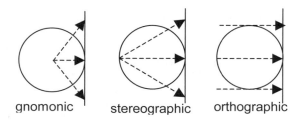

gnomonic projection. Gnomonic projections are typically used for aviation. The light source for *stereographic* projections is located at the antipode (the point exactly opposite the point of tangency of the projection surface). This light source typically creates conformal projections. The light source for *orthographic* projections is at infinity. True direction can be measured with orthographic projections.

There are three orientations of projection surfaces: normal (or regular), transverse, or oblique. The *normal* orientation for planar projections is at the pole, for cylindrical projections it is tangent along the equator, and for conical projections it is tangent along a parallel (line of latitude) with its apex over a pole. The *transverse* orientation occurs when tangency is changed by 90 degrees, so that a plane is tangent at the equator, a cylinder is tangent along a meridian (line of longitude), and the apex of a cone is above the equator. *Oblique* orientations lie in other locations besides the normal or transverse orientations.

Projection surfaces can be *tangent*, so their surfaces touche the globe at a point or along a line, or *secant*, when the surface intersects and passes through the globe. The secant case of projections is frequently used to minimize overall distortion when displaying continental-scale data. For example, the Albers Equal-Area projection is commonly used when displaying data for the coterminous United States. The secant case of this projection uses two standard parallels, typically at 29°30' and 45°30' latitude. In this projection, features that are between the standard parallels are reduced slightly, while above and below the standard parallels features are enlarged slightly. Distortion is minimal for features right at the standard parallels, while distortion is greatest at 37° and below 29°30' and above 45°30'. However, distortion is minimized for all features in the US compared to if a single standard parallel were used (tangent case).

3.4.2.2 Mathematical
Projections can also be defined by some mathematical formula. For instance, the Mercator projection (which is based on a normal, cylindrical geometric surface) is defined as:

$$x = R(\lambda\lambda_o)$$

$$y = R(\ln(\tan((\pi/4) + (\phi/2))))$$

where R is defined as the radius of the sphere at the scale of the map, λ is longitude east of Greenwich, λ_0 is longitude east of Greenwich of the central meridian or of the origin of the rectangular coordinates, and ϕ is north latitude. There are many other mathematically based projections.[9]

3.4.3 Distortion patterns

Because all projections have distortion, it is important to understand how the geometry of the projection leads to minimal distortion in one location and maximal distortion in others. Understanding these distortion patterns will help you choose a proper projection.

In the tangent case, distortion is minimal at the point of tangency and increases with increasing distance from the tangent (see Figure 3.2). In the secant case, there is minimal distortion at the line of tangency, and distortion increases at locations toward the center of the map away from the line of tangency. Also, distortion increases at locations away from the line of tangency toward the edges of the map. This pattern holds true for planar, cylindrical, and conical surfaces.

FIGURE 3.2. Distortion patterns on planar surfaces.[10] Higher levels of distortion are shown by darker shades.

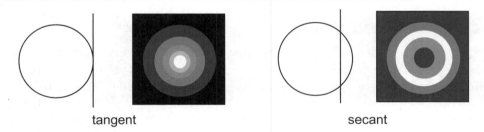

tangent   secant

In the 19th century, a French cartographer named Tissot devised a way to show distortion in both shape and size. His method, known as Tissot's indicatrix, simply plots circles at different locations of a projection. On conformal projections, the circles stay circles everywhere, while on equal area projections, they stay the same size.

9. Snyder, J.P. 1984. *Map projections used by the U.S. Geological Survey*. Geological Survey Bulletin 1532. US Government Printing Office, Washington, D.C.

10. Adapted from Muehrcke, P.C. and J.O. Muehrcke. 1992. *Map Use: Reading, analysis, and interpretation*. Madison, Wisconsin: JP Publications.

3.4.4 Selecting a projection

If you are making a fairly detailed map, for example of a city, or if the requirement for accuracy is minimal, then perhaps you need not worry too much about what projection you are using. However, if you are either making a map of a regional to continental to global scale *or* are interested in precise shape, area and/or distance measurements, then you should choose a projection carefully. For many applications or study areas, there is already a standard projection, such as Albers conformal conic for the coterminous US, the Universal Transverse Mercator (UTM) for state governments, or the State Plane Coordinate System for county and city governments.

There are limitations to accuracy even when using a projection, and understanding the limitations is critical. There are three factors to consider when selecting a projection: *latitude of area*, *extent*, and *theme*. For low-latitude areas (near the equator), use a cylindrical projection with normal aspect. For mid-latitude areas use a conical projection, and for polar regions use an azimuthal planar projection. If the extent of the area you are mapping is fairly broad in the east-west extent (e.g., the US), then a conical projection should probably be used, but if it is long in the north-south extent (e.g., Africa), then a transverse-case cylindrical projection should be used. If you are making a thematic map that compares different values in different locations, then typically you will use an equal-area projection.

3.4.5 Commonly used projections

ArcGIS supports a wide variety of projections. The available coordinate systems are organized by geographic region (e.g., polar, continental, world).[11] Some of the most widely used world projections are: Plate Carree, Robinson, and Sinusoidal. The Plate Carree is a cylindrical projection, creating a grid of equal rectangles. The polar regions are less distorted in area compared to Mercator. Robinson is a pseudo-cylindrical projection developed by Arthur Robinson (a.k.a. the "Dean of American Cartography") and used since 1988 by the National Geographic Society. Sinusoidal is also a pseudo-cylindrical projection, and the meridians are based on *sine* functions. In the US, two of the most commonly used projections are UTM and State Plane Coordinate System.

3.4.5.1 UTM

UTM stands for Universal Transverse Mercator grid. This is actually a system of a series of the Transverse Mercator projections that extend a flat grid from 80°N to 80°S. There are 60 zones, starting at 180° longitude and wrapping around Earth (Figures 3.3 and 3.4). Each zone is 6° longitude wide, with an additional 0.5° of overlap on each side. This makes

---

11. The ArcGIS desktop documentation provides a comprehensive list of coordinate systems that are supported. In ArcGIS Desktop help, go to the Contents tab, **Map projections** -> **Supported map projections** -> **List of supported map projections**.

it possible to have a maximum error of 1 per 2,500 in each zone.[12] The x coordinate within each zone starts at a false *easting* located 500,000 m west of the center of the zone. The y coordinate starts at a false *northing* located at the equator for the northern hemisphere and 10,000,000 m south of the equator in the southern hemisphere. Thus, to correctly specify a UTM coordinate, you need to specify the easting, northing, zone, and hemisphere (e.g., 100,000 m E; 3,700,00 m N; Zone 13, northern hemisphere). The coordinates units are in meters.

3.4.5.2 State Plane Coordinate System

The State Plane Coordinate System (SPCS) is a system that divides the US into about 120 zones. Each zone has a specific projection tailored to minimize distortion in that zone, so these are typically used for local areas (usually for counties or cities). Within each localized zone, each projection has a maximum error of 1 part in 10,000.[13] Each state is divided into a number of zones (up to five) (see Figures 3.5 and 3.6). For zones with a greater north-south extent, a UTM projection is used. For zones with a greater east-west extent, the Lambert Conformal Conic is used. SPCS

usually uses coordinates expressed in feet. The false origin is placed usually 2,000,000 feet to the west of the center of the zone, and some arbitrary but consistent distance south of the zone.

---

12. Muehrcke, P.C. and J.O. Muehrcke. 1992. *Map Use: Reading, analysis, and interpretation*. Madison, Wisconsin: JP Publications.

13. See an excellent discussion of these errors for Oregon: http://gisweb.iservices.state.or.us/coord/project/gpl.html.

FIGURE 3.3. **UTM Zones in the western hemisphere.**

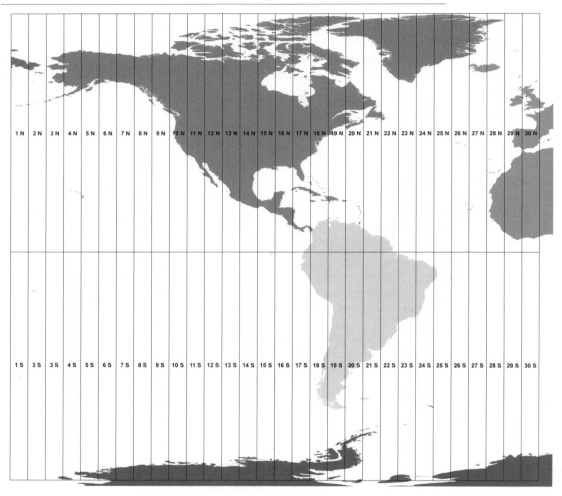

FIGURE 3.4. UTM Zones in the eastern hemisphere.

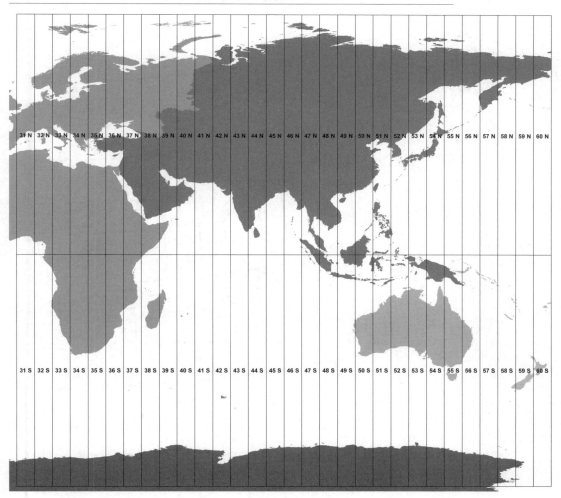

FIGURE 3.5. State Plane Coordinate System zones for the western US.

GIS Concepts and ArcGIS Methods

FIGURE 3.6. State Plane Coordinate System zones for the eastern US.

3.5 Changing coordinate systems

In order for ArcGIS to display layers so that they align properly, the coordinate systems for a dataset must be specified. Because geographic datasets often are stored in different coordinate systems, you will likely want to change coordinates to a different projection system at some point, and so another critical function of GIS software is the ability to manipulate coordinate systems. There are two ways to manipulate coordinate systems in ArcGIS so that data align properly. The first is to change the coordinates permanently through projecting the actual coordinates of the data. That is, if a dataset's coordinates were in latitude/longitude (so that its values ranged from + or -180° and + or -90°), you could create a new dataset with its data in a different coordinate system, for example in the UTM projection (which uses planar coordinates in meters). The second way is to change the coordinates temporarily by "on-the-fly" projection to a different coordinate system defined by the data frame in ArcMap. In order for both the permanent and temporary projection to work, ArcGIS needs to be able to determine the coordinate system of a dataset, which it does by looking for a projection definition file.

3.5.1 Projection definition file

One of the most important pieces of metadata for a dataset is its projection. Typically, the coordinate system parameters for a dataset are described in a *projection definition file*, in addition to any metadata files. If the dataset is in the geographic coordinate system, then the datum (based on a spheroid) is specified and the coordinates are in decimal degrees of latitude and longitude. If the dataset is specified in a projected coordinate system, then, in addition to the geographic coordinate system parameters, the

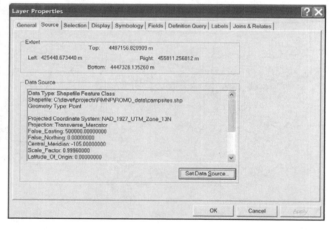

projected parameters are provided, including: datum, spheroid, units (e.g., meters, feet, etc.), projection name, and any parameters specific to that projection. For example, the zone would be specified for the UTM projection, while an Albers Equal Area would have the central meridian, central parallel, and standard parallels specified. Coverages and GRIDs have their projection definition in a file that is stored in the coverage folder, called prj.adj (which is a specially formatted text file). Shapefiles store the definition as a *.prj file and geodatabases store it in its database. You can easily access the coordinate system information for a given layer through the Source tab of a Layer's property dialog.

It is likely that at some point you will need to create or modify a projection definition file (*.prj), especially for shapefiles. Note that creating or modifying a projection definition file does *not* change the actual values of the spatial coordinates. In ArcGIS, you access this file principally through ArcCatalog, but also through ArcToolbox and ArcMap. In ArcCatalog, the coordinate system parameters of a shapefile can be viewed and edited. In the next dialog, you can select the coordinate system from a predefined list, import it from another existing definition file, or define a new coordinate system.

Creating a projection system definition file

1. In *ArcToolbox*, open **Data Management Tools**, then open **Projections and Transformations.**

2. Double-click on the **Define Projection** tool.

3. Note that a **Batch Define** tool is provided in the Samples tools to create definition files for more than one dataset at a time.

-- or --

1. In *ArcCatalog*, navigate to location of dataset and right-click on dataset and select **Properties**.

2. Select **Fields** tab.

3. Select **Shape** field, then click on ellipses button ("...").

4. Click on **Select** button, fill in information, then click **OK**.

In ArcMap, a projection definition file can be viewed, but not edited, through the Source tab in the Layer's Properties dialog. Note that at the ArcView level, you cannot create or modify projection definition files for coverages or GRIDs.

3.5.2 Permanent projection

To create a new dataset with its spatial data in a different coordinate system, you will need to project the data (sometimes called "reprojecting"). This is done in ArcGIS using the *Project tool* found in ArcToolbox. First, locate the source dataset(s) that you want to project. Second, specify the new dataset's name. Third, select the new coordinate

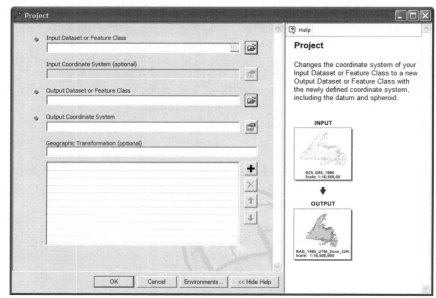

system (or modify an existing one to create a custom projection). Note that the Project Wizard requires that the source dataset must have a valid projection definition file first. At the ArcView level, coverages and GRIDs cannot be projected, only shapefiles and geodatasets.

Projecting a dataset

1. In *ArcToolbox*, open the Data Management Tools -> Projections and Transformations -> Feature.

2. Double-click on the Project tool to open the dialog.

3. Navigate to the location of the dataset to be projected.

4. Specify an output location by clicking on the folder button (or type in the file and pathname directly).

5. Click on the Output Coordinate System button.

6. Specify a Geographic Transformation if needed.

7. Click OK.

3.5.3 Temporary, on the fly, projection

A dataset can also be displayed in a different projection than its defined projection through *on-the-fly* projection. When you add a dataset to a data frame, ArcMap recognizes the coordinate system of the first dataset added (whether it is a geographic or projected coordinate system) and sets the existing data frame's coordinate system to its coordinate system. (Note that you can also later change the data frame's coordinate system.) All subsequent datasets are displayed using the data frame's coordinate system. If a new dataset's coordinate system does not match the existing data frame's, then ArcGIS automatically projects the data on the fly.

On-the-fly projection works by referencing a dataset's geographic coordinate system (that's why *all* datasets require a projection definition file), "back" projecting the native coordinates to geographic coordinates, and then "forward" projecting them as specified by the data frame's parameters. As a result, on-the-fly projection is most efficient when all the layers share the same geographic coordinate system. You will be warned if layers in a map have different geographic coordinate systems (see above right). For most situations where broad areas of Earth are being displayed (countries, states, etc.), the small differences in datums will not result in much difference in display or analysis. But, if your analysis has to be very precise or you are working in a very small area (e.g., city, parcel, etc.), then you should be sure that the datums match.

The advantage of on-the-fly projection is that, as long as your datasets have projection definition files associated with them, you can easily display datasets that are in different coordinate systems without much hassle. The downside is that the display time slows slightly when on-the-fly projection is needed. Also, on-the-fly projection is not as mathematically accurate, and some slight differences in analyses can result (e.g., selecting features within a given distance when on-the-fly projected vs. permanent projected).

Raster data are also on-the-fly projected during display. This works reasonably well for simply looking at patterns, but the on-the-fly projection for raster data is approximate. Because a low-order transformation is used, some distortion can be introduced. It is recommended when using these data in analyses to either make sure the data frame projection is set to be the same as the raster data set of interest, or that you permanently project the raster data using the Project tool—but this requires ArcEditor or ArcInfo level functionality.

3.6 The Global Positioning System (GPS)

The *Global Positioning System* (GPS) is a satellite-based system that provides locational information anytime, anywhere (or roughly so). The GPS was developed by the US Department of Defense for military and civilian use. Basically GPS works by having a number of satellites each broadcasting its status and location on a precise schedule. A GPS receiver on the ground picks up a signal, and determines the range (or distance) by computing the time delay between the scheduled and the actual arrival of signals. Signals from multiple satellites are required to fix a location on the surface of Earth. Prior to May 2000, the accuracy of GPS was degraded by "selective availability" scrambling.

There are three components to the system: the satellite constellation, the ground control network, and user equipment. The *satellite constellation* is based on a constellation of NAVSTAR satellites placed into orbit about 26,600 km from the center of Earth (see right, source US Dept. of Defense). The first GPS satellite was launched in 1978 and the full constellation of 24 active satellites (plus spares) was achieved in 1994. The satellites are scheduled so that at least 4 are "visible" anytime, anywhere, but most locations are likely to have 6 to 8 satellites available. There are 6 orbit planes with a 55° inclination, each containing 4 to 5 satellites. Each satellite makes roughly two revolutions per day (one-half of a sidereal day or 11 hours 58 minutes).

The *control network* maintains the system through five monitoring stations and a master control station at Schriever Air Force Base near Colorado Springs, Colorado. These stations correct orbit and clock errors.

The *user equipment* consists of individuals with one or more GPS receivers. A receiver collects measurements simultaneously from at least four satellites to solve for three dimensions of position (latitude, longitude, and altitude), typically measured in WGS84 datum.[14]

One of the main determinants of the precision of measurement is the satellite geometry, or the arrangement of satellites that are used to fix a location. The higher they are in the sky,

14. Obtaining precise altitude estimates is problematic though, because of real-world distortions in the shape of Earth -- see: Fraczek, W. 2003. Mean seal level, GPS, and the Geoid. ArcUser (July-September).

the lower the precision, so satellites lower in the sky provide a better measurement (but their signals are more likely to be disrupted!). This makes using a GPS problematic in landscapes with canyons and thick forests (e.g., Figure 3.7).

FIGURE 3.7. Hmmm, does this thing work? Waiting for a fourth satellite in a Nicaraguan rainforest.

The most common measurement of how precisely a GPS is recording locations is called *Positional Dilution of Precision* (PDOP). The higher the PDOP, the poorer the measurement. Generally, a PDOP value from 1-3 is considered very good, 4-5 good, 6 fair, >6 poor. Typical accuracies are between 10 to 30 meters.

Three techniques are commonly used to improve the accuracy of GPS measurements. A simple method involves collecting many position fixes (for 10-30 minutes) while remaining at the same location and then averaging the fixes to attain a location. A second method is to use *differential correction* that employs two receivers -- one receiver is established as a base station with a precise known location. The differences between the field-roving unit and the base station (see Figure 3.8) can be computed and used to correct the field-roving positions, providing sub-meter to centimeter (survey-grade) accuracy. Post-processing of GPS positions can also be done (but is of limited usefulness when precise navigation in the field is required).[15] A third method is to conduct real-time differential correction using the Wide Area Augmentation System (WAAS). WAAS is based on a network of ground reference stations that compute a differential correction, which is then transmitted to a geo-stationary satellite (i.e. a satellite that remains at one point in orbit over Earth). The correction signal is then broadcast back to the surface of Earth, where WAAS-enabled GPS devices can correct signals in real-time. This results in errors that are less than 7 meters 95% of the time.

FIGURE 3.8. Setting up a base station for differential correction west of Fort Collins, Colorado.

15. Post-processing correction files can be obtained online from: www.ngs.noaa.gov/OPUS

3.7 Geocoding

Most geographic datasets have their geometry derived either from paper maps or from GPS locations. Although relatively uncommon in the natural resources fields but commonplace in business applications, tabular datasets often have quasi-spatial attributes but are not tied to specific geometrical features. The most obvious example of this type of dataset is a file with customer names, addresses, and telephone numbers, and so these datasets are commonly called *address tables*. Through a process known as *geocoding* (also called *address matching*), these address tables can be combined with reference geographic datasets that have comparable attributes such as street address, street, city, and state names, and zip code. By linking the tabular data to the reference dataset through a series of rules, the locations of the tabular features (i.e. house locations) in the address table can be estimated. Geocoding databases power the browser mapping technologies such as MapQuest, allowing driving directions to be computed on the fly.

Occasionally the records in the address table can be referenced only to either a point or areal geographic feature. For example, if the address table contained just place names such as the city, state, zip code, or telephone area code (or a combination of these), then they could be linked only to point locations such as a city's x, y location or to polygons that represent a zip code. However, because usually there is no way to refine the location within a polygon, all the features are typically located to the center of the polygon. So, the spatial accuracy of the estimated locations in this case depend on the resolution of the polygon (e.g., five digit zip code vs. nine digit zip code), and typically this varies widely across different parts of a map (e.g., zip codes tend to be smaller in urban than rural areas).

It is fairly common, though, for an address table to have street addresses. By combining these data with a geographic dataset such as detailed roads that are attributed with address ranges, more accurate locations can be interpolated. For example, if you are trying to geocode the location of "950 West Oak Street," you would first find in a street database the polylines with their attributes "West Oak Street," and the starting address of 900 and ending address of 1000. Simple linear interpolation would then result in a point located at the midpoint of the street line. The reference geographic datasets for streets are available from a number of commercial vendors, including ESRI.[16]

Sounds great, in theory, but in practice it is slightly messier than this. Much of the messiness is caused by inconsistencies and data entry errors (e.g., "Georgetown" vs. "Georgetowne" vs. "George town"; "Street" vs. "St." vs. "St"), though these are fairly easy problems to clean up. Sometimes addresses are not unique, so that an address such as

---

16. For example, ESRI's StreetMap.

"1000 North College" may be a correct address for two different parts of town. More problematic are addresses that do not change linearly along a street, and the actual location of a house that may be set back some distance (e.g, a 1/4 mile or more in rural areas) from the street. For these reasons and others, agencies that provide emergency services (e.g., fire, police department, etc.) often need to expend huge effort to create and maintain accurate, up-to-date spatial databases. To reduce some of these problems, rural street addresses often correspond with the mileage (times 1000) from the start of the county road (e.g., the driveway of 1234 West County Road 29 is 1.234 miles from the start of County Road 29). Although this gets one closer to the house, this simply specifies the location of an intersection along a major road, and often houses are actually located some distance away along a complex network of private driveways.

Geocoding
ArcToolbox -> Geocoding Tools -> **Create Address Locator, Geocode Addresses**.

3.7.1 Geocoding services

In ArcGIS, geocoding is provided through a series of *geocoding services*. A geocoding service defines the reference dataset(s) that has spatial features, rules for standardizing the descriptions of features in the address table, and rules for how they are matched to the reference data and how the new features are created. To match an address, the geocoding service standardizes the address, searches the reference data for candidates, scores the candidates, and matches the best candidate. Before you create a service, you will need to understand the structure of your address table, particularly what fields have addresses, street names, directions, etc. For example, sometimes an address table will only have an "address" field (e.g., 950) and a "street" field (e.g., West Oak Street), while others may have the street broken into "street direction" (e.g., West), "street name" (e.g., Oak), and "street type" (e.g., Street).

A geocoding service is created in Arc-Catalog by locating the Geocoding Services folder in the Catalog, and then clicking on the Create New Geocoding Service folder to bring up the Create New Geocoding Service dialog. There are a number of different *geocoding styles* available—essentially you need to match how the reference geographic dataset is attributed. After the geocoding service is created and your address table matched,[17] you will likely want to examine your results. You can review the match scores, tweak some of the match parameters, and re-match your address table.

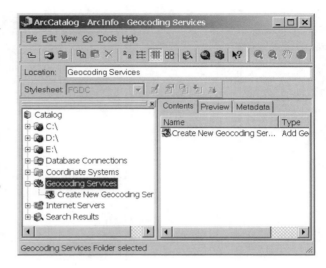

3.8 Chapter review

- Locations on Earth are defined by a *geographic coordinate system* (latitude and longitude).

- A projection is a systematic way to transform spherical coordinates to planar (Cartesian) coordinates, creating a *projected coordinate system*.

- The *scale* of a map is the *ratio* of a distance on the map to a distance on Earth.

- There are three geometric projection surfaces: the plane, cylinder, and cone. Each has a characteristic pattern of distortion.

- In ArcGIS, the coordinate system parameters for a dataset are described in a *projection definition file*.

- GPS works by having a number of satellites each broadcasting its status and location on a precise schedule. A GPS receiver on the ground picks up a signal, and determines the range (or distance) by computing the time delay between the scheduled and the actual arrival of signals.

---

17. For more information, see the ArcGIS Desktop Help, Geocoding addresses section.

Scale, coordinate systems, and projections

4 Cartography and geographic visualization

4.1 The art and science of cartography

Cartographers have been making maps for a long time and have developed a rich body of work on the art and science of making maps.[1] We can draw from this work a number of cartographic principles and rules of thumb that should be used to create a useful map. For example, Cynthia Brewer has written an excellent primer that provides more detail on designing maps for GIS users.[2] With the advent of computer-cartography and GIS, many cartographers have cautioned about the "democratization" that advanced computer technologies and software (such as ArcGIS) have enabled, providing neophytes who know little about cartography the power to create authentic maps. Because maps are a powerful way to communicate information, many fear that improper, or perhaps misleading, maps will be created through this enabling technology. While this perspective may be considered to be grumbling by the old guard, it is wise to heed their caution and learn

---

1. Probably the most widely used text book is by Arthur Robinson and others. Robinson, A.H., P.C. Muehrcke, AJ. Kimmerling, S.C. Gupti, and J.L. Morrison. 1995. *Elements of Cartography* (6th Ed.). New York: John Wiley & Sons.
2. Brewer, C.A. 2005. *Designing better maps: a guide for GIS users.* ESRI Press.

from their experience. And remember never to underestimate the power of even simple maps to convey critical information (e.g., Figure 4.1).

FIGURE 4.1. A white-board map of the boundaries of Chocoyero-El Brujo National Park, Nicaragua.

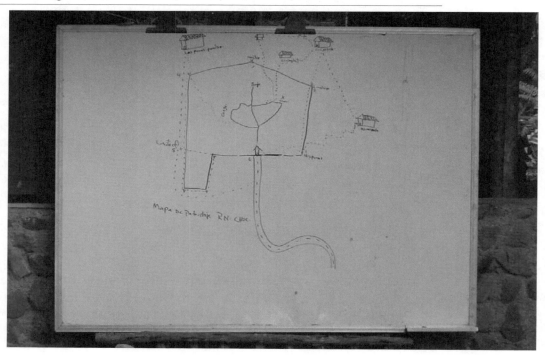

Part of this perspective can be explained by considering the roles of the map creator and reader in the long-established "map as communication" paradigm. In the past, maps were created primarily to communicate some geographic pattern to a map reader. The goal for map communication was to create a single map that displayed the "proper" geographic pattern because the map reader is essentially passive (again, an artifact of paper-based maps). This has led to the suggestion that the map maker has three responsibilities: a) to be fair to the data; b) to be clear to the map reader; and c) to anticipate ways in which a third person may be affected by a *foreseeable* misinterpretation of a map.[3] To be sure, many (perhaps most?) maps are still created and consumed in this fashion.

3. See: Gersmehl, P.J. 1985. The data, the reader, and the innocent bystander -- a parable for map users. *Professional Geographer* 37(3): 329-334.

More recently, there has been a slight paradigm shift, known as analytical cartography[4], that emphasizes the creation of maps that can be easily explored and analyzed. The goal in map analysis is to create a map that can be easily analyzed, because the map reader can query and explore the data behind the map.[5] Thus, the consumers of a map are no longer passive (indeed some would suggest they have a responsibility to be inquisitive), and so map exploration is best described as a set of steps that form an iterative process:[6] *frame* the question, *understand* the data, *choose* a display or analytical method, *examine* the results, and *revise* the question and start again.

This chapter describes how to create maps in ArcGIS from both a communication and an exploratory perspective. Again, much of the experience gained and rules of thumb developed in the context of cartographic display are still relevant, and some of the more important ones are described below. Also, MacEachren's primer on map symbolization and design is a very helpful, accessible guide to these principles.[7] But there are also some exciting opportunities for dynamic, "live" maps that transcend the limitations of paper and fully utilize the possibilities provided by digital technology. To this end, a *visualization framework*[8] can help set the broader context of the different roles of maps in GIS, as well as additional possibilities for visualizing spatial data beyond the traditional paper map. Although the framework is typically conceived of as a linear sequence, in reality it is a cyclic and dynamic process.

First, geographic data are gathered, then *explored*. Traditionally, numerous maps would be created to examine the geographic distribution, but with GIS, additional opportunities are available to explore the data, especially through interactive queries. Second, maps are occasionally used to *confirm* an assumption or hypothesis about the geographic phenomena. Perhaps more often, maps are used to generate hypotheses, and more rigorous statistical methods and spatial analysis are used to confirm a hypothesized pattern. Third, geographic data can be *synthesized*, to distill the patterns found, not only in a single map but through analysis of multiple layers of geographic information. Fourth, GIS are used to present geographic information. Again, the traditional format of this is a paper-based map, but increasingly their are opportunities for other types of digital presentations, such as animations and fly-throughs.

---

4. Waldo Tobler, Professor Emeritus at University of California, Santa Barbara, is widely regarded as the father of analytical cartography.
5. See: Muehrcke, P.C. 1981. Whatever happened to geographic cartography? *The Professional Geographer* 33(4): 397-405.
6. For example, see the analysis process described in: Mitchell, A. 1999. *The ESRI guide to GIS Analysis*. ESRI Press.
7. MacEachren, A.M. 1994. *Some truth with maps: A primer on symbolization and design*. Association of American Geographers, Washington, D.C. 129 pgs.
8. This framework is very loosely based on MacEachren's framework for the role of maps.

4.2 Thematic mapping

One of the main types of maps in cartography is a *thematic map*. A thematic map is designed to provide information about a single topic, or theme. For example, a thematic map might illustrate a particular phenomenon, such as how population is distributed throughout the US. Each "theme" can be represented by different data types, such as qualitative or quantitative. A map that showed the outlines of the major cities would provide qualitative data on the distribution of where population is distributed. A map that uses quantitative data might show the population size of each city using larger circles for more populated cities, smaller circles for towns, etc.

There are a wide variety of thematic map types that have been developed to portray the attributes of geographic features. The map type to use depends on the purpose of the map—what geographical aspect are you trying to visualize? For example, the locations of important bird areas can be shown within the spatial context of ecological regions. It also depends on the type of attribute data that is being displayed. Recall the discussion in Chapter 2 about attribute data types: qualitative (nominal) or quantitative (ordinal, interval, cyclic, ratio). Table 4.1 provides an overview of the mapping methods provided in ArcMap, organized by feature types. The map type is defined through the Symbology tab of the Layer Properties dialog (see graphics below). After the various types of maps are described, a detailed discussion about graphic symbology is provided.

TABLE 4.1. How different feature and data types are displayed using ArcMap methods. (N=nominal, O=ordinal, I=interval, C=cyclic, R=ratio).

ArcMap method	Point	Line	Area	Raster
Feature (shows location)	N, O, I, C, R	N, O, I, C, R	N, O, I, C, R	
Categories - unique values	N	N	N	N
Quantities - graduated color - graduated symbols - proportional symbols - dot	O, I, C, R O, I, C, R O, I, C, R	O, I, C, R O, I, C, R O, I, C, R	O, I, C, R[a] O, I, C, R O, I, C, R O, I, C, R	O, I, C, R

TABLE 4.1. How different feature and data types are displayed using ArcMap methods. (N=nominal, O=ordinal, I=interval, C=cyclic, R=ratio).

ArcMap method	Point	Line	Area	Raster
Charts				
- Pie	R	R	R	
- Bar/Column	R	R	R	
- Stacked	R	R	R	
Multiple				
- Quantity by category	R	R	R	

a. These are also known as choropleth maps when the data are normalized.

4.2.1 General features

The *features map* type simply displays the location of features using a single symbol—no attribute value is displayed. This can be valuable because it emphasizes the distribution of geographic features using vector a data model. For example, the capital cities are shown by blue stars, and they can be seen to be highly clustered in the New England region (due to the small size of states) and in some places in the west as well (e.g., Denver, CO and Cheyenne, WY; Sacramento, CA and Carson City,  NV). The US Interstate system is shown by the red lines, and again there is a higher density in the East, Midwest, and southern California. It is also interesting to note the Interstate 27 "spur" in northern Texas, dropping down from Interstate 40 to Lubbock and the Interstate 390 spur in western New York, terminating at the village of Bath. By comparing the location of a capital within its respective state, the geographic representativeness appears to be highly skewed in a number of states (especially Florida, Nevada, and Wyoming).

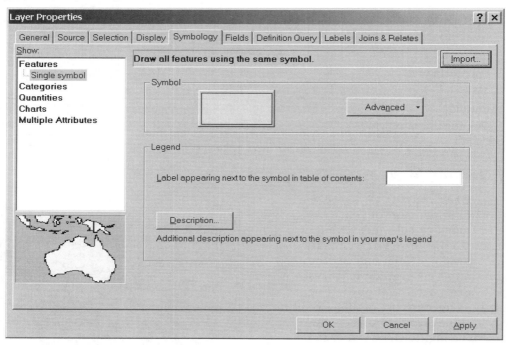

A specialized features map type is an isoline map that displays the values of a continuous phenomenon. An *isoline* connects points of equal value, and this map is commonly used to show the distribution of continuous surfaces, not by changing their symbology, but simply through their location in relation to other isolines. For example, contour lines are isolines that map locations of equal elevation (Figure 4.2).

FIGURE 4.2. Isolines, or lines of equal elevation, are commonly used in topographic map series. Here, the general landforms around Livermore, Colorado can be seen.

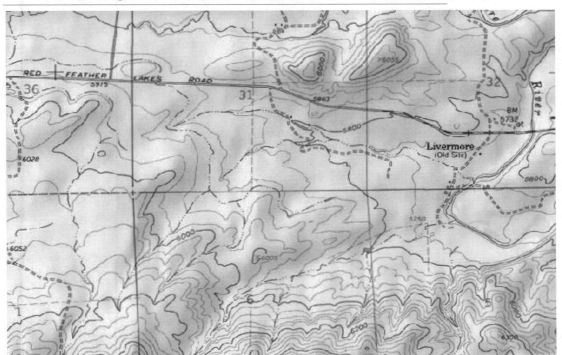

4.2.2 Categories

The *Categories map* type is typically used to portray nominal data, such as land use classes or vegetation types—based on *unique values* of an attribute. Nominal data are qualitative, not quantitative data. Features with unique values are drawn with a different color or symbol. This type of map shows the geographic distribution of features, but also differentiates them by an attribute. It also shows visually how many are in a category compared to others. For example, the states (right) are grouped into

different divisions, each displayed with a unique color. Also, most locational and road maps are this type, simply showing the difference in roads (e.g., interstate, state highways, secondary, local roads, etc.). For raster datasets, nominal data can also be portrayed using the unique values option. Note that the unique values can be drawn from the values found in one field or multiple fields (up to three). This second option allows features to be differentiated based on their unique combination of two or three attributes.

This is an effective method for displaying nominal data, but humans have difficulty distinguishing between color hues when there are more than ten or so classes (and ideally around seven). Therefore, it is recommended to combine classes to create groups of values or categories to reduce the number of classes. With more than a dozen classes, this legend type is occasionally used to distinguish locations, but the resulting map is too visually complex to be useful for examining categories. Typically, when using a unique value classification, similar colors will be used for related categories. For instance, for urban classes (residential, commercial) use shades of red, or for forest classes (ponderosa pine, Douglas fir, etc.) use shades of green. In addition, classes can be grouped manually.

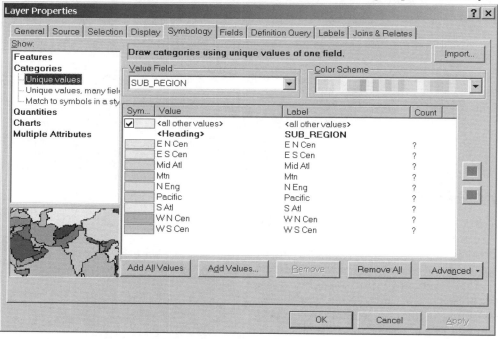

Grouping classes in a legend

1. In *ArcMap*, right-click on a layer and select **Properties**.
2. Select the **Symbology** tab.
3. Select **Categories** and then **Unique Values,** then specify the **Value** field, then click on **Add All Values**.
4. Select the classes to be grouped (using shift-click and/or ctrl-click).
5. Right-click and select **Group values.**
6. Repeat for each group.
7. Click **OK**.

4.2.3 Mapping quantities

The *Quantities map* type displays quantitative attribute data, such as daily maximum temperature, the population change in the past decade in the US, the Nielsen rating for NBC's television show at 7:00 p.m. on Thursdays, the annual sales generated in a territory, or the number of acres of habitat for an endangered species. There are four different display methods for quantitative data: *graduated color*, *graduated symbol*, *proportional symbol*, and *dot density*. Which type should you use? The main consideration is the type of attribute data that is to be mapped (i.e. whether it is ordinal, interval, cyclic, or ratio). For line and areal data, also consider whether the geographic features that will be portrayed with some attribute value vary in size or length. For example, an attribute might contain ratio values that represent a count or raw amount (e.g., the population per state in 2000). It might also contain ratio values that represent densities (e.g., population density per state in 2000)—this is called a ratio (because it is normalized by some denominator). When geographic features are fairly uniform, then mapping raw counts or amounts is reasonable. However, when geographic features vary (especially the size of areal features), then you should portray the data as densities, not raw counts— cartographers call these *choropleth* maps. The reason is that raw counts are highly correlated with the area of a feature—the larger a state, the more likely it is to have more people than a small state. So, large counties, like San Bernadino, CA, stand out disproportionately (Figure 4.3). Also, choropleth maps are typically used when the polygons (e.g. counties) are determined independently of the phenomenon. Raw count data should be converted to ratio or density data by *normalizing* them with another attribute (e.g., area of a state or total US population). In order to better understand the various situations in which particular map types are used for displaying quantitative data (which are discussed in detail below), a short discussion about classifying data is warranted.

FIGURE 4.3. A comparison of raw values and normalized display of population by county in 2000. Note that when geographic features vary in size, it is recommended to portray data as normalized values (right).

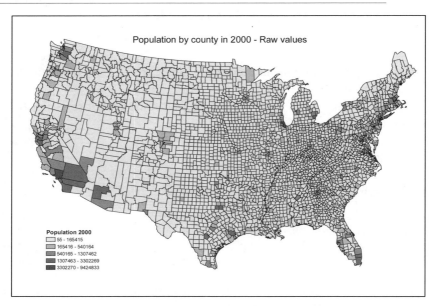

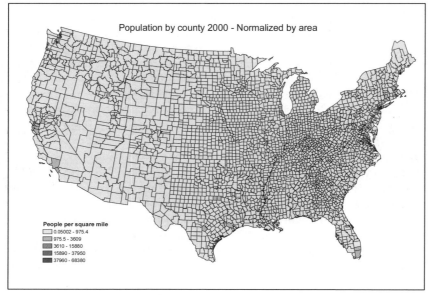

4.2.3.1 Classification

A *classification* is a method that groups similar features based on an attribute value into a smaller set of groups or classes by assigning the same symbol to each member of the class. This helps to simplify the visual complexity of a map, making the map easier to read and understand. First, select the number of classes, which typically should be between 3 and 10. Why 3 to 10? The smaller the number of classes, the more simplified a map will be and greater within-group variation, but using fewer than three classes causes vast generalizations that are rarely helpful. The larger the number of classes, the closer the attribute values can be portrayed and the within-group variation decreases. But because humans are limited in our ability to differentiate shades of gray and colors and because too many classes make a map complex, the cartographic rule of thumb is to use somewhere between 3 to 10 classes.[9] Note that even this first, fairly arbitrary decision, can result in maps that are quite different.[10]

There are six standard classification schemes that are available in ArcMap. The standard classifications are: *defined interval, equal interval, natural breaks, quantiles, geometric interval* and *standard deviation*. A seventh classification is called *manual*, where the class limits can be adjusted to create your own classification.

---

9. Dent, B. 1985. *Principles of thematic map design*. Addison-Wesley Publishing.

10. Indeed, some have offered a cynical view of mapping, for example: "One of the trickiest ways to misrepresent statistical data is by means of a map. A map introduces a fine bag of variables in which facts can be concealed and relationships distorted." From Huff, D. 1954. *How to Lie with Statistics*. W.W. Norton.

The *defined interval* method allows you to specify an interval value that is used to equally divide a range of values (Figure 4.4). ArcGIS then computes the number of classes.

FIGURE 4.4. **Defined interval classification.**

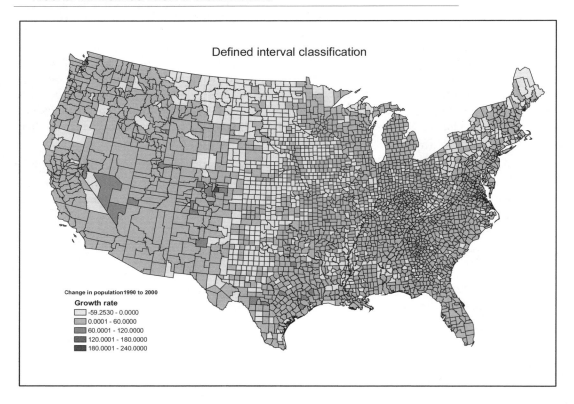

The *equal interval* method divides the full range of attribute values into equally sized sub-ranges, then the features are classified based on those sub-ranges (Figure 4.5). Equal-interval legends are also fairly intuitive to map readers. A closely-related method is the *defined interval* method, which divides the full range of attribute values into equally sized sub-ranges that are based on a specified interval size. Rather than specifying the number of classes and calculating the resulting interval, the interval is set and the number of classes is calculated.

FIGURE 4.5. Equal-interval classification.

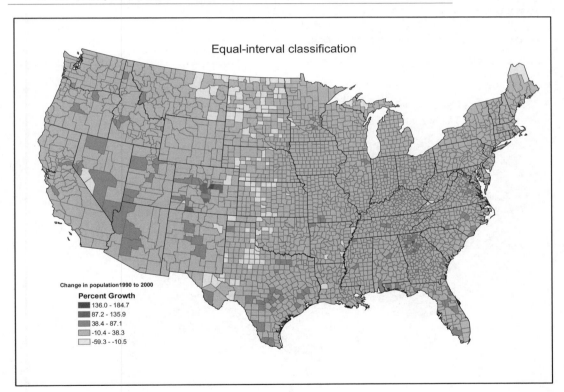

The *natural breaks* method identifies breakpoints between classes to form groups that are internally homogeneous while assuring heterogeneity among classes (Figure 4.6). This method uses a statistical formula that minimizes the sum of the variance within each of the classes, often called Jenks optimization.[11] This is the default classification. Because the legend values change with each distribution and therefore with each map, beware when comparing maps depicting similar, but different data. The differences you observe might simply be artifacts of the class ranges, rather than differences in the data themselves. For example, do not use this classification type when comparing data between years, because the class ranges will change depending on the data, making inter-year comparisons very difficult.

FIGURE 4.6. Natural breaks classification.

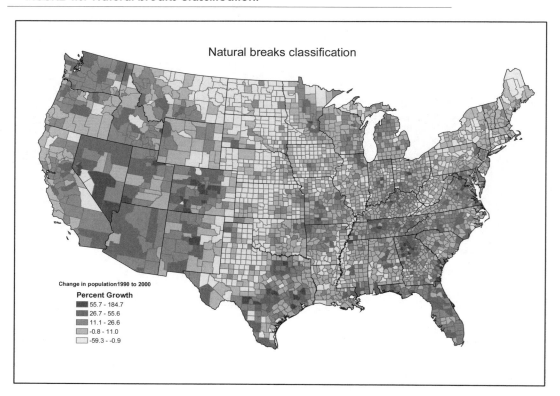

11. The primary reference for Jenks optimization procedure is: Jenks, G.F. and M.R. Coulson, 1963. Class intervals for statistical maps. *International Yearbook of Cartography* 3:119-134. Also see: Fisher, W.D. 1958. *On grouping for maximum homogeneity*. American Statistical Association Journal 53: 789-798.

The *quantiles* method identifies breakpoints between classes so that each class contains approximately the same number of features (Figure 4.7). If the number of classes is five, then the data is broken into quintiles. If the number of classes is four, then it results in quartiles. This method is well suited for data that is linearly (or uniformly) distributed.

FIGURE 4.7. Quantile classification method.

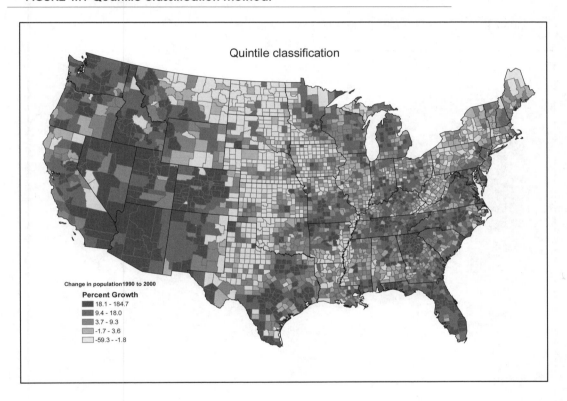

The *geometric interval* method was designed specifically for continuous data and results in a visually appealing classification (Figure 4.8). It finds the range of values (maximum minus minimum) and then places class breaks based on a geometrical series, which generates a pattern where a constant coefficient is multiplied by each value in a series. For example, if the minimum value was 0.0 and maximum 16 (for 6 classes), then the coefficient would be 2.0.

FIGURE 4.8. Geometric interval classification method.

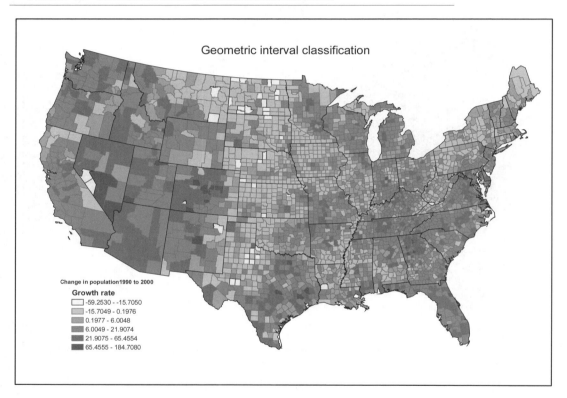

The *standard deviation* method finds the mean value and then places class breaks above and below the mean at intervals of either one-fourth, one-half, or one standard deviation until all the data values are contained within the classes (Figure 4.9). This classification should be used only when the data approximate a normal distribution.

FIGURE 4.9. **Standard deviation classification method.**

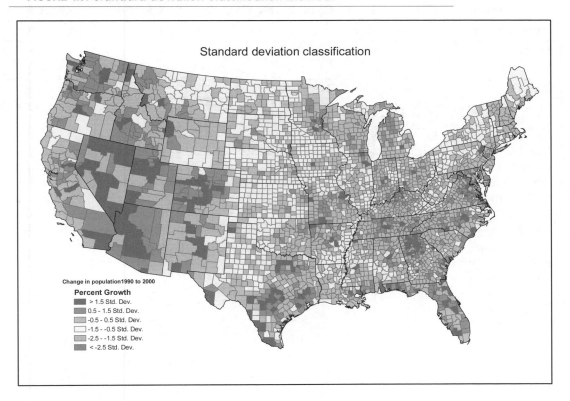

To summarize, there is no "correct" way to classify data, no one "right" map. Changing the number of classes or the class ranges through different classification schemes creates maps that emphasize different aspects about the distribution of an attribute (as the figures above demonstrate and Table 4.2 shows). A useful exercise is to understand the distribution of attribute data to see if they are overly skewed, lumped, bi-model, or perhaps have outliers that will bias statistics. It is important to explicitly consider the goal for making a map—different goals require different strategies. A different approach will be taken if the goal is to communicate some known distribution rather than to explore geographic data to notice possibly unexpected distributions.

TABLE 4.2. The class values for the different classification methods.

Classification method	Class 1	Class 2	Class 3	Class 4	Class 5
Defined interval	-59.3 - 0	0 - 60.0	60.1 - 120.0	120.1 - 180.0	180.1 - 240.0
Equal interval	-59.3 - -10.5	-10.4 - 38.3	38.4 - 87.1	87.2 - 135.9	136.0 - 184.7
Natural breaks	-59.3 - -0.9	-0.8 - 11.0	11.1 - 26.6	26.7 - 55.6	55.7 - 184.7
Quantiles	-59.3 - -1.8	-1.7 - 3.6	3.7 - 9.3	9.4 - 18.0	18.1 - 184.7
Geometric interval	-59.3 - -21.2	-21.1 - 4.2	4.3 - 42.2	42.3 - 99.2	99.3 - 184.7
Standard deviation	-29.9 - -14.3	--14.2 - 1.2	1.3 - 16.8	16.9 - 32.5	32.5 - 184.7

Occasionally, there will be some additional guidance—perhaps the classification needs to conform to specific criteria or to some standard format. For instance, there may be a specific threshold value that is either mandated in a regulation or has simply emerged as a useful comparative value (e.g., greater than 50% cover, slopes greater than 25%, etc.) As a result, ArcGIS also allows the classification to be customized by editing class values directly to change the breaks between classes. This is accomplished through interacting with a histogram of the attribute values (Figure 4.10).[12] For example, often data is classified in comparison to some statistical average—here we'll map the county population growth rates as compared to the national average.

---

12. This is a big improvement over ArcView v3.2, which provided no easy means of viewing the distribution.

FIGURE 4.10. Classification dialog illustrating Natural Breaks (Jenks) setting of classes.

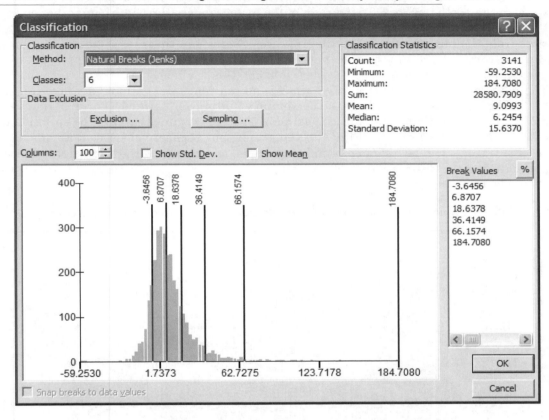

Displaying a histogram

1. In *ArcMap*, right-click on a layer and select **Properties**.
2. Select the **Symbology** tab.
3. Click **Classify**....

At the top of the Classification dialog, change the classification method to "Manual." Note the *classification statistics* in the top right corner showing count, minimum, maximum, sum, mean, median[13], and standard deviation of the attribute values. In the lower part of the dialog is the histogram, with the data aligned from minimum to maximum values. The

---

13. New with v9.1.

number of histogram columns or bins shown in the graph can be adjusted by changing the value in the "Columns" box. To the right of the histogram are the *break values* that specify the class limits. In the break values list, the first class of the US population growth rates runs from the minimum value to the first break value—in this case 0 (so the first class ranges from -59.2530 up to and including 0). The next value is 9.0992, the average percentage growth per county from 1990 to 2000 (this is slightly less than 1% annually). The next values represent twice, five times, and ten times the national average (Figure 4.11). The last break value is also the maximum value of 184.7—which is over 20 times the national average (Douglas County, Colorado)! The break values can also be specified by click-dragging on the vertical lines in the graph that separate classes. Note also that specific features can be excluded from being displayed by clicking the Exclusion... button and entering the desired value. This feature is useful when some particular feature(s) should be removed temporarily from the list of features.

FIGURE 4.11. Manual classification method comparing growth rates to national average.

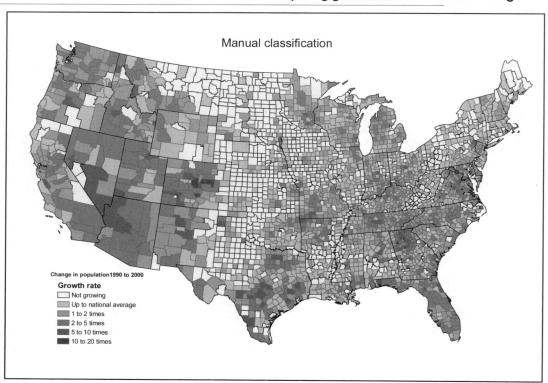

4.2.3.2 Representing classes

A common method of displaying quantitative attribute data is to vary the color of features according to an attribute value. Population density and growth rates (at right) are typically portrayed in this fashion.[14] This method works for point, line, and areal geographic features (and raster data as well). The cartographic rule of thumb that applies here is the *greater* the attribute value, the *darker* (more intense) the color value. In this way, features with higher values are visually dominant.

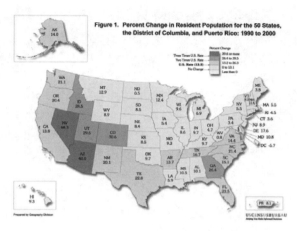

Figure 1. Percent Change in Resident Population for the 50 States, the District of Columbia, and Puerto Rico: 1990 to 2000

When depicting ratio data, it is best to use *monochromatic* color ramps, where darker color values correspond to higher values in your data. If the phenomenon being depicted naturally has a division, has both negative and positive values, or if you want to show areas above or below an average, then *dichromatic* ramps are useful. For example, if you are portraying temperature, then use a dichromatic ramp with blue symbols depicting values lower than freezing and red for values higher than freezing. Otherwise, avoid using dichromatic ramps, especially for data with no natural separation in the distribution. There are a number of other "specialty" color ramps available, such as for elevation, sea floor elevation, and land cover, which are available by clicking on the **Color Ramp** drop-down list.

---

14. Source: US Census Bureau, 2002.

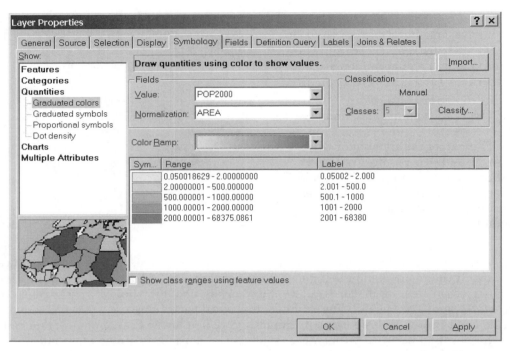

Another type of isoline map is called a *shaded isoline* map. Recall that an isoline map shows locations of equal value. Often, the interior areas of an isoline map are shaded so that colors represent an attribute value. A common example of this is a weather map showing temperature, or perhaps precipitation amounts (Figure 4.12).

FIGURE 4.12. In contrast with the map in Figure 4.2, a shaded isoline map shows areas of equal value—in this case precipitation in Colorado (center) and Utah (left). Notice the dry, interior deserts in Utah and Arizona, the wet "islands" in blue, and the rain shadow effect of the Rockies (this time distinguished by color differences in the two large polygons of lower precipitation to the east of the Front Range) (download color figures from www.consplan.com).

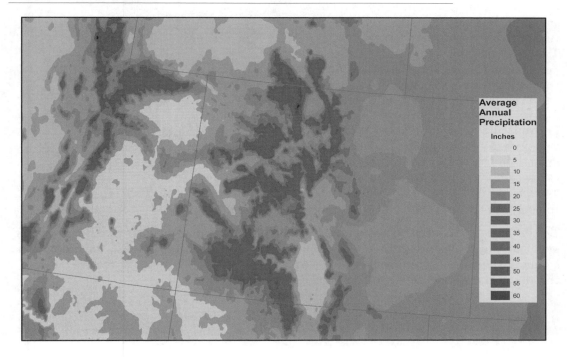

Average
Annual
Precipitation

Inches

0
5
10
15
20
25
30
35
40
45
50
55
60

For raster datasets, quantitative data can be displayed using the *classified* option, which is essentially the same as the graduated color option for feature data. In this case, the number in the value attribute table is displayed with a color. For example, the mountain ranges of the world can be seen by the yellow-red-brown values (right).[15] The only aspect of a raster cell that

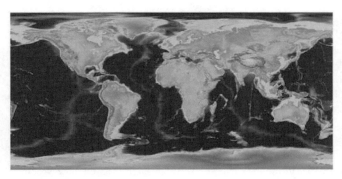

can be controlled is the interior color—the outline color or fill pattern of a raster cell cannot be changed. Raster data can also be displayed using the *stretched* classification type, which stretches values along a color ramp. This is used mostly for adjusting images and photographs.

Another way to symbolize quantitative data is to keep the color and symbol constant, but vary the size of a symbol in relation to the attribute value. Typically, point feature data, such as population of cities, are portrayed in this fashion (right), though this method can also used for linear features (e.g., different stream orders). In ArcGIS, graduated symbols for areal features are portrayed by placing a marker symbol in the center of the polygon. A *cartogram* is another type of graduated symbol method that varies the size of

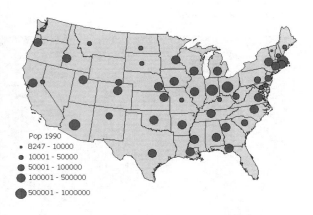

the polygon features, but this type of map is not a standard feature of ArcGIS.[16]

The difference between *graduated symbols* and *proportional symbols* is that, for graduated symbols, the values are grouped into a few, discrete classes. In contrast, for proportional symbols, the values are considered to be continuous and no discrete classes are formed, so the size of the symbol reflects the actual data value.

---

15. This shows world topography, stored as a MrSID image using GTOPO30.

16. Discontinuous cartograms can be easily created, however, by scaling the area of polygons in relation to the attribute value. A classic paper on cartograms is: Olson, J.M. 1976. Noncontiguous Area Cartograms. *The Professional Geographer* 28(4): 317-380. Also see: Jackel, C.B. 1997. Using ArcView to create contiguous and non-contiguous area cartograms. *Cartography and Geographic Information Systems* 24(2): 101-109.

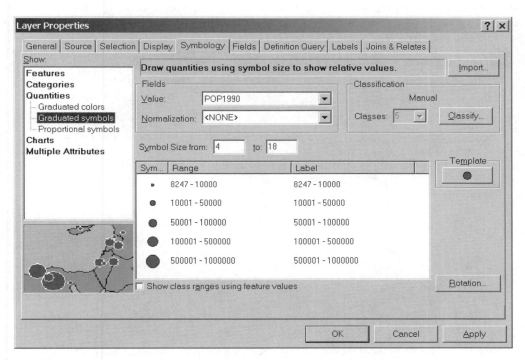

A *dot density* map displays quantitative data values for polygon features only by adjusting the density of dots in relation to the value of an attribute. Each dot represents a specific number that can be set, and the more dots in an area, the higher the value. However, you will need to trade off the number of dots, which is controlled by the attribute value and the *dot value* setting that specifies the value represented by a single dot, and the *dot size*, or the point size of a dot. Dots are distributed randomly throughout a defined area

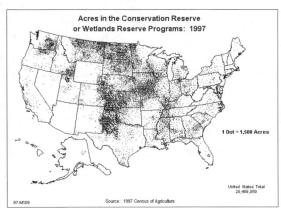

specified by a polygon, and because of this random component, this type of map "fuzzies up" the location of features, so that the exact location of a geographic feature cannot be discerned. For example, the number of acres placed into the US Conservation or Wetland

Reserve Program is shown (above right), but not the precise location of leases.[17] Several variables can be displayed at once by selecting multiple attributes that use a distinct color to portray the dots and a transparent background.

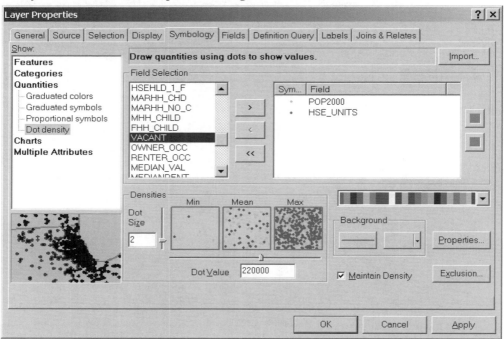

Dot maps are fairly intuitive to most map readers, but they can be very misleading as well. Beware of maps that use this type of legend, especially when showing population density, because the human eye naturally infers pattern, even if none exists. For example, although population in Nevada (Figure 4.13) is highly clustered around Las Vegas, the randomly located points within the state give the impression of a fairly homogenous distribution, even though only about 10% of Nevada is private land. A powerful feature provided in ArcGIS to address this issue to some extent is the ability to force dots to be either included in or excluded from areas defined by a *mask* layer (that must be a polygon type). This is a type of *dasymetric* mapping.[18]

---

17. Source: US Department of Agriculture, Natural Resource Conservation Service.
18. This technique was first developed to map population density in Cape Cod: Wright, J.K. 1936. A method of mapping densities of population. *Geographical Review* 26: 103-110. Also see: Eicher, C.L. and C.A. Brewer. 2001. Dasymetric mapping and areal interpolation: Implementation and evaluation. *Cartography and Geographic Information Science* 28(2): 125-138; and Theobald, D.M. 2001. Land use dynamics beyond the American urban fringe. *Geographical Review* 91(3): 544-564.

FIGURE 4.13. Population in California, Nevada, and Utah using dot density mapping. Notice that lakes were used to exclude dots from being located there randomly.

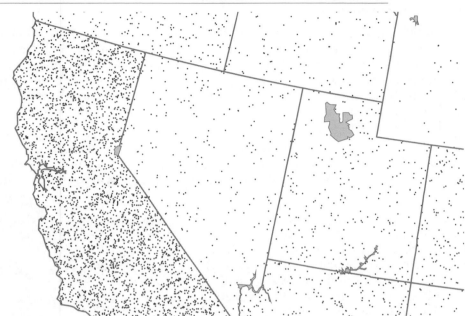

4.2.4 Symbolizing data

Depicting distributions of geographic phenomena rely on our well-developed ability to visualize and comprehend spatial patterns. Graphic primitives, such as color, symbol size, and arrangement, can be used to portray spatial patterns. One of the most comprehensive efforts to create a typology of graphic variables was Bertin's classic study: *Semiology of Graphics*.[19] The graphic primitives he identified, with more recent extensions,[20] include the following: location in space (x,y,z), size, shape, color, texture, orientation, arrangement, and focus. These are the building blocks of symbols that are used to depict geographic phenomena on maps.

Obviously, mapping the *location* of geographic features allows one to distinguish their geographic distribution and their interrelationships. Changing symbol *size* is particularly effective because sizes are easily differentiated by human perception. Larger sizes are intuitively associated with higher attribute values, but nominal values should not be

19. Bertin, J. 1983. *Semiology of graphics: Diagrams, networks, maps.* Madison, Wisconsin: University of Wisconsin Press.
20. DiBiase, D., J.B. Krygier, C. Reeves, A.M. MacEachren, and A. Brenner. 1991. *An Elementary Approach to Cartographic Animation.* Penn State University, University Park, PA.

portrayed by different sized symbols. *Shape* is well suited to represent different nominal values. Human perception is sensitive to different shapes, but there is essentially no intuitive ordering to different shapes.

Color *hue* is what most people associate with the word "color." Technically, hue is defined by a color's wavelength. Remember "ROYGBIV" from high school physics? Those hues can be seen (right, the *Color Selector* dialog) as: red, orange, yellow, green, blue, indigo, violet. Changes in hue are well suited for depicting nominal data. However, a common mistake is to use hue to map quantitative data (e.g., blue to red) because we quickly are overwhelmed with maintaining a sense of order with hues. That is, there is no inherent hierarchy or ordering between the hues.

Color *saturation* is the purity or brilliance of a hue. Technically, saturation is the range of wavelengths—a narrow range is perceived as a pure hue, while a wide range of wavelengths results in a cloudier color. Saturation is well suited to represent numerical values.

Color *value* is the variation in lightness or darkness of a color, which ranges from 0 to 100%. High color values are light (i.e. white) while low color values are dark (i.e. black). Because color value clearly has an order, variations in color value are useful for depicting quantitative data, although we have a limited ability to distinguish color value (up to 10 or so) and grey tones (about 7 or so). Two hue-value combinations are useful for ordinal data: yellow through green to blue or violet and yellow through orange to red. The Hue Saturation Value (HSV) color model (as depicted in the Color Selector dialog right) compensates better

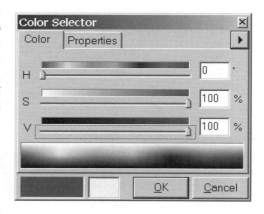

for the non-linear changes in human color perception, as compared to the RGB color model (red, green, blue).[21] The color model of the Color Selector can also be changed to the RGB or CMYK (cyan, magenta, yellow, black) models that are used by printers and photographers as well, using the arrow button at the top-right.

---

21. The RGB (red, green, blue) color model is particularly popular in for color video monitors. The intensity of color lies along the axis of 0, 0, 0 (black) to 100, 100, 100 (white), when all RGB values are equal. One of the problems with RBG is that linear changes in RGB values do not correspond to linear changes in color perception—for example, the human eye is less sensitive to changes in blue (see Bonham-Carter 1996). One alternative model is the HSV, which uses the same intensity as RGB. *Hue* refers to the angle in a plane normal to the intensity axis, while *saturation* is the radius from the intensity axis. Also see: Shih, T.Y., 1995. The reversibility of six geometric color spaces. *Photogrammetric Engineering & Remote Sensing* 61(10): 1223-1232.

Texture describes the spatial pattern of geographic features (see right). Changes in texture are best used to symbolize areal features. Different textures can be applied to features using the different fill patterns available, as well as through dot density mapping.

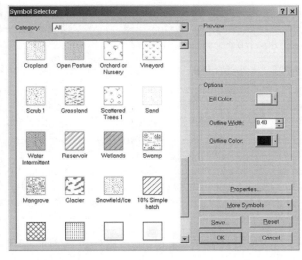

Orientation of a symbol can be used to depict either nominal or quantitative data. It is most often used in combination with texture to create fill patterns (see right). A really good use of orientation is to describe cyclic data (particularly aspect) by rotating a point symbol or marker, to show wind direction for example. *Arrangement* is also an aspect of pattern, and so it is most useful to depict areal features. *Focus* describes the clarity of a symbol, and is ideally suited to depict uncertainty or accuracy.

But what symbology should be used to depict a feature in ArcMap? Symbology in ArcMap is set in the *Symbology tab* of the Layer Properties dialog, as has been shown in the discussion of different classification types above. Note that the symbol can be adjusted through the *Symbol Selector* dialog, and there is a unique dialog for points, lines, and polygons. *Marker* symbols are used for point features, and the symbol shape, size, angle, fill color, and outline color can be changed. There are four types of markers: simple (fast-drawing based on "glyph" patterns); character (based on TrueType font), arrow, and picture (that uses a bitmap or enhanced metafile graphic). There are many, many existing marker symbols that are available by clicking on the **More Symbols...** button (and additional ones can be loaded from files as well). Note that the color can also be transparent (no color). There are five types of line symbols: simple (fast-drawing, one-pixel lines with predefined pattern); cartographic (straight lines with template patterns); hash (these use hachures and template patterns); marker (use marker decorations); and picture (a continuous tiling of a bitmap or an enhanced metafile graphic).[22] For area features, there are five types of *fill symbols*: simple (fast-drawing fill with optional outline); gradient (linear, rectangular, or circular color ramp fills); line (hatched lines at any angle, separation and offset); marker (marker symbols drawn randomly or ordered); and picture

---

22. There are some very powerful combinations here, including a symbology method to virtually "dissolve" boundaries between same-value features. See: ArcGIS Desktop Help, ArcMap, Symbolizing your data, Working with advanced symbolization.

(continuous tiling of a bitmap or an enhanced metafile graphic).[23] You can also bring up the *Color Selector* dialog and the *Symbol Property Editor* dialog (these dialogs are shown on the two previous pages).

4.2.4.1 Layer files

After a geographic dataset has been added and the layer has been symbolized and classified in ArcMap, the settings of how to display the data can be saved to a *layer file* (*.lyr). A layer file exists outside of the map document on disk, and in it are all the settings that specify the way the features are symbolized and the classification applied.[24] These layer files can be added to a map document, just like an existing dataset. Also, the symbology can be imported from an existing layer file and applied to a target dataset by clicking on the Import... button in the Symbology tab of the Layer Properties dialog of the target layer. Importing existing layer files is a useful way to save time and hassle so that existing legends can be applied to a new layer.

Note that a layer file simply points to the dataset it is based on, but does not store the actual data itself. So, if you would like to share a layer with someone, you need to provide both the dataset and the layer file. There are two ways that ArcGIS stores that pathname to the datasets in a layer file. The default method is to use the *absolute* or *full pathname* (e.g., c:\esri\data\usa\counties.shp). This requires that those who wish to use the layer file have the data on their computers using the same folder structure. Datasets can also be referenced using *relative* pathnames (e.g, \usa\counties.shp). Because relative paths do not contain drive names, data can be moved more easily between computers.

Changing absolute or relative pathnames

1. In *ArcMap*, click File ->Map Properties....

2. Click on the Data Source Options... button.

3. Click the radio button to set Store full path names or Store relative path names.

4. Click OK.

When a layer in ArcMap references data that does not exist at the specified location on a computer, ArcMap flags the layer using a red exclamation point next to the layer's name in the table of contents. This is called a *broken link*. Links can be broken when a dataset is

---

23. There is a lot more to symbols in ArcMap than can be adequately covered here. Please see ArcGIS Desktop help, type "symbols, marker," "symbols, line," or "symbols, fill" in the Help Index.

24. Layer files also typically save the selected features as well—though you can change this in the Selection Options dialog.

---

moved, renamed, or deleted, or if it is inaccessible for some other reason such as a downed database connection. Broken links can be repaired either one at a time, or for multiple layers.[25] Note that the data source for a layer can be changed even when the link is not broken. Indeed this is a useful technique to apply a particular legend onto a different or updated dataset.

Repairing broken links

One layer at a time:

1. In *ArcMap*, right-click on the layer with a broken link and select Properties.

2. Select the Source tab.

3. Click on the Set Data Source... button and navigate to find the desired dataset, then click OK.

Multiple layers:

1. In *ArcMap*, right-click on a layer with a broken link and select Data->Set Data Source....

2. Navigate to find the desired dataset, then click OK. (Arc-Map looks for other layers in the same folder).

4.2.5 Advanced symbology

There are numerous advanced methods for customizing symbology. One of the more useful tools is to specify the *transparency*

of a layer.[26] In this way, features can be displayed that allow underlying features to be viewed as well. Transparency, which ranges from 0 to 100% transparent, can be specified in three different ways. The same transparency for all features in an individual layer can be set through the layer properties (on the **Display** tab) or through the Effects tool (above). The transparency can also vary by feature, as specified in a field (values in percent) in a layer's attribute table. Note that the *brightness* and *contrast* can also be set. Another useful technique is to use a polygon feature layer to define an area to virtually clip the map to. That is, you can display an irregular portion to "clip" a map to (e.g., a couple of counties), and exclude the other areas, without having to permanently clip your layers. This is done through the data frame properties.

---

25. A broken link is roughly parallel to the dreaded project repair process (i.e. Where is file....?) in ArcView v3.x. The ability to repair multiple broken links at once, however, is a big step forward.

26. In ArcView v3.x, this concept of transparency only worked for GRID data, but now it applies to all layers (including feature types).

Setting the transparency of a layer

Layer properties:

1. In *ArcMap*, right-click on the layer and select **Properties**.
2. Select the **Display** tab.
3. Set the "Transparent:" value as a percentage (~40-50 works well), then click **OK**.

Effects tool:

1. In *ArcMap*, select **View->Toolbars->Effects**....
2. Set the "Layer" drop-down list to the desired layer.
3. Click on the transparency button ( ), then set the transparency percentage.

Feature specific:

1. In *ArcMap*, right-click on the layer and select **Properties**.
2. Select the **Symbology** tab.
3. Click on the **Advanced** button, then select **Transparency**.
4. Select the desired field that contains transparency values (ranging from 0 - 100), then click **OK**.
5. Click **OK**.

Another interesting tool that is helpful to visualize features below a polygon or raster layer is called the *Swipe* tool. This tool is found on the Effects toolbar (the button on the far right).

Whether a layer is displayed at a given scale or not can be controlled by setting a layer's *scale range* on the General tab of the Layer Properties dialog. You can set both the minimum and maximum thresholds, so that when the data frame is outside the minimum to maximum range, the layer is not drawn (even if you have the display checked in the TOC). This feature is useful when you want to prohibit users from zooming in too far and making decisions that the data may not support. Or it can be used to show layers with different representations of the same geographic features. These layers can also be combined into a *group layer* and then the scale range for the group layer can be set. For example, at a coarse scale, cities would be displayed as points, but at a finer scale, a different layer representing cities as polygons could be displayed.

Custom color ramps can be created for quantitative maps. Set the top and bottom (and any intermediate) color symbols, and then ramp colors (using right-click). If you wish to save

---

this customized color ramp, right-click on the color ramp drop-down arrow and select "Save." Note that the names of color ramps can be displayed instead of the color ramp graphic (again, right-click on drop-down arrow).

4.2.5.1 Styles

Styles are used to describe how maps are drawn, including symbol properties, label specifications, color schemes, legend and scale bar characteristics, and the location and the appearance of other cartographic elements. Styles help you to manage a familiar "look-and-feel" of a map, so that standard symbols, colors, and patterns can be maintained. In ArcMap, styles are accessed through the Style Manager dialog by clicking Tools->Styles->Style Manager....

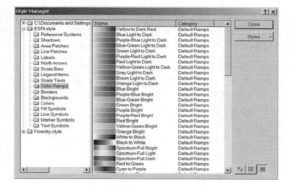

4.2.6 Multiple attributes map type

This type of map, also known as a *multi-variate* map, displays two or more attributes simultaneously on the same map, including a combination of categorical and quantitative data. Point and line features are commonly portrayed using multi-variate maps. For example, the size of marker symbol could show population, while the color could show the proportion of that population that is of Hispanic origin. There is a variety of combinations of maps, but you must be cautious when displaying multi-variate data because the map may become overly complex and hard to read.

4.2.6.1 Charts

Charts are used to display the values of multiple attributes of a feature. For example, the metropolitan and non-metropolitan percent change in population can be compared by region (right). In ArcMap, pie, bar, and stacked charts can be created. *Pie charts* are useful for showing proportions or ratios. *Bar charts* are useful for comparing amounts of related values (see right[27]), and to show trends over time. *Stacked bar charts* are useful for comparisons and relative relationships.

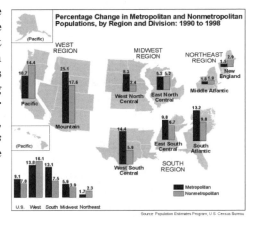

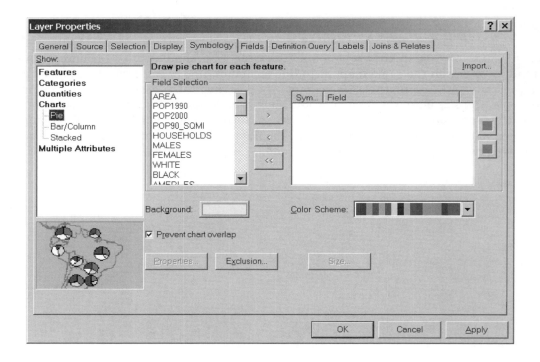

4.3 Landform maps

In addition to thematic mapping that was described above, a second common form of mapping is to depict landforms (Figure 4.14). For many centuries cartographers have developed clever ways to portray Earth's surface, or topography. Early explorers used symbols and hatch marks to delineate mountain ranges and canyons. These techniques reached their pinnacle in Erwin Raisz' work of landforms, which shows land features in intricate detail.[28]

FIGURE 4.14. The beautiful landforms formed by sand dunes in Death Valley National Park, California.

28. See: Raisz, E. 1962. *Principles of Cartography*. McGraw-Hill. Also see: http://www.mercatormag.com/article.php3?i=66.

Probably the most important type of map developed to portray terrain are maps that use contour lines (or their below sea level counterparts, *bathymetric contours* or *isobaths*) (Figure 4.15). This type of map, of course, has been well utilized in the USGS Topographic map series.

FIGURE 4.15. Contour lines (lines of equal elevation) in Colorado and Utah depicting 1000 m intervals.

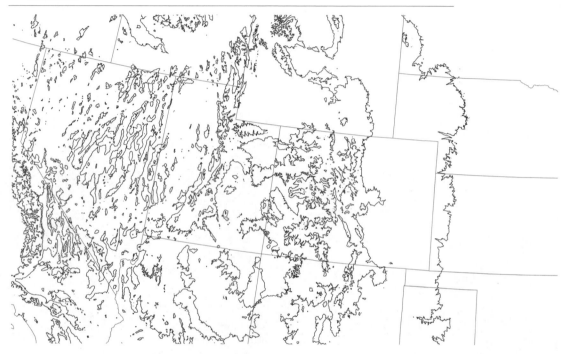

An early innovation of computer cartography and GIS was a series of alternative methods to depict landforms from an *oblique perspective,* in contrast to the *orthographic perspective* (essentially looking straight down on a surface). An oblique perspective typically allows map readers to more readily understand spatial relationships between features because the landscape appears much as it does when looking out of the window of an airplane. An oblique perspective requires three inputs: the zenith angle (the angle measured from a horizontal, which ranges from 0° to 90°), the viewing azimuth, which specifies which direction you are looking (0° to 360°), and the viewing distance (how distant the observer is from the surface). One of the first innovations was to create *fishnet* or *wire-frame* diagrams to depict terrain using vector graphics (e.g., the SYMVU program).

The next major advance in landform visualization was the development of *hillshade* maps, which is an approach that models the hypothetical illumination of a surface (Figure 4.16). Hillshade maps can be created using the Spatial Analyst, 3D Analyst, and Geostatistical Analyst extensions, and are discussed in detail in Chapter 7. A further innovation that has taken full advantage of powerful computer graphics is to represent features in three dimensions, from which surfaces, terrain, and whole landscapes can be visualized and analyzed. This is what the ArcScene and 3D Analyst extensions allow you to do.

FIGURE 4.16. Hillshade map showing the dramatic relief of the Rocky Mountains around the Roaring Fork Valley, home to Aspen, Colorado.

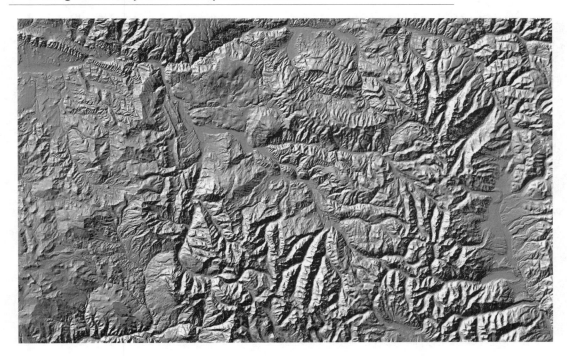

4.4 Labeling maps

In addition to portraying geographic features using symbology, you may want to label features simply with their names. A *label* is some descriptive text that is associated with a feature. For point features, it is important to[29]:

- position labels shifted up from the feature (to the right or left) and on the same side of a linear feature as the point feature;
- maintain consistent distance between features and label.

For line features, try to:

- position labels above and at the straightest and most horizontal portion of a feature;
- use italicized font for water features;
- follow natural features and repeat labels for long line features (e.g., rivers).

For areal features, it is best to:

- expand the label to suggest the spatial extent of an areal feature through providing spaces between characters of the label;
- use uppercase characters.

If labels are to be added to only a few features, then perhaps it makes sense to add them manually. This can be accomplished by creating a text graphic, placing it near the

feature to label, and then typing in the desired description. The *Labeling toolbar* (above) provides easy access to the Label Manager dialog and a variety of ways to prioritize and weight labels for each layer.

Four types of labels are available. First, simple text that follows a straight line (usually horizontal, but it can be rotated) can be entered using the *New Text* tool. Second, text can be added so that it follows a curved line using the *splined text* tool, for example, when labeling a winding river. Third, features can be

---

29. This section borrows heavily from Brewer's 2005 book: *Designing Better Maps*, ESRI Press.

labeled with one of their attributes by clicking on a feature with the *label* tool. Fourth, text can be added in a callout box using the *callout* tool.

Labeling features

1. In the Draw toolbar, select one of the four text tools: *New Text*, *New Splined Text*, *Label*, or *Callout*.

New Text: **A**

2. Click at a location and enter the text label in the properties dialog. Click **OK**.

New Splined Text:

2. Click to add vertices that follow a curving feature and double-click to end the line, then type in the dialog.

Label:

2. Set the field to label features from the Labels Tab of the Properties dialog.

3. Click on a feature.

Callout:

2. Click at a location, then type text into the dialog.

New polygon text:

2. Click the vertices of a simple polygon (double-click to close), then type desired text into the dialog.

New rectangle text:

2. Click and drag a rectangle, then type desired text into the dialog.

New circle text:

2. Click and drag a circle, then type desired text into the dialog.

4.4.1 Dynamic labels

If many or all of the features on a map are to be labeled, then it makes sense to automatically label a layer with what are called *dynamic labels*. To do this, select **Label Features** from the context menu of a layer. You can specify the attribute that will be used to label in the Labels tab of the Layer Properties dialog. Note that if an attribute value is changed, the label for that feature changes as well. Also, all features can be labeled the same way, or differently by groups (again specified by selecting an attribute). Labels can be turned off by selecting **Label Features** again. The placement of labels can be controlled, because sometimes in a location dense with features, labels may overlap or conflict. One of the options is to set labels with a priority value.

4.4.2 Annotation

To provide more control over label placement, labels can be converted to *annotation*. Annotation labels can be worked with independently, so the location or font size can be adjusted. Note that other graphic features (points, lines, circles, etc.) can become annotation as well. Annotation (text and graphics) is stored with the map document, or alternatively as a feature type in a geodatabase. One advantage of storing annotation in a geodatabase is that *feature-linked annotation* can be created, which creates a strong linkage between an annotation and its feature. This means that if a feature is moved, then the annotation moves as well. (Note that this functionality requires the ArcEditor or ArcInfo level.)

Note that although there are basic capabilities provided for automatic placement of labels in ArcGIS, there is an extension called *Maplex* that adds advanced label placement and conflict detection. It can also generate saved text with map documents and annotation layers as well. This extension is part of the ArcInfo license (but must be purchased for ArcView license).

4.4.3 Label expressions

To provide more control over how a label appears, ArcGIS allows you to use *label expressions*, along with ArcGIS formatting tags that are special characters you can use to change the appearance of labels. For example, you can automatically add a particular string to your label (e.g., to add "Starbucks" before the store numbers) or concatenate two or more fields together. This is done through the expression window in **Label Expression** dialog (right).

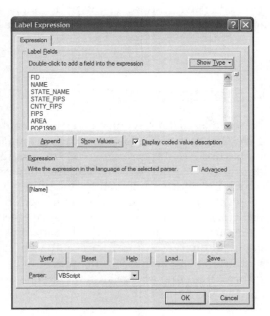

- "Starbucks " & [STORENO]
- [COUNTY] & " " & [FIPS]

To round a number (e.g., area of polygon) to a certain number of places, use:

- Round ([AREA], 1)

To convert labels to upper case, use:

- UCase ([NAME])

Separate fields with the Visual Basic variable vbNewline (or vbCrLf) to create "stacked text" (fields on separate lines):

- "State: " & [NAME] & vbNewline & "County: " & [COUNTY]

You can also format labels automatically through formatting tags, such as bolding the FIPS portion of the string below.

- [COUNTY] & " " & "<BOL>[FIPS]</BOL>"

Change the label format based on the value of a field using a conditional if-then-else statement:

- Function MyLabel ([Name], [Population])
-     if ([Population] >= 10000) then
-         MyLabel = "<CLR red='255'> + [Name] + </CLR>
-     else
-         MyLabel = [Name]
-     end if
- End Function

Other tags include: font (FNT), italics (ITA), underline (UND), all capitals (ACP), small capitals (SCP), superscript (SUP), subscript (SUB). Note that "&" and "<" are special characters inside label expressions, so use &amp or &lt for those characters.

4.5 Map layout

Numerous books have been written about map design and composition, so the approach here is to mention a couple of cartographic rules of thumb, to introduce you to some of the tools that ArcMap provides and to provide references for additional information where appropriate. Also, ArcGIS has implemented what it calls *cartographic representations*, which are more advanced and sophisticated ways to create maps, which is beyond the scope of this book. Maps are composed in the layout view of ArcMap. A layout can have multiple data frames in it to show different views or maps (Figure 4.17). Also, various elements can be added to the layout to provide additional information needed to make a comprehensive, stand-alone map. The typical elements that are found on a map, in addition to the map itself, include: a map title, legend, map scale, north arrow, projection information, and source statement. These elements can be added to a layout view through the **Insert** menu.

The *map title* needs to describe, through a short phrase, the essence of the map—what is trying to be conveyed to the reader. Some description of the source data that were used to produce the map, the date of the data, and the map projection should be provided as well. A *neatline* can be added to frame or organize map elements. These elements can be placed on the map using a *text* graphic. The *legend* explains the symbols that are found on the map. A *north arrow* shows the orientation of the map. The *scale bar* shows the amount of detail (or generalization) displayed on the map through a graphic, and the *scale text* portrays the same information, but using words (e.g., "1 inch equals 1 mile"). Finally, other pictures or images can be added as well, for example to incorporate a company logo. A *graticule*, which provides a grid of spatial coordinates on top of the map, can be added to a data frame through its Properties dialog.

4.5.1 Templates

ArcMap provides the ability to create a map template. *Templates* are used to standardize layouts so that map series can be easily created and to provide a jump-start to create comprehensive maps. A number of templates are provided with ArcGIS as well, and templates can be shared within and between organizations. Map templates are actually a special type of map document (*.mxt), and so existing template files can be opened by selecting **File->Open**..., then modify the "Files of Type:" drop-down list to templates. Templates can be saved in the same fashion (**File->Save as**...). Templates also store the state and configuration of the user interface, such as whether additional toolbars are being used, or whether they are "docked" or not. Also, custom tools are stored in templates.

FIGURE 4.17. Example map layout of the Democratic Republic of Congo.[30]

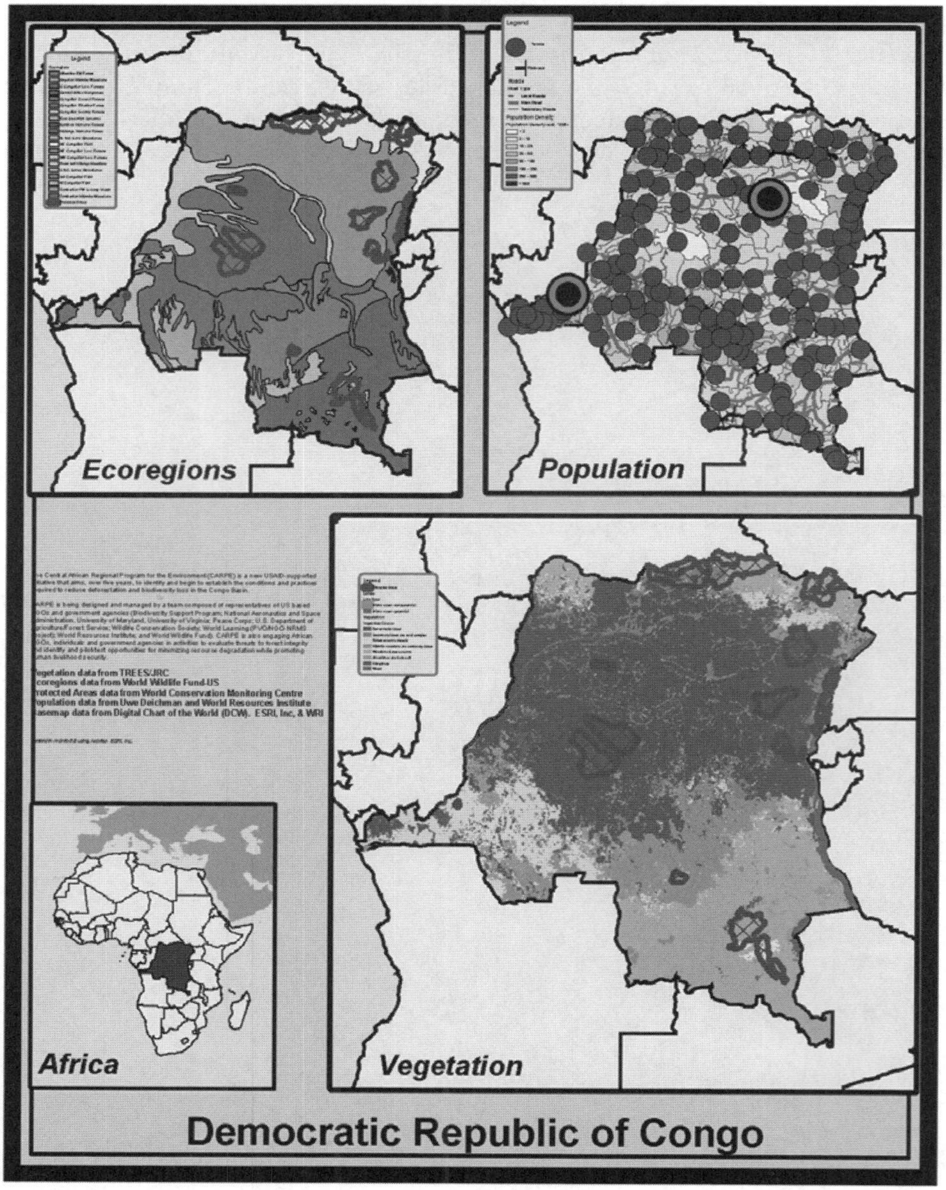

4.6 Exporting and printing

There are a number of ways a map can be exported to output maps, shown in the data view or layout view, onto different media (Table 4.3). First, a map can be exported to a graphic format that can be incorporated into a digital document (e.g., Portable Document Format). Second, it can be printed directly or from one of the exported formats (e.g., Encapsulated PostScript). Third, interactive maps can be created that are web-browser compatible.

TABLE 4.3. Types of maps and their media.

	Media	*Advantages*	*Disadvantages*
Map Document	ArcGIS	Full display, query, analysis Hyperlinks, map tips	
Internet Map	ArcIMS	Full dynamic browsing	
Interactive map	ArcPublisher & ArcReader		
Image map	DHTML	Fast, very stable, very portable, low technology investment	
Google Earth	KML	Drape vector-based features within Google Earth, including attributes	
PDF	Adobe Reader	Standard format Control layer visibility	Cannot query specific features, information content low
Graphics format	E.g., Enhanced Metafile	Can resize without distortion	
Paper		Easy to read	Expensive, static

Maps created in ArcMap can be exported to a number of different graphic files[31]—the choice of which method is best depends on a couple of factors. First, does your map contain raster layers, just vector layers, or both vector and raster? Vector layers can be exported to what is called vector graphic format, which keeps the features intact and allows the graphic to be resized with little distortion. Second, large-format maps can create very

---

30. Source: from ArcGIS Sample maps, DemocraticRepublicOfCongo.mxd.
31. Compared to ArcView v3.x, the exporting capabilities are much improved, and the application is much more stable.

large graphic files (i.e. megabytes to gigabytes in size). As a result, some graphic formats use compression, but it is important to understand whether the compression technique is lossy or lossless. A *lossy* compression technique results in smaller file sizes, but can result in slightly degraded image quality—notably JPEGs. A *lossless* technique compresses files but does not result in image degradation (e.g., GIFs and PNGs). A number of export options are available (Table 4.4).

Also note that a world file can be generated for all graphic file types. A *world file* is an additional file that contains information to tell other software where the image is located in the world -- that is, it stores spatial coordinates (but not projection information). This is only necessary if the image will be used in a GIS program -- it is not required if the image will be viewed or used in a non spatial context. The file typically will have the same name as the image file, with the file extension based on the first and last letters of the image's file extension, plus "w" (e.g., *.tif --> *.tfw, though for a JPEG it should be either *.jpw or *.jpgw). This option is only available when exporting in the **Data** view.

TABLE 4.4. Graphic formats available when exporting ArcMap data and layout views.

Format (*ArcPress)	Type	Comments	World file?
Adobe Illustrator (*.ai)	vector and raster		No
Bitmap (*.bmp)	raster		Yes
Encapsulated PostScript (*.eps)	vector and raster	transparency, standard format for printing industry	No
Windows Enhanced Metafile (*.emf)	vector and raster	Can be resized	No
GIF (*.gif)	raster	transparency	Yes
JPEG (*.jpg)	raster, lossy compression		Yes
Adobe Portable Document Format (*.pdf)	vector and raster	transparency, retain annotation, labeling, and layers from ArcMap	No
Portable Network Graphic (*.png)	raster	transparency	Yes
SVG (Scalable Vector Graphics)	vector and raster		No
TIFF	raster	transparency	Yes

Adobe Illustrator Format (*.ai)—This is a useful format for post-processing maps in Adobe Illustrator (v6.0 and above is supported). Not only does it export maps at 720 dpi, it exports colors in CMYK and preserves most layers from ArcMap, including annotation, labels, and data frame graphics.

Bitmap (*.bmp)—This is a native Windows graphic format, but it can handle only raster images, though it does resize very well. The color depth can also be specified: use 24-bit for maps with color gradients and fills, 8-bit for plain color, and 1-bit for black and white maps. A background color and header file (*.bpw) can be exported to georeference the image (only available with data view).

Computer Graphics Metafile (*.cgm)—This format is a standard in the oil and gas industry. The best resolution choice is 300 dpi.

Encapsulated PostScript (*.eps)—This is the most commonly used format for high-end cartography and printing, and it can handle both feature and raster data. A resolution of 300 dpi produces a good quality graphic, and fonts can be downloaded as well.

Enhanced metafiles (*.emf)—This is a native Windows graphic format that can handle both vector and raster graphics. A nice feature of this format is that these files can be resized without much distortion inside another document (e.g., Microsoft® Word, Microsoft® Powerpoint, Adobe Acrobat PDF, etc.). A resolution of 300 dpi produces a good quality graphic.

Graphic Interchange Format (*.gif)—This is a standard raster format ideally used for the web. GIFs are limited to 256 colors (8 bit) and can have transparent color.

Joint Photographic Experts Group (*.jpg)—This is a format for raster graphics, and because it utilizes compression, it has been a favorite for web graphics. However, this format uses a lossy compression technique, and because lines and text in particular become fuzzy, it is recommended to be used only for printing images (like an aerial photograph).[32] Reasonable quality images can be created using 72 or 96 dpi and medium to medium-high quality settings. A progressive JPEG displays as a series of scans as the file downloads (useful for the Web). Selecting Clip removes the white margin of the map (when you are in layout view).

Portable Document Format (*.pdf)—This format is robust and works well across computer platforms, and handles both raster and vector graphics well. A resolution of 300 dpi produces a good quality graphic, and you can also choose to download any fonts used. Layers in PDF v8 are now supported (Figure 4.18). Group layers in ArcMap are consolidated into a single layer in the PDF. Layers that cause rasterization, such as a raster dataset, transparent layer, or layer that uses a picture fill symbology (unless you use the option "vectorize picture marker/fills"), consolidate all layers below them into a single layer in the PDF called "image". Text, picture, and north-arrow map elements that

---

32. In the past, this was one of the old standards, but there are much better alternatives available.

are part of a layout are placed into a PDF layer called "other". Dynamic labels are placed into a PDF layer called "labels." It is also wise to check the "Embed All Document Fonts" option so that the PDF looks the same on the destination computer than as it does when it was created. Also note that you can do some basic queries of the labels embedded in a PDF through the Find function.

FIGURE 4.18. An example of maintaining layers from ArcMap into a Adobe Portable Document Format file for Bear Lake, Rocky Mountain National Park, Colorado. Note that each of the layers can be turned on or off.

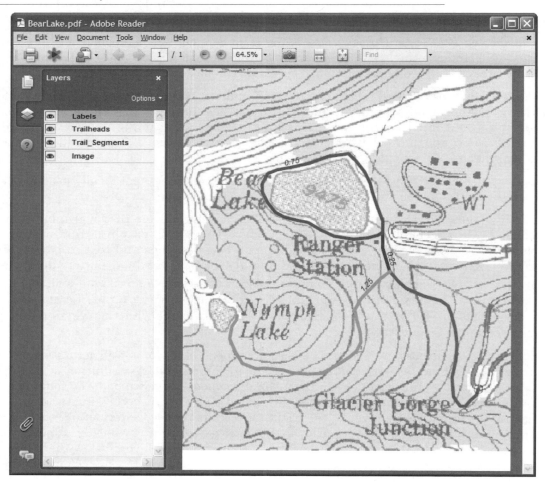

Portable Network Graphics (*.png)—This a very useful format as it uses a lossless compression technique and it improves on the older *.gif format by supporting 24-bit color. Use 72 or 96 dpi for web graphics. It also supports transparency (use 24-bit color).

Scalable Vector Graphics (*.svg)—This is an XML-based file format designed for viewing graphics over the Web, and is the standard vector Web format. It is rescalable.

Tagged Image File Format (*.tif)—This format is very robust for handling raster images, and because it works well across computer platforms (e.g., Windows, Mac, UNIX), it is often the format of choice. The background color and a header file (*.tfw) can be exported to georeference the image (only available with data view). If you have the *ArcPress* extension, then a number of additional options are available. ArcPress is a PostScript-based raster image processor that converts maps into high-resolution bitmaps for high-quality printing. When ArcPress is used to print, first the map is exported to an Enhanced Metafile, which is then converted to Encapsulated Postscript. Then, the EPS file is rasterized into a printer-specific bitmap image. The advantage is that the printer does not need to process the image, making it print faster, and making it more robust for really big graphic files. ArcPress is especially useful to print maps with large raster data sets and transparent or complex symbology.

Exporting a map

1. In *ArcMap*, select File->Export Map..., then choose the format from the dialog.
2. Navigate to the desired location and specify the filename.
3. Set the "Save as type:" drop-down list to the desired format.
4. Modify the options as necessary.
5. Click Export.

4.6.1 Creating interactive maps

An interactive map allows users to query and manipulate the display of a map, either stand-alone on a computer or through the World Wide Web.[33] There are a number of methods to create interactive maps.

A common format of interactive maps uses Dynamic HTML, particularly an *imagemap*, that allows users to click at a location to bring up specific text or images (Figure 4.19), and to move their cursor to a feature (a "mouse-over") to display text information. Also,

---

33. For example, see: Peterson, M. 1995. Interactive and animated cartography. Prentice Hall. 257 pgs.; Kraak, M.J. and A. Brown. 2001. Web Cartography. Taylor & Francis. 213 pgs.

clicking at a specific location on a map triggers something, typically a new hyperlink or perhaps a zoomed-in image. ArcGIS does not provide a method to create imagemaps directly, but a number of third-party extensions have been developed that do this.[34]

FIGURE 4.19. An example image map allowing users to click at a location and bring up additional information, as well as providing mouse-over information as a "map tip."[35]

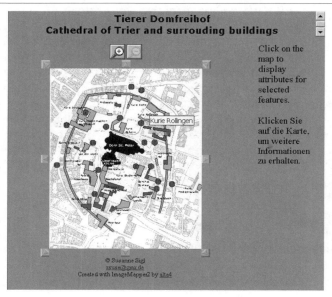

A new type of interactive map can be produced by ESRI's *ArcPublisher* extension, and read by a free plug-in called *ArcReader*. This type of map does not contain the data itself— rather it simply points to data elsewhere on the computer (or Internet). This is a powerful method to create very simple, intuitive interfaces for the general public to gain access to current data.

A slightly more powerful way to serve maps over the Internet is called *Internet mapping*. This generally requires specialized software (e.g., ArcIMS) to serve data over the Internet (Figures 4.20 and 4.21). One of the main advantages of this method is that it allows users to be able to zoom and pan to their areas of interest, rather than preparing set levels of zoom. It is perhaps most useful when data is updated on a frequent basis (e.g., daily).

---

34. For example, Alta4's ImageMapper: http://www.alta4.com/eng/products_e/im/im8/
35. http://www.swegis.com/english/software/imagemapper/samples/im2/dom/index.html

---

FIGURE 4.20. An example Internet Map Service application—the GeoMac Wildland Fire Support system. Here the perimeter (as of August 15, 2002) of the largest fire in Oregon's history is displayed.[36]

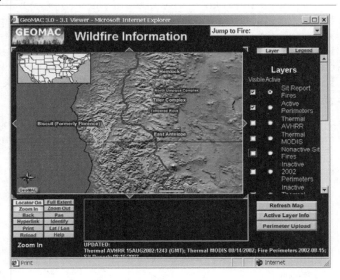

FIGURE 4.21. An example Internet Map Service application showing the Colorado Ownership, Management, and Protection spatial database displayed in the Colorado Division of Wildlife's Natural Diversity Information Source (www.ndis.nrel.colostate.edu).

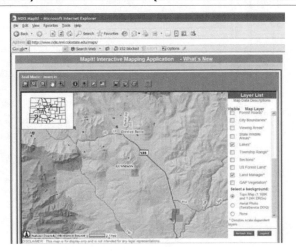

36. http://geomac.usgs.gov/

4.7 Graphs

In addition to maps, geographic data can be visualized using a *graph*, which portrays information about geographic features in a slightly different way than a map. A graph typically aligns attribute values against two dimensions (sometimes three). Often, graphs are used to present summary information that has been gleaned from a spatial analysis (Figure 4.22). Graphs are dynamically linked to their source tables so they are updated as the selection of records (and features) changes. There are a number of different types of graphs available, including the option of overlaying lines on bars (Table 4.5).

FIGURE 4.22. An example of a graph showing summary statistics for major land cover types in Colorado. Note that the graph properties can be modified by right-clicking in the graph title bar.

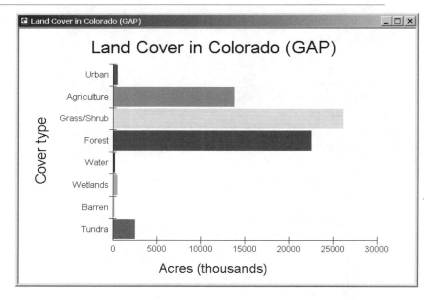

<table>
<tr><td colspan="2" align="center">Creating a graph</td></tr>
</table>

Creating a graph
1. In *ArcMap*, select Tools->Graphs->Create.... to open the Graph Wizard.
2. Select the type of graph.
3. Specify the layer and select the attribute values to graph.
4. Specify the look of the graph.
5. Click Finish.

TABLE 4.5. Available graph types in ArcGIS.

Type	Description	Picture	3D?
Area	Like a line graph, but shades between lines emphasizes quantities. Useful for showing the relationship of several attributes over time.		Y
Bar and column	Consists of two or more parallel bars, each represents an attribute value. Useful to compare amounts between different attributes or trends over time.		
Box Plot	This provides a graphical display of the statistical distribution of values. The box shows the middle 50% of data points (ranging from first to third quartile of the data -- the horizontal line in the box marks the median value (second quartile).		
Histo-gram	This is a sub-type of the vertical bar graph that shows the frequency distribution of values.		
Line	Shows trends in a value along a continuous scale using one or more lines or sequences of symbols drawn on a Cartesian grid. They can be used to display rising and falling trends among several variables, and can be oriented horizontally or vertically.		Y

TABLE 4.5. Available graph types in ArcGIS.

Type	Description	Picture	3D?
Pie	Shows the relationship of proportions or between parts and the whole.		Y
Scatter	Plots points based on link attribute values to the x and y axis. These are useful for examining the relationship or correlation between two variables.		Y
Scatterplot matrix	This is a data exploration tool that shows several variables on the same graph.		

Specify the data the graph will be displaying by selecting the records (or fields for most graph types) that will be linked to the x and y axes. Here you can also choose to have the graph change according to the selected set of records, or show all the records all the time.

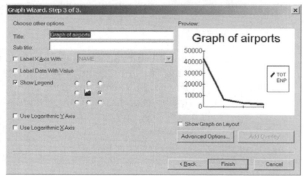

Finally, specify the appearance by setting the title and labeling the axes. There are a number of additional, advanced features as well, accessed through the **Advanced Options...** button. You can specify titles; modify axis tick, color, and labels; set the fonts for the text; change the markers and symbology; add statistical lines (e.g., min, max, mean, etc.); fit trend lines (e.g,. linear, power, log, etc.) and add a second y-axis[37] by using an *overlay graph*; add error bars (e.g., standard deviation or standard error); and set the style of the background.

Graphs can be added to the layout view, managed through the *Graph Manager* dialog, and accessed through **Tools-->Graphs**.... They can also be exported to a graphic file by selecting **Export...** from the graph's context menu (*.bmp, *.jpg, *.png, *.wmf).

4.8 Chapter review

- Cartography is the art and science of making a map.

- Key to making a good map is to clearly identify the *purpose* of the map—what geographical aspect are you trying to visualize?

- In general, in a quantitative thematic map, the *greater* the attribute value, the *darker* (more intense) the color value so that features with higher values are visually dominant.

- A *layer file* stores the symbology of a dataset, but simply points to the dataset and does not store the actual data itself.

---

37. Only available on the area, column, high-low-close, and scatter graph types.

Cartography and geographic visualization

5   *Querying spatial data*

As was discussed in the first chapter, one of the important characteristics of GIS is that it is "maps and more...". The previous chapter covered a lot of material about map making and cartography. This chapter we'll explore the "more" part. One of the critical differences between an electronic map displayed in GIS and a paper map is the ability to access or query the data "behind" the map. To *query* a map is to pose a question or inquire about a feature (or features) represented in a GIS dataset. Queries about geographic features can be accomplished in two ways. An *attribute query* (also called aspatial) utilizes attribute data of features to identify a sub-set of features that are of interest. For example, if you wanted to identify relatively populated places in the US, you might pose a query that would find the counties in the US that have greater than 100,000 people. S*patial* queries utilize spatially explicit data and relationships between spatial features. An example of a spatial query would be to identify all counties that have an interstate highway passing through them.

5.1 Selection method

If you recall from Chapter 2, an important concept is the idea of the *selection set*. A selection is a subset of features that is displayed as selected rows in an attribute table and/ or a subset of features in a spatial dataset (or feature class). Knowing what features or rows are selected (and which are not) is important because ArcGIS can perform different operations to a feature or row depending whether it is in the selection set or not. But how do you create a selection set? Through a query!

Queries can be used to identify and distinguish certain features with desired attributes from the rest of the features of a dataset (see Table 5.1). The selection of features is often talked about in terms of sets, based on Boolean logic operations: AND, OR, NOT, and XOR (Table 5.2).

There are a few *selection methods*, or ways to instruct ArcMap to recognize or ignore an existing selection set. That is, a query can disregard the currently selected set of features (i.e. create new), recognize the current selection and add to it, remove from it, or select from it. The most commonly used (and by default) selection method is *create a new selection,* which ignores (does not recognize) the selected set of features before the new query is applied. Another method is to *add to current selection*, which adds those features selected by the new query to the current selected set. You can also *remove from current selection,* which removes features selected in the new query from those that were already selected. Finally, *select from current selection* respects the current selection and returns only those already-selected features that meet the new criteria. For example, to select US counties with at least 100,000 people in 2000, you would do a query (using the Select by Attributes tool) using the *create a new selection* method (this would result in a selection set with 524 counties).

Selection of features has changed slightly in v9 to make it consistent with the geoprocessing framework. Previous versions did not differentiate between the situation where zero features were selected and where no selection set existed (a selection has to be made to in order for a selection set to exist). This enabled functions in the past to assume that "no selection is the same as all the features selected." Now, with v9, these states are differentiated. If you query a feature dataset and the selection criteria results in zero features being selected, then the next Geoprocessing operation will use 0 features (instead of all that would have occurred pre-v9).

TABLE 5.1. Examples of applying different selection methods on a table with five counties (labeled a, b, c, d, and e). The population (pop) of the counties (in order) is: 1000, 2000, 5000, 5000, and 10000.

Method	Current selection	Selection query	Resulting selection
Create a new selection	- none -	pop > 2000	c, d, e
	- none -	pop > 0	a, b, c, d, e
	a, b, c	pop > 2000	c, d, e
Add to current selection	- none -	pop > 2000	c, d, e
	- none -	pop > 0	a, b, c, d, e
	a, b, c	pop > 2000	a, b, c, d, e
Remove from current selection	- none -	pop > 2000	- none -
	- none -	pop > 0	- none -
	a, b, c	pop > 2000	a, b
Select from current selection	- none -	pop > 2000	- none -
	- none -	pop > 0	- none -
	a, b, c	pop > 2000	c
Switch selection	- none -	N/A	a, b, c, d, e
	- none -		a, b, c, d, e
	a, b, c		d, e

5.2 What is here?

5.2.1 Identify

One of the first and common ways to ask questions and interact with a map of spatial data is to ask the question: "what is here?" This allows you to obtain the background or underlying information about a particular feature. To query a particular location, use the *Identify* tool 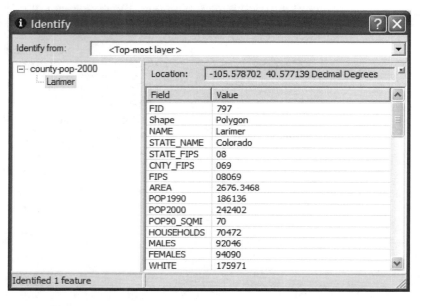 (found in the **Tools** toolbar). Clicking with this tool on a feature in a layer brings up the **Identify** dialog that displays the attribute values for the feature. For example, from a county dataset, clicking with the Identify tool in Larimer County, Colorado brings up the listing of attributes associated with that feature. The attributes (stored in fields) can be sorted by the field name (click on the Field tab). Also note that you can copy and paste a value (or values) from a particular field.

In contrast to queries that select features, the Identify tool does not change the selection set. Also note that you can specify which layers will be searched: *top-most layer, visible layers* (those that are displayed or drawn in the view portion of ArcMap), *selectable layers, all layers,* and each layer in the data frame by name.

In a fashion similar to Identify, the primary attribute or label of a feature can be easily displayed using *map tips*. The display value for the feature at the location of the cursor is updated as the cursor is moved across the map. Note that more than one layer can have map tips on, and that map tips also works on raster datasets.

Turning map tips on
1. In *ArcMap*, right-click on the layer and select **Properties**.
2. Select the **Display** tab.
3. Check the **Show Map Tips** box. If this is greyed-out, add a spatial index to the dataset and try again.
4. Click on the **Fields** tab to set the primary display field.
5. Click **OK**.

5.2.2 Interactive selection

Features can be interactively selected using the cursor and clicking on desired features. The attributes of the selected features can then be examined in the attribute table. To query a layer through *interactive selection,* use the *Select Features* tool( ). First, you need to specify which layers to select features from, and that is typically accomplished through the *Selection tab* in the Table of Contents. One common source of confusion is that as a layer is added to a data frame, it is automatically made selectable, so features from many layers may get selected by default. To display the number of selected features for a single layer, click on the layer name and the status bar will display "*n* features selected", where *n* is the number of selected features. Note that the number of features selected is displayed in the status bar in the lower-left part of the ArcMap window.

Setting the selectable layers
1. In *ArcMap*, click **Tools->Options...**
2. Click on the **TOC** tab.
3. Check the **Selection** box (at the top).
5. Click **OK**.

Features can also be *deselected*, or removed from the selected set by shift-clicking, and also by *switch selection*, which reverses the selected features.[1] Note that interactive selection actually selects all the features within a *selection tolerance*, that is, those features that are found within a radius of a specified number of pixels (three by default).

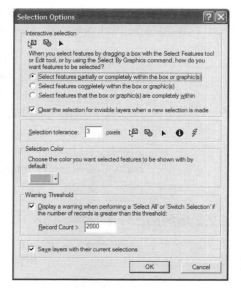

Interactively selecting features

To add to the selected set

1. Select the *Select Features* tool(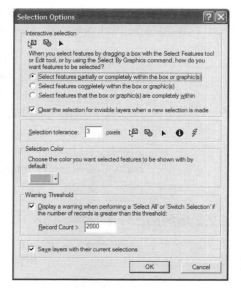).
1. Select the first feature, then shift-select subsequent features.

To switch selection

1. In *ArcMap*, right-click on the layer and select **Selection->Switch Selection**.
2. Select the **Display** tab.

To modify selection tolerance

1. In *ArcMap*, click **Selection->Options...**
2. Set the **Selection tolerance** (in pixels).
3. Click **OK**.

---

1. To avoid the warning message about the amount of time to perform a "switch selection" (which can become annoying), set the record count to a large number, such as 1,000,000 (it really doesn't take that long).

5.3 How big? How long? How far?

Another common way to query a feature is to investigate its spatial properties (in this case, not its attributes). That is, how big? How long? One way to determine the area of a feature is to use the *Identify* tool to get the value of the area field in a polygon coverage theme. You will need to know what units represent this value, which are usually based on the projection. Many times, however, there is not an area field in the attribute table (though you can create one). In this case, you can visualize the size of certain features on a theme by placing a graphic in the data view and resizing it through the

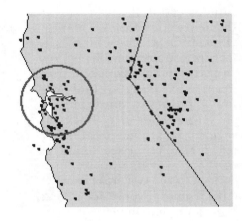

Properties dialog, using the "Size and Position" property. For instance, if you want to see how features on the map compare to a 100 km radius circle (above right), you could add a circle and change the radius value. This is useful when trying to visualize features that are within a certain distance or how large features are compared to a benchmark (e.g., an acre, hectare, soccer field, city block). One caution: it is recommended to calculate length and area only when your dataset (data frame) is displayed using a projection (rather than in geographic coordinates), because distance is greatly distorted as a function of increasing latitude with geographic coordinates. (Otherwise, spherical distance and area calculations are needed).

Another way to determine the area or length of a feature is to use the *Measure tool* 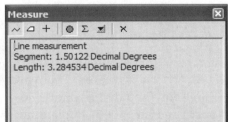. A nice interactive dialog (see right) can be used to measure the area and length of different aspects of features that you click on. You can also change the units that distance and area are measured in.

It can also be used to determine the distance between features. After selecting the tool, click on the map at the start of a feature, then click at the end of the feature you are measuring. You can also measure a complex feature by using a number of line segments to approximate a curvilinear feature. Both the segment length and total length (of all segments) are displayed in the status bar in the units defined in the General tab of the data frame's Properties dialog. For example, the as-the-crow-flies distance between Denver, Colorado and Santa Barbara, California is 918 miles. The display units can be changed through the properties (General tab) of the data frame. Note that

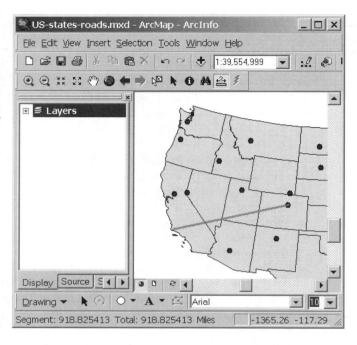

you can get the *geodesic distance* (computed using spherical geometry) by holding the shift-key down while using the measuring tool

5.4 Where is...? Where are...?

A common query of spatial data is to simply find where a particular feature that meets certain criteria is located. There are two methods to locate a feature through its attributes: through the Find dialog and through the Select By Attributes dialog.[2] Which to use? Find is best used for fairly simple queries, while Select By Attributes provides the ability to develop more complicated queries involving several attributes and even compound Boolean logic.

---

2. In ArcView v3.x, this was called the Query Builder dialog.

5.4.1 Find

You can quickly find features in ArcMap through the *Find* dialog.[3] For example, where is the US zip code 90210 anyway? By default, *Find* searches through string and numerical fields in all *visible layers* in ArcMap, finding matches to the input search string. Matched records are listed at the bottom of the dialog, and by right-clicking on the value, you can flash the feature(s) on the map, zoom to the feature(s), and even set the spatial extent that contains the features as a bookmark. You can list all the

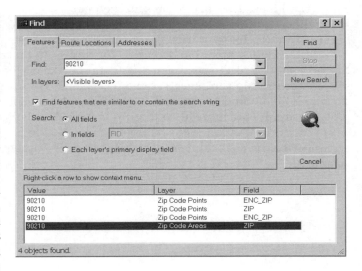

attributes of that feature (like Identify), and you can also select the features by clicking on them—selected features on the map are shown by a highlighted color (default is cyan).

Querying using Find
1. In *ArcMap*, click **Edit->Find...** (or click on the Find button 🔍).   2. Fill out the "Find:" string and other parameters.   3. Click **Find**.

---

3. Note that ArcCatalog's Search feature finds whether a dataset is within some geographic region that you specify.

There are a number of options to modify the way Find works. First, the layers that are to be searched can be specified to find values in: all visible layers (default), selectable layers, all layers (in data frame), all layers in all data frames, and individual layers by name. Second, you can match strings that are similar to the search string (default, like a wildcard search), or exactly the search string (case-sensitive as well). Third, all fields can be searched, a specific field you choose, or just the field that is used to display a layer's labels (the *display field*). Also note that the search string is automatically recorded and available for subsequent searches.

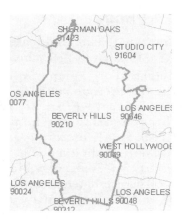

5.4.2 Select By Attributes

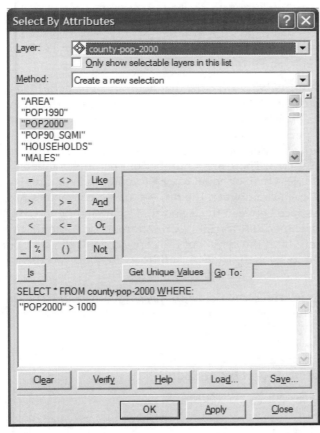

Probably the most commonly-used and powerful method to query datasets is through the *Select By Attributes* query. This approach lets you specify a query expressed through a text string, called a *query expression*, that follows a particular format (called the *Structured Query Language* or SQL formalism). A proper expression is formed by a threesome of field, operand, and value.[4] There are five steps to use this powerful dialog.

• First, select the layer you want to query (only those layers in a data frame are listed). The list of fields in the selected layer's attribute table is updated automatically (and notice there is plenty of room for long field names). Note that you can limit the entries in this list to only "selectable" layers through the check box.

• Second, select one of the four selection methods: the default is a to create a new selection.

• Third, specify a query expression in the expression text box. One way to do this is to click in the box with the mouse and then simply type in an expression. A faster, easier, and less error-prone way to form the query expression is to generate it interactively by clicking on the fields, buttons, and values. This way you will not need to recall the syntax! Double-click on the desired field to add the quote-delimited field name to the expression text box. Click on one of the operand buttons (=, <>, >, >=, <, <=, Like, or Is). To get the unique values associated with a given field, click on the "Get Unique Values" button. Then, double-click on the desired value(s).

---

4. Expressions must be in the form: <field> <operand> <value>, while compound expressions can be formed as well: <field> <operand> <value> {AND | OR | NOT} <field> <operand> <value>

- Fourth, decide if you want to save your expression for later (this is a good habit to form!).
- Fifth, press **OK**. Voila!

For example, for our earlier query to locate the Beverly Hills zip code 90210, the expression will look like: **"ZIP" = '90210'**

The field is "ZIP", operand is "=", and value is "'90210'". Note that fields must be delimited by double-quotes ("", no spaces!), strings must be enclosed in single quotes, and numbers cannot have delimeters—for file-based datasets such as file geodatabases, shapefiles (dBASE) and coverages (INFO). Otherwise, for the personal geodatabase, enclose the field in square brackets (e.g., [ZIP]). (Table 5.2). Numerical values have no delimeters (and you cannot use comma delimeters for thousands, millions, etc.). There are a number of operands available: = (equals), < (less than), > (greater than), <= (less than or equal to), >= (greater than or equal to), and <> (not equal to). There cannot be a space between the <=, >=, or <> characters (e.g., **"Field" > = 23** is invalid because of the space between the > and =). Use matching left/right parentheses if you need to change the assumed left-to-right evaluation order. Note that the *Select By Attributes* tool is a bit persnickety with the syntax of the expression. If the equation does not work initially, then a good thing to try is to delete the entire expression and then re-build the expression by clicking on the field names, buttons, and values.

Note that you can also modify the order in which the fields are presented by right-clicking in the field listing of the dialog (so the fields can be sorted ascending, descending, or the order found in the table).

Querying using Select by Attributes

1. In *ArcMap*, click **Selection->Select by Attributes....**

2. Select the desired *layer*.

3. Select the desired selection method.

4. Create the query expression by typing the expression in or clicking on the desired *field*, the appropriate operand (action), and the value.

5. Save your expression to an expression file (for later use and documentation).

6. Click **OK**.

GIS Concepts and ArcGIS Methods

TABLE 5.2. Summary of SQL idiosyncrasies

Dataset	Field delimiter	Case sensitive	Wildcard
File Geodatabase	"AREA"	Y	_ , %
Shapefile (dBASE)	"AREA"	Y	_ , %
Coverage (INFO)	"AREA"	Y	_ , %
Geodatabase (ACCESS)	[AREA]	N	? , *
SDE	AREA		

Some additional examples and comments are as follows (assuming file-based datasets):

("area" >1500) do not enclose values in quotes

("pop2000" < "pop1990") finds all counties with declining population

("area" * 0.000247105 <= 25) can include calculations—convert area in m to acres

("pop1990" / "area" <= 25) can include fields in calculations

("state_name" = 'colorado') strings are enclosed by single quotes

("county_name" LIKE 'rio%') use % as a multiple character wildcard

("owner_name" LIKE '_aul') use an "_" (underscore, not hyphen) as a single character wildcard, gets Saul and Paul

("county_name" >= 'r') select counties with names beginning with R to Z

Compound queries can be created that use the Boolean logic operators: AND (both criteria must be true), OR (either criteria must be true), and NOT (exclude). Compound queries query values from multiple fields (Table 5.3).

("area" > 1500) and ("garage" > 3) select houses that are at least 1,500 square feet and have at least three garages

TABLE 5.3. Compound statements using Boolean AND, OR, and NOT. The table below describes the possible combinations of conditional statements (T = TRUE, F = FALSE). Both statements must be true when using the AND operator, and either statement can be true when using the OR operator.

A	B	A AND B	A OR B	NOT A	NOT B
T	T	T	T	F	F
T	F	F	T	F	T

TABLE 5.3. Compound statements using Boolean AND, OR, and NOT. The table below describes the possible combinations of conditional statements (T = TRUE, F = FALSE). Both statements must be true when using the AND operator, and either statement can be true when using the OR operator.

A	B	A AND B	A OR B	NOT A	NOT B
F	T	F	T	T	F
F	F	F	F	T	T

5.4.2.1 Advanced query expressions

Note that there are a number of additional SQL operators that can be used in the Select by Attribute dialog, in addition to standard operators such as =, >, >=, etc. (Table 5.4).

TABLE 5.4. Advanced expressions using additional operators and functions in an expression.

Operator/ Function	Example	Description
ABS	ABS ("NET_ELEV")	returns the absolute value
BETWEEN x AND y	"AREA" BETWEEN 15 AND 20	
CHAR_LENGTH	CHAR_LENGTH ("STATE") > 4	returns state names longer than 4 (sorry Iowa)
CURRENT_DATE	"DATE" < CURRENT_DATE	returns the current date
DATE	"DATE" < DATE '1999-12-25'	select records before Christmas 1999 DATE returns the string in the correct DATE format
IN	"STATE" IN ('Alabama', 'Alaska', 'California', 'Florida')	true if one of these in list
IS NULL	"STATE" IS NULL	find records where no values has been entered yet
LIKE	"STATE" LIKE 'New%'	returns New Hampshire, New Jersey, New Mexico, New York
LOWER	LOWER("STATE") = 'colorado'	converts text to lower case, only in Access and SDE
MOD	MOD ("LENGTH", 2)	returns the remainder of division

TABLE 5.4. Advanced expressions using additional operators and functions in an expression.

Operator/ Function	Example	Description
NOT	NOT "STATE" = 'California'	finds all states but California
UPPER	UPPER("STATE") = 'COLO-RADO'	converts text to upper case, only in Access and SDE

Also note that you can save and recall (load) query expressions to and from the disk using an *expression file* (*.exp). It is good practice to save the file in a project workspace or directory to help document your work. Unfortunately, only one query can be saved at a time per file—make sure the filename captures what the expression does. The most recent query is also left in the dialog. It is also good practice to index an attribute field if you are going to do many queries on it or if fast performance is required.

5.4.3 Definition query

By default, all features of a layer are displayed and queried. In certain situations, however, it is useful to restrict a layer to a subset of its features temporarily. For example, you may only care about major rivers instead of all rivers contained in a layer. Instead of creating a separate dataset that contains just major rivers from a dataset of all rivers, you can *temporarily* remove the unwanted features by applying a *definition query*. An advantage of temporarily subsetting a layer is that if the dataset is updated or modified, changes will be automatically reflected in the layer the next time the map document is opened. Using a subset of the data also speeds up the drawing speed and any analytical operations on a layer. Definition queries are specified through the Definition Query tab in the Layer Properties dialog (using the same interface as the Select by Attributes).

Setting the Definition Query

1. In *ArcMap*, right-click on the layer and select Properties.
2. Select the Definition Query tab.
3. Click on the Query Builder... button.
4. Create a query using the Select by Attributes dialog, then click OK.
5. Click OK.

5.5 What features are near another feature?

Another powerful method of selecting features of a layer is through their
spatial relationships with another
layer(s). ArcMap allows you to select
features of a layer based on their relationship to features of another layer
using the *Select Layer by Location* tool.
With this *spatial query* method, questions that involve issues of proximity,
adjacency, and containment can be
addressed. For example, what cities
and towns in the western US are
located within the forest fringe
(right)? To answer this question, distances between features from two different layers will need to be
measured.

This type of operation requires you to specify
target and *filter* layers. The *target* layer(s) is
the layer that contains the features you want
to select (e.g., towns and cities—black dots).
The *filter* layer contains the features that you
want to use as a filter (e.g., forest land cover—
in green). Note that you can specify multiple
target layers. Also, to speed up your spatial
queries considerably, add a spatial index to
your layer.

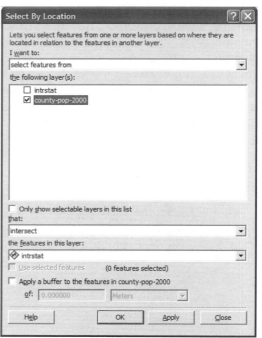

Querying using Select by Location
1. In *ArcMap*, click Selection->Select by location... to bring up the dialog.
2. Specify the type of selection in the "I want to:" drop-down list.
3. Check the box next to each *target* layer you want to select from.
4. Set the spatial relation type (e.g., intersect).
5. Set the filter layer you want to select features in relation to.
6. Click Apply.

Indexing the shape field
1. In *ArcCatalog*, navigate to the desired folder.
2. Double-click on shapefile to open up the Properties dialog.
3. Click on the Index tab.
4. Click on the Add button at the bottom of the dialog (if greyed out, make sure layer is not open in another application and ensure you have write-access).
5. Click OK.

5.5.1 Spatial relation types

ArcMap provides eleven ways to relate features from one layer to another. Recall from the discussion of *spatial relations* in Chapter 1, that the main classes of spatial relations were proximal, directional, and topological relationships. ArcMap provides methods for both proximal and topological relationships in the Select By Location query tool.

5.5.1.1 Proximal

The *are within a distance of* method selects features near or adjacent that are within a specified distance. A useful feature in the Select Layer by Location dialog is the *apply a buffer to the features of* option. This applies a buffer of a specified distance from the features in the filter layer.

5.5.1.2 Topological

The *are identical to* method is used to test whether two or more features (of the same feature type) are spatially equivalent. This means that for features to be the same, they must be the same size, shape, and be placed directly on top of one another. They also must have the same number of vertices and the vertices must be in the same location.

To test whether two or more features are partially equivalent (meaning that they overlap one another or cross one another), the *intersect* method is used typically. Polygon features intersect if they overlap, if they share a line segment, or even if they share a point. The *are crossed by the outline of* method is similar, but a feature is only selected if the area of overlap (two polygons) or length (line/line, line/polygon) is greater than 0. Shared segments or vertices do not count. The *have their centroid in* method requires that not only the area of overlap (or length) exceeds 0, but a feature's centroid is within the polygon feature as well.

The *are within (Clementini)* method (aka are completely within) requires a feature to be contained in another so that all of the overlapping areas (or length) are within the polygon, and they cannot share any boundary segments or points. The *are within* method also requires all of the area (length) to be overlapping, but the features can touch at a point or share a line segment. The reverse methods are: *contain (Clementini)* and *contain*.

Adjacency occurs when two features share a common boundary or meet at a point. The *share a line segment with* method means that two features will be selected if they share a line segment (defined by two consecutive vertices). The *touch the boundary of* method means that two features are adjacent when they share even a single point.

Features that are separate or disjoint cannot overlap or touch (not even a single vertex).

5.5.2 Examples of common selections

A common need in locational queries is to select point features that are near a linear feature (*point near line*). For example, to select locations that occur within 25 m of a river, set the linear feature (e.g., rivers) to be the *filter* layer, and then select point features using *are within a distance of* 25 m.

Often the points that are found within polygon features are needed (*point in polygon*). For example, to determine the number of people who are potentially at risk from forest fires, the points (e.g., towns and cities) that *intersect* the forested area (polygon layer) could be selected. The features from the filter layer (the forest polygon) could also be buffered (e.g., by two miles) to extend the notion of the forest fringe, so potentially some locations are at risk outside of the forested area.

You can also select linear features that pass through or intersect polygonal features (*line in polygon*). For example, you could select administration units (e.g., counties), using *intersect* or *are crossed by the outline of*, that have interstates running through them. You might also select wilderness areas that have roads running directly on their borders using *share a line segment with*.

Linear features that occur within certain polygonal features can also be selected (polygon on line). For example, you could select stretches of streams and rivers in the western US that occur on public land. By using the *intersects* method, you would find any stream that even touched public land, for example if the stream formed the boundary of public land. By using the *have their center in* method, you would likely find the large stretches or rivers within public land. If you used the *are completely within* method, then the entire river stretch would need to be on public land.

5.5.3 What is adjacent?

A simple way to determine features that are spatially adjacent (a.k.a. *first-order neighbors*) to a particular feature is to select them interactively using the *Select Features* tool. However, interactively selecting features can be a time-consuming and error prone process for complex themes. So, how can adjacent features be found in a more automated process? Adjacent features *can* be selected in ArcMap, but the same dataset must be represented by two different layers in order to trick the Select Layer by Location dialog. To do this, first make a copy of the layer in the data frame so that two layers depict the same dataset (select Copy from the layer's context menu, then Paste layer from the data frame's context menu). Then, set the relation type to *intersect*, and choose the layer and the copy of the layer for the layer selections.

Finding adjacent neighbors

1. In *ArcMap*, right-click on desired layer and select Copy.

2. Right-click on the *data frame,* then select Paste layer.

3. Bring up the Select Layer by Location dialog, the box next to each *target* layer you want to select from.

4. Set the spatial relation type (e.g., intersect).

5. Set the filter layer you want to select features in relation to.

6. Click Apply.

5.6 Chapter review

- To *query* a map is to pose a question or inquire about a feature (or features) represented in a GIS dataset.

- The two main types of queries are an *attribute query* that uses attribute data of features to identify a sub-set of features that are of interest and *spatial* queries that use spatially explicit data and relationships between spatial features.

- The Select By Attributes tool allows you to formalize a query expression.

- The main classes of spatial relations are proximal, directional, and topological relationships.

6 Acquiring, editing, and creating vector datasets

The previous chapters have discussed different geographic data types, how to visualize datasets, and how to query them. But where do you get the datasets to do your work on in the first place? Good question! There are three general answers. First, it's best to acquire existing datasets when they are available (duh). But there are a number of important issues to think about, including what are the sources, cost, consistency, trustworthiness, etc. Second, occasionally the datasets that are available are not quite right for your needs: perhaps they are out of date, incomplete, or in separate datasets that need to be synthesized. There are numerous ways to edit existing datasets in ArcGIS. Third, you might need to start from scratch and create a brand new dataset (rats!).

There are two issues of particular importance in this chapter that provide some broad context for dealing with acquiring, editing, or creating vector datasets. The first issue is to understand the trade-offs involved with creating new spatial data vs. dynamically subsetting or joining data. The second issue is about creating and/or maintaining map topology. Although ArcMap does not automatically check topology, the tools *are* provided that allow for the creation and maintenance of topologically valid (planar enforced) datasets.

6.1 Acquiring existing datasets

There are a wealth of existing datasets available. Below are a variety of sources of data that are generally available at no cost. There are at least six criteria to judge a dataset's suitability for your task at hand:

- Geographic extent: Does the dataset provide coverage for your area of interest? Will you need to merge or synthesize several datasets together into a cohesive dataset?

- Geographic unit: Are the data provided at a scale for geographic features that are of interest? Are the geographic units (e.g., states, counties) of adequate resolution for your question?

- Thematic: Does the dataset provide appropriate data on the theme or topic of interest? Is there an attribute associated with the geographic features?

- Scale: Were the data generated from a map or dataset of adequate scale to allow reasonably precise answers to your questions?

- Temporal: Do the data represent the geographic features during a time that you are interested in?

- Metadata: Does the dataset have adequate metadata associated with it? Is there a projection file associated with the feature dataset?

Be sure to spend some time "getting to know" your data -- both the geographic features and the attributes. After you've located a dataset of interest, download it and then inspect it. Add it to ArcMap and visually explore it. Does it cover the broad geographic extent that you are interested in? Zoom to an area that you are very familiar with and examine the geographic features that are represented. Does it make sense? Are the features that you would expect there? Are there additional unexpected features? Why? Zoom into a detailed area for which you are not familiar with. Does this help you to understand what is there? Can you see the "geographic fabric" in that place? Use the Identify tool to query features and examine what attributes are associated with each. Make a few maps of some attributes that you are interested in by using the Symbology tab from the Layer properties. Does the distribution of values make sense? What are the units in?

Open up the attribute table. Locate a field (attribute) of interest and peruse the list of values. Do all features (rows) have a value or are there some blank or missing values? Do they make sense? Sort the table from descending to ascending and examine the values at the top (the largest values). Can a feature with the largest value actually exist? For example, could there be a county in the US that had a population in the 2000 Census of 14,000,000? Now reverse it and examine the smallest values. Do they make sense or are there some extraneous values? For an attribute that is of nominal type (e.g., vegetation classes), summarize the field to identify the unique values that are found in the field. Are there more than you thought? Are there some different values that are likely duplicates with some typos or spelling errors (this is a common occurrence!).

Be sure not to let your excitement (or the teacher's or boss's demands) allow you to skip some quick and basic "checking out" of your dataset. Spending a couple of minutes early on understanding the appropriateness and/or quality of your data is worth hours and days later.

6.1.1 FTP or seamless?

Increasingly data downloading is being provided through interactive web services. An advantage of these websites is that data can be bundled together to get small geographies in a seamless fashion, automatically merging spatially adjacent datasets together. The disadvantage of this approach is that only small geographies can be downloaded. On the other hand, some websites still provide access through ftp sites where data are packaged via larger geographies (e.g., for an entire state or watershed) that can be downloaded quickly and efficiently.

6.1.2 ESRI Data and Maps

The ESRI Data and Maps for 2006 provides a variety of national, international, and global datasets that are organized on five DVDs, available for free. These data are provided in a format that is ready to go, with solid metadata, and usable straightaway in ArcGIS. These datasets include:

> World - country boundaries, continents, cities, drainage systems, lakes, latitude/longitudes, times zones, WWF ecoregions, elevation (ETOPO2, GTOPO30, and Shuttle Radar Mission), imagery;

> Europe - cities, countries, transportation, lakes & rivers, NUTS demographics, places, urbanized areas;

> USA - census-based data such as congressional districts, block groups, census tracts, urbanized areas, cities, counties, population places, states, zip codes, etc.; hydrography; landmarks such as hospitals, institutions, parks, recreation areas, etc.; transportation such as airports, highways, railroads, etc.; miscellaneous such as time zones, quadrangle indexes, etc.

> Canada - highways, postal zones, cities, indian reserves, transportation, telephone area boundaries, rivers & lakes;

> Mexico - cities, elevation contours, transportation, state boundaries, urban areas, hydrology.

6.1.3 Government sources and clearinghouses

In the US, a variety of governmental agencies have generated a plethora of publicly-available datasets. Some of the more useful repositories are:

> National Atlas - providing nationwide datasets for a variety of themes: http://nationalatlas.gov/atlas-ftp.html.

US Geological Survey, National Elevation Dataset - elevation data at a variety of resolutions: http://ned.usgs.gov/

US Geological Survey, National Hydrography Dataset - hydrology data for rivers, streams, and water bodies: ftp://nhdftp.usgs.gov/SubRegions/

Multi-Resolution Land Characteristics Consortium - a consortium of 11 federal agencies have collaborated to generate the National Land Cover Dataset (1992) and the National Land Cover Database (2001): http://www.mrlc.gov/

US Geological Survey, Seamless Data Distribution System - variety of elevation and land cover datasets: http://seamless.usgs.gov/

TerraServer - ortho-rectified aerial photography: http://terraserver-usa.com/

CIESIN's Socio-economic Data and Applications Center: http://sedac.ciesin.org/data.html

6.1.4 Commercial

GIS Data Depot - from GeoCommunity, a variety of free datasets compiled into datasets that are available for a CD write-fee: http://data.geocomm.com

GeoWarehouse - http://www.geowarehouse.com/

GfK GeoMarketing - http://www.globalmaps.com/

6.2 Converting a dataset

Occasionally the situation occurs where you have the perfect dataset, but it happens to be in the wrong format (or dataset type). For example, you might want to convert a dataset to another format to be consistent or to standardize with other existing datasets, or to provide data in a format for users who may be limited by their software license.

There are a variety of conversion tools to help you convert datasets to other formats, the main tool being the *Feature Class to Feature Class* tool. This tool allows a user to convert from a shapefile, coverage, or geodatabase feature class over to a shapefile or geodatabase feature class. Another useful tool is the *Import from CAD* tool that allows CAD files to be imported into a geodatabase file.

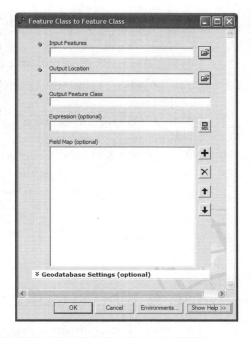

Converting a feature class to another format

ArcToolbox -> Conversion Tools -> To Geodatabase -> **Feature Class to Feature Class**.

A few other possible reasons might be to create a new dataset containing a subset of the original dataset; to create a dataset in a different coordinate system; to speed up display time (e.g., using shapefiles). Note that raster-vector conversions is covered in Chapter 7.

Exporting a dataset to a shapefile
ArcToolbox -> Data Management Tools -> Features -> **Copy Features**.
- OR -
1. In ArcMap, right-click on layer to export and select Data -> Export Data...
2. Select the features to export: all, selected, or in view extent.
3. Choose whether to use the layer or data frame's coordinate system.
4. Click on the folder icon to navigate to a desired location, and select the output format.
5. Click OK.

6.3 Sub-setting a dataset

A common way of generating a dataset is retaining some features (sub-setting) of an existing dataset, and removing the rest (Table 6.1). If the features themselves do not need to be modified, then a new dataset can be created that is simply a subset of the original dataset. The new dataset can be either a permanent new dataset or a temporary, dynamic layer that subsets a dataset. To create an entirely new dataset, the data can be exported using the *Copy Features* tool. To subset a dataset, a definition query is applied. Definition queries are specified through the Definition Query tab in the Layer Properties dialog (described in detail in Chapter 5).

TABLE 6.1. Advantages and disadvantages associated with permanent or dynamic subsetting of a dataset.

Data type	Function	Advantages	Disadvantages
Spatial	Dynamic (Definition query)	Subsets features, both visibly in the layer and in attribute table Less confusing Updates to layer automatic	For large layers, possible long query times when opening map document
	Permanent (convert)	Smaller datasets Can edit individual features	Updates to parent layer not automatic
Table	Dynamic (Relate/Join)	Less storage Updates automatic	Cannot edit the related table
	Permanent (Export joined file)	Smaller file size Can edit joined field values	Not automatically updated

---

Sub-setting a dataset in current extent

1. In *ArcMap*, select **Tools -> Options...**

2. Select the **TOC** tab, and check the box to show the Selection tab. Click OK.

3. Click on the Selection tab in the Table of Contents.

4. Select only the features in the current extent using the Select features tool.

5. Right-click on desired layer and select **Create Layer from Selected Features**. Note that the new layer trimmed to the current extent is automatically added to the map document.

6.4 Editing and topology

As was discussed in Chapter 2, topology plays a central role in GIS. Planar topology has been employed traditionally in GIS through the use of topological data structures, chiefly for two reasons. First, explicit depiction of neighborhood relationships allows advanced spatial analysis to be conducted on a set of geographical features. Second, topology provides a rigorous method to clean up spatial data that have been created during digitizing and editing to identify artifacts that result during the creation of spatial data. The traditional *modus operandi* of creating digital spatial data has been to digitize a map by following the borders of features, crossing from one to another without respect to the feature. This so-called *spaghetti digitizing* developed historically because computers and display technology were too slow to conduct any real-time checking of the input geometry, so topology was employed to post-process digitized data to ensure topological consistency. This provides a practical means to build large spatial datasets in a rigorous manner. As a result, a whole GIS lexicon has formed over the process of digitizing, editing, and building topology.

To illustrate how spaghetti digitizing works and why topology is needed, imagine that the boundaries of four rural residential blocks are being digitized from an aerial photo in order to create areal units for census-related activities (Figure 6.1). First, the boundary is digitized by starting at one corner, then intermediate vertices are placed along the roads, going around the perimeter of the blocks and ending back at the starting point. Second, the three lines that separate the blocks are digitized. Next, labels are added to uniquely identify each polygon. Finally, the data are ready to be post-processed to remove spurious artifacts.

FIGURE 6.1. "Spaghetti" digitizing of four polygons: 1) outer boundary is digitized (upper left); 2) three bisecting lines are digitized (upper right); 3) clean up overshoots and undershoots (lower left); 4) add ID labels (lower right) (download color figures from www.consplan.com).

Recall that a polyline (or chain) has a node at the start and end point, with a series of segments called arcs. By definition the starting and ending point of a polygon must be at the same location, but in practice it is virtually impossible to click exactly at the location of the starting point when digitizing. If the start and end nodes do not touch, the polygon is not closed (called an *undershoot)* (Figure 6.2). So, to ensure that polygons close and polylines intersect, start and end vertices are purposefully placed such that the polyline crosses another line and the small fragment that extends beyond the intersection to the end node is called an *overshoot.* As a result, spaghetti digitizing creates numerous *dangling nodes*, both of the overshoot and undershoot variety, that need to be cleaned up.

FIGURE 6.2. Common artifacts created during spaghetti digitizing and "cleaning and building" of topology.

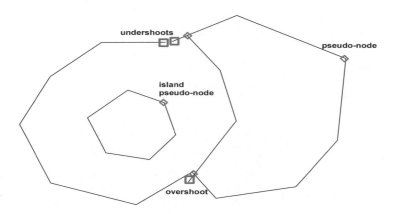

The "clean and build" process enforces planar topology by identifying all the line intersections. If two lines intersect, but not at the location of two nodes (the start or end point of one line and the start or end point of a second line), then the line(s) is cut into two lines forming nodes at the intersection. The next step is to automatically identify and remove dangling nodes, which requires that a *dangle length* be defined such that overshoots that are less than the dangle length are removed. Here we are stuck with a problem reminiscent of one that Goldilocks faced—the "just right" problem, solved best by trial-and-error. That is, the dangle length must not be too large such that undershoots that represent parts of a polygon boundary are removed, nor should it be too small so that overshoots are left remaining. Also, a *fuzzy tolerance* must be defined, such that if two vertices are within a given distance, they will be snapped together. In this way lines that have been *double digitized* are cleaned up, but if the fuzzy tolerance is too large, then real features can be simplified and possibly removed altogether. This is especially problematic when editing maps with a large extent, because the default tolerance is typically set to a fraction of the spatial extent (e.g., 1/10,000). Further compounding the difficulty of clearly identifying dangling nodes is that there are a number of real-life features that are legitimate dangling nodes. For example, roads often stop abruptly a short distance from an intersection, often in cul-de-sacs. Occasionally, when only two polylines touch, a feature called a *pseudo-node* is created. These are typically artifacts of the digitizing process where two individual lines were digitized, and are generally not needed. Some pseudo-nodes are needed, however, such as *island pseudo-nodes* that are required to create an island polygon.

6.5 Feature-oriented digitizing

Although it remains important to understand how topology is used to post-process spaghetti-digitized data, currently the tools exist to digitize from a vector or feature-oriented perspective.[1] This approach to digitizing and editing spatial data also ensures a planar-enforced map, but does not require post-processing and thus artifacts such as overshoots and undershoots do not need to be cleaned up! To illustrate the difference between spaghetti and *feature-oriented digitizing*, let us return to our example of digitizing the boundaries of four residential blocks from an aerial photo (Figure 6.3).

The feature-oriented approach creates one feature at a time and for polygon features, relies on three main editing tools provided in ArcGIS: *create new feature*, *auto complete polygon*, and *cut polygon features*. These tools ensure that adjacent polygons share boundaries—which means that planar topology is enforced (this is called *topological association* in ArcMap) to prevent overlaps. First, a new polygon can be created by digitizing individual vertices and then double-clicking within the snap distance of the starting point to close the polygon. Second, adjacent polygons can be created using the auto complete tool by beginning at one corner and digitizing the three edges of the second block, ensuring that the two adjacent polygons share boundaries. Third, a single large polygon can be "cut" into multiple smaller polygons. The resulting four polygons have topology without clean and build operations, nor arc-node features.

Topology is fully implemented in Geodatabases in ArcGIS v8.3.[2] It is important to note that the approach to topology in Geodatabases reflects this feature-oriented perspective and is a significant departure from topology as implemented in the past. There are two main differences in this new approach to map topology. First, rather than storing topological relationships explicitly in data files (i.e. like coverages do), Geodatabase topology stores the rules, ranks, and cluster tolerance that are applied to check topology on-the-fly, rather than as a final editing process (i.e. as in CLEAN and BUILD with ArcInfo v7). Second, topological relationships can be examined not only between features within a dataset (e.g., a vegetation layer), but also between datasets (e.g., a vegetation layer and a road layer). This is a powerful addition that enables coincident geometry between datasets.

---

1. Actually, as early as 1987 a GIS system was designed to approach digitizing from this perspective: White, D., J. Corson-Rikert, and M. Maizel. 1987. "WYSIWYG" map digitizing: Real time geometric correction and topological encoding. *Proceedings from Auto-Carto 8*: 739-743.
2. For a helpful introduction to topology at v8.3, see: Childs, C. 2003. ArcGIS topology for ArcView users. *ArcUser* (July-September): 48-49.

FIGURE 6.3. Feature-centric digitizing of four polygons: 1) create new, closed polygon (upper left); 2) add adjacent polygon using the "auto-complete" tool (upper right and lower left); 3) "cut" polygon into two polygons (lower left) to create the four polygons that are planar-enforced (lower right). Note that no post-processing is needed.

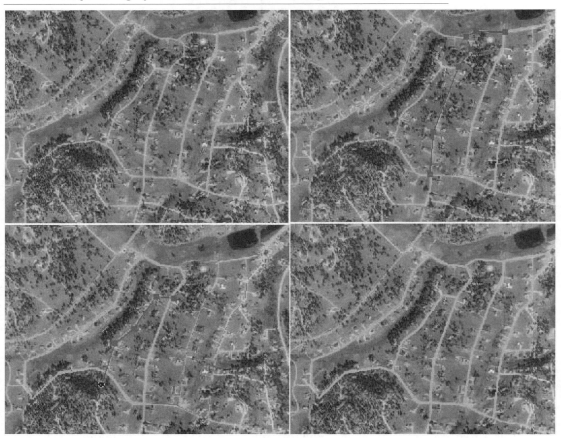

6.6 Feature editing basics

When editing spatial data in ArcMap, there are a couple of important ways to control how the editing tools work. A primary means is the snapping environment that specifies whether Arc-Map recognizes existing features that are found either in the same layer that is being edited or in a different layer. Editing is accomplished through the Edit toolbar after an edit session is established. Editing allows you to populate a data set once it has been established or created using ArcCatalog.

6.6.1 Starting an edit session

After a dataset has been added as a layer to ArcMap, an edit session can be started. To edit layers, the Editor Toolbar must be added to the ArcMap interface (Figure 6.4; or already available). Only one collection of datasets can be added at a time from the currently active data frame. When you start an edit session, ArcMap will notify you if there are multiple datasets available in your ArcMap document, and then you will need to choose one. Once an edit session is established, all the changes made are placed into a temporary buffer. These changes are not made permanent until the edits are saved, and adding, moving, deleting features can be incrementally undone (ctrl-Z).

FIGURE 6.4. Editor toolbar in ArcMap.

When you begin editing, you'll need to think about the "3Ts" of the editor toolbar: *target, task,* and *tool*. First, think about the *target*—what dataset do you want to edit? Second, what is the edit task? There are a dozen or so different tasks available that are used to create or modify features. Third, which tool will be used to accomplish the task? The sketch ( ) and edit ( ) tools are the main tools you will use, but there may be other tools available depending on the task. Basically, a tool is used to perform some task on a particular target.

Starting an edit session
1. In ArcMap, add the Editor Toolbar by selecting View -> Toolbars -> Editor.
2. From the Editor Toolbar, select Editor -> Start Editing.
3. If multiple datasets are in ArcMap, select the desired one to edit.

Note that editing datasets with a large amount of data may be fairly slow, so to speed things up a bit you have the option to create an *edit cache* to store in memory all the features found within a user-defined extent.

6.6.2 Setting the snapping environment

One of the principal ways to ensure that features line up, connect, or directly abut another feature when you are creating or editing features is through the use of *snapping*. Snapping allows newly created or modified features to coincide with existing features within the same layer or from different layers. The snapping environment controls how features relate to one another.The snapping tolerance specifies the distance within which a feature is snapped to another feature, or the pointer is snapped to another location. The snapping tolerance is typically defined in map units, but can also be specified by the number of screen pixels. Graphically, the snapping tolerance is shown by a circle around the pointer. If the pointer is within the snapping tolerance, then the

circle snaps to the location; otherwise, the circle stays centered on the pointer. The snapping properties specify the part of a feature that the snapping responds to. That is, snapping can respond to all vertices, the edge, and/or the endpoints of a feature. These properties can be set independently for each layer listed in the Snapping Environment dialog, and the priority follows the order of the listing of the layers.

Setting the snapping environment

1. From the Editor toolbar, select Snapping...

2. Check the boxes for the feature parts for each layer.

3. Prioritize the snapping order if needed by click-dragging on a layer name.

4. To change the snapping tolerance, from the Editor toolbar select Options..., then the General tab.

6.6.3 Adding new features

Typically, new features are drawn or digitized in relation to existing features. *Heads-up digitizing* is a method that is commonly used, which describes digitizing when looking at the monitor and occurs when other spatial data, usually an image, is used as a base map. This contrasts with *paper-map digitizing*, which employs a paper map mounted to a digitizing tablet. Another method of digitizing is used, though less frequently, when a description of the geometry of the feature is known. This is typically from descriptions of metes and bounds or coordinate geometry, for example from a surveyor or from a land plat map.

To illustrate how creating new features occurs using the heads-up digitizing method, let's digitize some geographic features from an aerial photograph (right). The location of buildings may be digitized as points that mark the location of each building. Trails are typically digitized as lines (also called *polylines*), which are represented by a start point, a series of intermediate points or vertices, and an end point. In *point mode digitizing,* vertices are established at a location (by clicking on it), and you are actually sampling a real-world feature by approximating it with line segments. Another method, though perhaps less common, is *stream mode digitizing*, where points are

established at defined intervals along a feature as the cursor is moved across the map. Typically, lines should not be self-intersecting (Figure 6.5). Areal features such as parking lots or vegetation patches would be digitized as *polygons*, where the starting point and ending point of a line are the same. Care must be taken when creating polygons so that non-valid polygons (so called *weird polygons*) are not created (Figure 6.5).

Note that ArcMap provides a number of digitizing options through the Sketch tool's context menu (right-click), for example, to remove the last vertex digitized. Also, a number of digitizing methods are available that utilize "CAD-like" editing methods. For example, a vertex can be established by providing an *absolute x, y* location by typing in the x and y coordinates, or through providing *relative x, y* coordinates from the last vertex. A vertex can also be located by providing an *angle* and *length* from a known location. *Parametric* and *tangent* curves can also be created.[3]

---

3. See ArcGIS Help -> Editing in ArcMap --> Creating new features --> Creating features from other features.

FIGURE 6.5. Common digitizing problems: A self-intersecting line (left) is a polyline that crosses itself. A self-intersecting polygon (right), also known as a "weird polygon," crosses itself with no vertices at the boundary intersection(s).

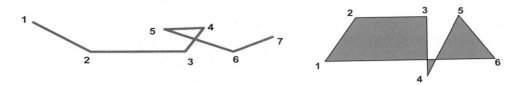

Note that there are a number of techniques available to help ensure that data are planar enforced. One common method is simply to set the snapping environment so that new vertices snap to existing vertices in a layer that is being edited. In this way new polylines and polygons can directly connect to adjacent features. Polylines should touch one another only at the end points (Figure 6.6).

FIGURE 6.6. Polylines should connect or touch one another only at the ends of lines (right), rather than at the mid-point of lines (left).

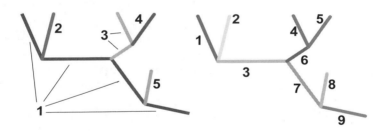

Creating a new feature.

1. Establish an edit session and set the desired *target layer*.

2. Select the Sketch tool (✏️).

3. Set the task to: **Create New Feature**.

4. Digitize the location(s):

Points

Single-click on the desired location (double-click to end for lines and polygons).

Lines

Click at the beginning of a line, then click on intermediate vertices, then double-click at the endpoint.

Polygons

Click at the beginning of the polygon, then click on intermediate vertices, then double-click on the start point to snap the polygon closed.

5. Click on the Attribute button (▦) to enter attributes through the Attribute dialog.

6. Save edits.

Also, when digitizing a new polygon adjacent to an existing one, to make sure the boundaries match you must create vertices that duplicate every vertex and only the vertices from the existing polygon. Because this can be both tedious and fraught with error, ArcMap has a powerful task called *Auto Complete Polygon*, which allows a new polygon feature to be digitized such that it automatically shares the boundaries of existing features. After setting the snapping environment on, start at the vertex where the new feature starts from an existing feature (see point 1, right)—which is called the *common vertex* (like a node), then digitize the new points that form the new polygon (2, 3, 4). Then close the polygon back on the vertex of an existing polygon (5).

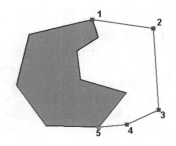

Creating a new polygon adjacent to an existing polygon

1. Select the Sketch tool.

2. Set the task to: Auto Complete Polygon.

3. Set the snapping environment to vertices.

4. Click at the first common vertex, then click on intermediate vertices, then double-click on the last common vertex to snap the polygon closed.

5. Click on the Attribute button (▦) to enter attributes through the Attribute dialog.

6. Save edits when finished.

6.7 Common editing tasks

6.7.1 Splitting a feature

Occasionally, an existing polyline or polygon feature needs to be split or cut into two or more features. Because you are cutting a particular feature(s), then you'll need to first select the feature to be cut into pieces. This can be accomplished for line features using the Split tool (✐). Note that if you want to split the line at a particular vertex, then set the snapping environment appropriately. A second way to split a line is to specify the location by defining a distance or percentage from the starting (forward) or ending (reverse) point. For polygon features, use the *Cut Polygon Features* task. Polygons can also be split to cut out an *island polygon* or *doughnut* from the parent polygon by drawing a line that closes on itself (an interior polygon) but does not cross the boundary of the polygon that is being cut. To test whether a polygon is an island polygon or is simply overlapping on top of another polygon, click on the island with the Identify tool—if only one record was found, then it is an island polygon. Note that ArcMap automatically updates the length (for polylines) or area (for polygons) field for geodatabases only—but not for shapefiles.

Splitting features

Polylines

1. Select the target polyline layer.
2. Select the feature to cut using the Edit tool.

3. Select the Split tool ( ), then click on the line at the location to split the line. To split the line via a distance or percentage, select Editor->Split..., then use the Split dialog.

4. Save edits when finished.

Polygons

1. Select the target polygon layer.
2. Select feature(s) to cut using the Edit tool.

3. Set the task to: Cut Polygon Features.

4. Draw the "cut" line by beginning and ending the split line at a boundary vertex, on the boundary line, or outside the polygon boundary. Double-click to end the line.

5. Save edits when finished.

6.7.2 Deleting features

Once an edit session has been established, features can be easily deleted by first selecting the features to be deleted, then by simply pressing the Delete key. Recall that a deletion can be undone using ctrl-Z.

6.7.3 Modifying features

Existing features often need to be modified to add, delete, or move vertices, for example.

Note that ArcMap provides a *Shared Edit* tool ( ), which is similar to the *Edit* tool ( ), but allows features to be modified that maintain shared boundaries. At v8.3 of ArcGIS, the Shared Edit tool was moved from the Editor toolbar to the *Topology Edit Tool* ( )located in the Topology toolbar. A number of common ways to modify features is summarized in Table 6.2. Two principle "tasks" allow you to modify features. The first task is *Modify Feature*, which allows you to work directly on vertices. A second task is *Reshape Feature*, which operates on a sketch that is drawn on top of the existing feature. This second method is useful when editing a complicated shape, and where knowing the "old" location of a line is helpful.

There are also a number of methods to affect how two nearby, adjacent, or overlapping features *from the same layer* interact (Figure 6.7): merge, union, intersect, or clip. Features can be *merged* or *unioned* so that two or more features from the same layer become one feature. Typically, adjacent features such as two polygons (either sharing a common boundary or overlapping) are merged into a single feature. However, *disjoint features* (features that are not spatially connected) can also be merged together into a single, but *multi-part*, feature. Multi-part features can also be created during digitizing by creating individual parts, then grouping parts by "finishing the sketch."[4] The constituent parts of a multi-part feature can be obtained by *exploding* a multi-part feature. For example, if you had a single feature (polygon) that represented the Hawaiian Islands and needed the individual islands, the so-called explode method could be used. This functionality is available through the *Multi to Single Part* tool in the Features toolset (in Data Management). Also, all adjacent features in a layer that have the same attribute value can be merged so that their shared boundary is *dissolved*. Dissolving a layer is accomplished using the *Dissolve* tool in the Generalization toolset (Data Management toolbox), which is covered in depth in Chapter 7. Like merge, features can be *unioned*, but the union command combines features from *different layers* into a single new feature in the target layer. This method allows features from other layers to be easily incorporated into the target layer.

FIGURE 6.7. Common editing procedures with two or more features. These include merge or union (left, center-left, and center), intersect (center-right), and clip (right).

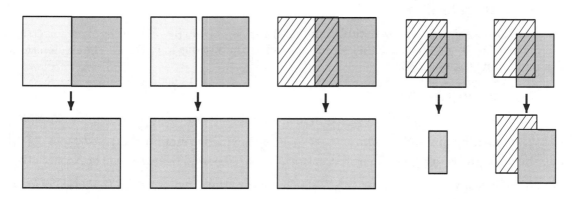

When two features from the same layer overlap, the *intersection* (left) can be found or a feature can be clipped from the other (right). With intersection, note that the original

4. See ArcMap help: Editing in ArcMap -> Creating new features -> Creating lines and polygons.

features remain and a new feature that represents the intersection is added. Alternatively, when two features overlap, one feature can be used to subtract or *clip* the other feature. The top polygon gets subtracted from the bottom polygon, so the overlap portion of the bottom polygon is clipped, while the top polygon remains unchanged. Note that the feature that is being used to clip can also be *buffered* by a specified distance (in map units).

TABLE 6.2. Summary of step-by-step methods for common modification editing tasks.

Method	*Tool*	*Task*	*Step by step*
Clipping features	Edit	Modify features	1. Select two features that overlap. 2. Select **Editor -> Clip....**
Deleting a vertex	Edit	Modify features	1. Select feature. 2. Right-click on a vertex, select **Delete Vertex**.
Flipping polylines	Edit	Modify features	1. Select polylines to flip. 2. Right-click, select **Flip**.
Inserting a vertex	Edit	Modify features	1. Select feature. 2. Right-click on line segment, select **Insert Vertex**.
Intersecting overlapping features	Edit	Modify feature	1. Select two features that overlap. 2. Select **Editor -> Intersect**.
Merging features	Edit	Modify feature	1. Select two or more features to merge. 2. Select **Editor -> Merge**.
Moving a shared boundary	Shared Edit	Reshape Feature	1. Click on the common boundary between two polygons (it will turn orange). 2. Click and drag the line to a new location.
Moving a shared node	Shared Edit	Reshape Feature	1. Click on the node location where two or more polygons come together (an orange dot should appear). 2. Click and drag the node to new location.
Moving a shared vertex	Shared Edit	Modify feature	1. Click on the common boundary between two polygons (or common vertex between two polylines). 2. Click on a vertex and drag to new location.

TABLE 6.2. Summary of step-by-step methods for common modification editing tasks.

Method	Tool	Task	Step by step
Moving a vertex	Edit	Modify features	1. Select feature. 2. Move cursor over vertex to move, then left-click and drag to new location. Or, right-click and select **Move To** to specify a new x,y coordinate location. Or, right-click and select **Move** to specify distance and direction to move.
Unioning features from different layers	Edit	Modify features	1. Select a feature from the target layer. 2. Select a feature from another layer. 3. Select **Editor -> Union**.

6.7.4 Removing an overlap

An *overlap* occurs when a feature overlaps another feature, where two features are coincident and the area of overlap for polygons and length of overlap for polylines is greater than 0. Although sometimes it is valid and useful to have overlapping features, typically these are considered to be errors in planar topology created during digitizing or editing. Typically overlaps are removed by simply clipping one of the features from the other(s).

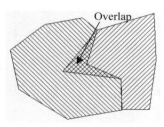

6.7.5 Removing a sliver polygon

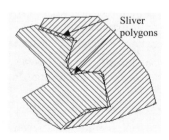

Sliver polygons are small, usually narrow, and almost always unwanted polygons. Two processes typically create these artifacts. The first is that a sliver polygon is an artifact of digitizing boundaries of two adjacent polygons where the vertices are not snapped together.[5] Sliver polygons are characterized by high perimeter-to-area ratios. The paradox of sliver polygons is that in trying to more precisely digitize two boundaries, more, albeit smaller, sliver polygons are created.[6] Sliver polygons are also created occasionally when overlaying two layers whose features are roughly coincident in some locations. For example, if a layer of soil boundaries was overlaid (e.g.,

5.   DeMers, M. 1997. *Fundamentals for Geographic Information Systems*. New York: John Wiley & Sons.
6.   Goodchild, M.F. 1978. Statistical aspects of the polygon overlay problem. In: *Harvard papers on geographic information systems*, vol 6, Ed. G. Dutton. Reading, MA: Addison-Wesley.

unioned) on top of a layer of vegetation polygons, then because the ecotones, or edges, of vegetation polygons sometimes follow the boundaries of a sharp change in soil type, sliver polygons along this ecotone may be created. The challenge of sliver polygons is not merely in their ubiquity, but lies more in the difficulty of deciding whether a small polygon is an artifact and should be removed or is simply just a small polygon that should be retained. As a result, sliver polygons are the bane of GIS.

It is important to identify and remove these sliver polygons. When you are displaying maps at fine scales, sliver polygons can make your boundaries look poor. Probably more importantly though, computing statistics on an attribute table of a theme that contains slivers may introduce errors because of the additional polygons. For example, if you want to compute the average population in your state by county, and you have 5 sliver polygons in addition to the 20 "legitimate" polygons representing counties, you will be significantly underestimating the average value (because you will be dividing by 25 instead of 20). So, take care and screen maps by both visually inspecting them for sliver polygons (but these can be hard to see) and by comparing the number of records (polygons) in the attribute table to the number you would expect.

To remove a single sliver polygon, simply union or merge the sliver polygon with an adjacent polygon. Although you can select for sliver polygons by building a query that tests for polygon size and/or perimeter length, unfortunately there is not an easy way in ArcMap to eliminate many sliver polygons at once. However, the *Eliminate tool* in ArcToolbox[7] can be used to merge selected polygons that have the longest common boundary between them, or the polygon with the largest area.

Another type of sliver polygon is created when joining a number of map tiles together. If neighboring features on the border of a tile do not join perfectly, *merge slivers* are created (see right). These are more problematic to remove, because an operation such as eliminate does not reliably remove these artifacts. However, there is a specialized method to join or *append* map tiles together (also called *mapjoin*). This method is available through the *Append tool* in ArcToolbox.[8] Note that appending datasets enforces planar topology and typically assumes that features from adjacent layers typically do not overlap. A similar method is to *Merge* layers using the Merge tool in the General toolset (Data Management toolbox), which is usually used to

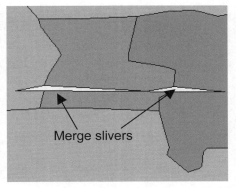

Merge slivers

---

7. Not available at ArcView functionality level.
8. Also not available in ArcView functionality level.

combine layers with the same feature type representing features that are adjacent and do not overlap. However, Merge does not enforce topology, and so features at the edge can overlap, or merge slivers can be created accidentally as well.

6.7.6 Patching a gap

A *gap* is a hole in a polygon layer where no feature exists, but it is surrounded by polygons. Gaps are occasionally created (usually accidentally) through editing in a non-topological fashion, or when a layer is created from a selection of another layer. Probably the easiest way to patch a gap, if the gap is fairly small and simple, is to simply create a new polygon ensuring the vertices snap to the surrounding polygon vertices. For large, complex-shaped gaps, this might not be feasible, however, and so a more robust method is needed. A process likened to patching a hole in a bike tire works reasonably well (Figure 6.8).

FIGURE 6.8. Graphical depiction of steps in patching a gap polygon (see step-by-step instructions below). To patch a gap (left), place a "patch" polygon over the gap (left-center). Then select a polygon that overlaps the patch (center), and clip the patch (right-center). Repeat with all other polygons that surround the gap to create a new polygon that fills the gap (right).

Patching a gap
1. Create a new polygon "patch" over the gap.
2. Select an original polygon that intersects the patch polygon.
3. Select Editor -> Clip, use a buffer distance of 0 and check "Discard the area that intersects." Click OK.
4. Repeat steps 2 and 3 using another original polygon, working around the gap.
5. Save edits when finished.

6.7.7 Integration

Another editing method available in ArcMap is *integration*, which essentially snaps vertices together that are within a certain distance as specified by a *cluster tolerance*. This is a potentially powerful method to remove a number of common artifacts, such as overlaps, gaps, sliver polygons, and merge slivers. It works by searching through the features in a layer, and determines if two vertices are within the cluster tolerance. If two or more

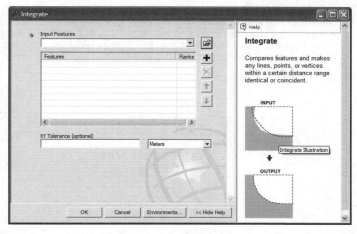

vertices are within the tolerance, then a single vertex replaces them approximately midway between the original vertices (Figure 6.9). The cluster tolerance is specified in map units, and because it searches from two (or more) nearby vertices, the tolerance needs to be set at half the required distance. For example, if you want to integrate vertices that are 100 units or less away, then use a cluster tolerance of 50. Again, we are faced with the Goldilocks problem: you must be careful to choose a "just right" tolerance that cleans up unwanted artifacts, but does not overly simplify features by removing needed vertices (including nearby vertices on the same feature).

Integrating a layer

ArcToolbox -> Data Management Tools -> Feature Class -> **Integrate**.

FIGURE 6.9. Integrating a layer to remove artifacts and assisting in creating a dataset that conforms to planar topology. The original two polygons have a gap with vertices separated by 100 units and an overlap with vertices separated by 50 units (left). Also notice the small peninsula at the bottom of the right polygon with vertices separated by 75 units. A cluster tolerance of 25 removes the overlap (upper right). Increasing the tolerance to 35 does not clean up the gap, but removes the peninsula (lower right). A tolerance of 50 units is needed to clean up both the gap and overlap, but again has removed the peninsula (lower right).

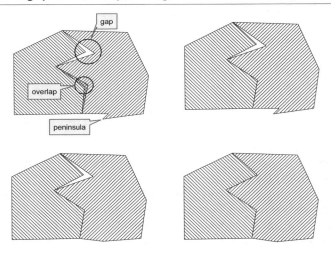

6.8 Map topology

Beginning with version 8.3, map topology has been fully implemented in ArcGIS. A map topology can be imposed on simple geometric features during an ArcMap edit session. Features can be from either a shapefile or geodatabase dataset. There are generally two steps where topology comes into play. The first is when you are editing features by reshaping or moving features. The second is termed *validation* and is used to examine whether a dataset or set of datasets conform to the specified topology rules. Note that validation can only be done using Geodatabase topology, available with an ArcInfo license.

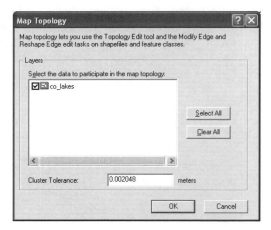

Defining a map topology

1. From the Editor toolbar menu, select More Editing Tools -> Topology. This adds the Topology toolbar.

2. From the Editor toolbar menu, select Start Editing.

3. Select the source dataset to be edited on the Editor toolbar.

4. From the *Topology* toolbar, click the Map Topology button ( ).

5. Check the feature classes that will take part in the map topology.

6.8.1 Topology rules

The types of topology rules allowed are based on spatial relation types (see section 5.6.1) between the geometric primitives (points, lines, polygons) that make up features. There are a number of types of geometry that are used when editing a topology, including edges, nodes, pseudo-nodes, and vertices. *Edges* are line segments that define polyline features or polygons. *Nodes* are the ending points of an edge. *Pseudo-nodes* are the end points that occur at the intersection of two (and only two) edges. *Vertices* are the non-end point *x, y* locations that define the geometry of an edge. When features have intersecting (adjacent) or overlapping (partially-equivalent) features, the edges and nodes that comprise these parts are termed *shared*. Topology edit tools allow you to move vertices, nodes, or whole edges of shared features, thus maintaining planar topology.

There are a variety of rules that can be imposed on Geodatabases (Table 6.3). Rules define the possible (allowed) spatial relationships between features within a dataset or between datasets.

TABLE 6.3. Topology rules between feature types in a Geodatabase.

Feature types	Rule	Example uses	Possible fixes
Polygon-polygon	**Must not overlap** - polygon interiors must not overlap, though polygons can be disconnected or share edges or vertices. This is used to enforce planar topology.	Ensure that administrative boundaries (e.g., counties, states, etc.) are mutually exclusive	Reshape a polygon to move vertices of one to another (use snapping) Subtract one polygon from the other Merge two polygons into a single polygon
Polygon-polygon	**Must not have gaps** - there cannot be voids between polygon interiors, though polygons can share edges or vertices. This is used to ensure that polygons are completely space-filling and tesselate the whole study area.	Ensure there are no gaps between land ownership parcels or vegetation polygons	Reshape a polygon to move vertices to snap to the nearest polygon Create a new polygon that fills the void
Polygon-polygon	**Must not overlap with** - the interior polygons of one feature class must not overlap with those of another feature class	Ensure that features from two layers are mutually-exclusive, such as lakes and soil types	Reshape a polygon to move vertices to snap to the nearest polygon Subtract a polygon from another
Polygon-polygon	**Must be covered by feature class of** - a polygon in one feature class must cover polygons in a second feature class	Ensure that hierarchical relationships are maintained (e.g., states are completely covered by counties)	Subtract one polygon from the other Create a new polygon that fills the void
Polygon-polygon	**Must cover each other** - polygons in one feature class must share all of its area with polygons of another class	Ensure that hierarchical relationships are maintained (e.g., nested watersheds)	Subtract one polygon from the other

TABLE 6.3. Topology rules between feature types in a Geodatabase.

Feature types	Rule	Example uses	Possible fixes
Polygon-polygon	**Must be covered by** - polygons in one feature class must be contained within polygons of another class	Ensure that hierarchical relationships are maintained (e.g., counties are completely covered by states)	Create a new polygon that fills the void
Polygon-line	**Boundary must be covered by** - boundaries of polygons must be covered by lines from another feature class	Ensure that area feature boundaries are marked by linear features (e.g., parcel boundaries are formed by major roads)	Create a new polygon that fills the void
Polygon-polygon	**Area boundary must be covered by boundary of** - boundaries of polygon features must be covered by boundaries of polygon features from another feature class	Ensure that polygons share boundaries when features naturally nest (e.g., parcels within a subdivision)	Create a new polygon that fills the void
Polygon-point	**Contains point** - a polygon contains at least one point from another feature class. Points must be in the polygon interior, not on the boundary.	Ensure that each polygon has at least one point associated with it	Add additional points
Line-line	**Must not overlap** - lines must not overlap (share an edge segment) lines within the same feature class, though lines can cross or intersect	Ensure that line segments are not duplicated (planar enforcement)	Subtract one line from the other
Line-line	**Must not intersect** - line features from the same feature class must not cross or overlap, though lines can share endpoints	Ensure that lines do not self-cross (e.g., a contour line)	Subtract one line from another. Split a line at intersection

TABLE 6.3. Topology rules between feature types in a Geodatabase.

Feature types	Rule	Example uses	Possible fixes
Line - line	**Must not have dangles** - a line feature must touch lines from the same feature class at both end points, though cul-de-sac or dead end streets are common exceptions	Ensure that lines from closed loops (e.g., a linear representation of a lake)	Extend line to intersect other line Trim part of line Snap end point to line
Line - line	**Must not have pseudo-nodes** - a line must connect to at least two other lines at each end point	Ensure closed loops or when line features should connect to two other features (e.g., a hydrologic network)	Merge the two features that share the pseudo-node
Line	**Must not intersect or touch interior** - a line must only touch other lines of the same feature class at the end points	Ensure that lines only be connected at end points	Subtract features Split features at intersection
Line - line	**Must not overlap with** - a line from one feature class must not overlap with line features of another class	Ensure that linear features do not share the same space (e.g., a road and a river)	Subtract features Move features
Line - line	**Must be covered by feature class of** - lines must be covered by lines from another feature class	Ensure that lines are coincident (e.g., a bus route follows a street network)	
Line - polygon	**Must be covered by boundary of** - lines must be covered by the boundaries of polygons	Ensure that linear features are coincident with polygon features (e.g., a lot line with the edge of a lake)	Subtract features
Line - point	**Endpoint must be covered by** - endpoints of linear features must be covered by points from another feature class	Ensure that a point feature occurs at all line junctions (e.g., a water line junction)	Create feature Remove pseudo-node

TABLE 6.3. Topology rules between feature types in a Geodatabase.

Feature types	Rule	Example uses	Possible fixes
Line	**Must not self overlap** - a line feature must not overlap itself, though they can cross or touch themselves	Ensure that linear features like bus routes do not duplicate a segment, but can cross	Simplify
Line	**Must not self intersect** - line features must not cross or overlap themselves	Ensure planar topology (e.g. contour lines cannot cross themselves)	Simplify
Line	**Must be single part** - line features must be composed of only a single part	This is useful to reduce linear features to their elemental aspects	Explode
Point - polygon	**Must be covered by boundary of** - points must fall on the boundary of polygon features, not the interiors	Ensure markers are placed on the boundary	
Point - polygon	**Must be properly inside polygons** -points must fall in polygon interiors, not outside or on the boundaries	Ensure points are within an areal feature (e.g., a well inside an aquifer)	Delete features
Point - line	**Must be covered by endpoint of** - points must be covered by the end points of linear features	Ensure that markers are located only at the end of a line feature	Delete Move feature
Point - line	**Must be covered by line** - points must be covered by lines from another feature class	Ensure that points are located on a line (e.g., road sign locations on a road)	

6.8.2 Cluster tolerance

The *cluster tolerance* specifies the maximum distance between vertices of features that will be considered coincident. That is, if the distance between vertices is less than the cluster tolerance, then the vertices will be snapped together. With v8.3, a second aspect of map topology is the definition of the cluster tolerance. Usually the cluster distance is set to be a small distance to minimize the movement of features. The default tolerance is calculated as the minimum possible cluster tolerance. Increasing the tolerance causes more vertices to snap together, though large distances can begin to collapse features.

6.8.3 Topological or shared editing

The *Topology toolbar* provides additional editing tools. These include shared editing using the *Topology Edit tool*, validating topology, and fixing topological errors. Note that the first step in using the Topology tools is to set up map topology using the Map Topology button ( ).

6.8.3.1 Editing shared geometry

With the Topology Edit tool ( ) you can edit edges and nodes that may be shared by more than one feature. When you move a vertex, a node, or an edge, all of the features that share the vertices that are edited are updated as well. The *Show Shared Features* tool ( ) is useful to display the features that were selected using the Topology Edit tool. If you want to remove a particular feature from participating in the shared edit, you can

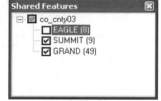

interactively remove the feature from the check list. For example, the node located at the intersection of three counties in Colorado could be selected, but Eagle County might be removed from participating in the shared edit (see right above). Note that at the ArcView level, a few additional tools are provided, but are not typically located on the Topology toolbar, including the *Explode tool* ( ) that converts multi-part features to single-part features. With an ArcInfo license, additional ways to edit and create topological features are provided, including splitting lines at their intersections (Planarize Lines), constructing new features from different geometry types (Construct Features), and generalizing features (Generalize).

Editing shared geometry

Selecting and moving a node

1. From the *Topology* toolbar, click the Topology Edit tool ( ).
2. Click on the node you want to select (holding the N key down helps).
3. The node should be symbolized by a thick point (purple by default).
4. Click and drag the node to a new location. You can also move the node a specified distance by right-clicking, selecting Move To, and entering the absolute X and Y coordinates.

Selecting and moving an edge

1. From the *Topology* toolbar, click the Topology Edit tool ( ).
2. Click on the edge you want to select (holding the E key down helps).
3. The edge should be symbolized by a thick line (purple by default).
4. Click and drag the edge to a new location.

Modifying an edge

1. From the *Topology* toolbar, click the Topology Edit tool ( ).
2. Click on the edge you want to select (holding the E key down helps).
3. The edge should be symbolized by a thick line (purple by default).
4. Select Modify Edge from the Task dropdown arrow on the Editor toolbar.
5. To insert a new vertex, right-click a segment of the edge and select Insert Vertex. To delete a vertex, right-click on a vertex and select Delete Vertex. To move a vertex, click on a vertex and drag it to a new location. To split an edge, ctrl-click at the location where you want to split (you should see a circle symbolizing the "anchor"), then right-click and select Split Edge at Anchor.
6. To finish the sketch, right-click anywhere in the map and select Finish Sketch.

6.9 Creating a new dataset

Frequently, a new dataset will need to be created from scratch. The process of defining the type of feature and attributes needed is accomplished through ArcCatalog, and then new features are created through ArcMap. Another common way to create a new dataset is through some selection (either all or some features) of an existing dataset, and then individual features are edited. Occasionally, features themselves do not need to be modified, rather simply a selection of features from an existing dataset is needed. In this case, either a new dataset can be created, or a dataset can be dynamically subsetted.

New shapefiles, geodatabases, and coverages[9] are created in ArcCatalog, and the properties cannot be modified after the new dataset is created. The properties that need to be specified for a shapefile include its name, the type of features it will contain (point[10], polyline, polygon), whether it also stores m values (measured values) at each vertex (used for routes), whether it stores z values (elevation) at each vertex, and the coordinate system. After the dataset is created, then the attributes can be specified through the layer's properties (right).

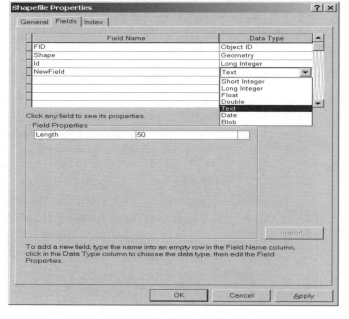

For geodatabases, the process is similar, but slightly more complicated because of the numerous feature datasets, classes, and relationships that can be specified. Recall that only personal geodatabases can be created with ArcView-level functionality.

---

9. Coverages cannot be created with ArcView-level functionality, but shapefiles and simple geodatabases can be created.

10. A multi-point feature type can also be created.

Creating a new shapefile dataset

1. In ArcCatalog, navigate to a desired folder (remember it should not have non-alphanumeric characters).

2. Select **File -> New -> Shapefile**. If this is greyed-out or not available, be sure that you do not have a dataset already selected.

3. Specify the name of the shapefile (again, use only alphanumeric and the underscore characters).

4. Select the feature type.

5. Click on the **Edit...** button to specify the coordinate system.

6. Check the *m value* and/or the *z value* check-boxes, as desired.

7. Click **OK**.

8. Find the newly-created shapefile and right-click, then select **Properties**.

9. Add a new field by clicking in the **Field Name** column in the space below the last existing field, and type in a field name.

10. Specify the field type by clicking in the **Data Type** column and selecting the desired type.

Creating a new geodatabase dataset

1. In ArcCatalog, navigate to a desired folder (remember it should not have non-alphanumeric characters).

2. Select **File -> New -> Personal Geodatabase**. If this is greyed-out or not available, be sure that you do not have a dataset already selected.

3. Specify the name of the geodatabase (again, use only alphanumeric and the underscore characters).

New feature dataset

4. Right-click on the geodatabase and select **New -> Feature dataset...** Name it, then click **OK**.

New feature class

5. Right-click on the geodatabase and select **New -> Feature class...** Name it, then click **Next**.

6. Specify the configuration keyword, then click Next.

7. Click on the **Shape** field name, then specify the feature type by clicking on **Geometry Type.**

8. To add other attribute fields, click in the **Field Name** column in the space below the last existing field, and type in a field name.

9. Specify the field type by clicking in the **Data Type** column and selecting the desired type.

10. When finished adding fields, click **Finish**.

6.10 Creating and editing attribute data

There are a couple of basic ways that attribute data can be created and edited. Recall that attributes can be edited from a feature-centric perspective by changing values for a particular feature through the Attributes dialog. A second way is to open an attribute table and edit it directly. Like a spreadsheet, attribute data can be edited cell-by-cell by simply typing in a value—but this is available only when a dataset is in edit mode. The header cell of editable fields is shown in white. Values can be copied and pasted from one field to another. Note that to put the original value back into a cell, press Escape.

6.10.1 Field calculator

A third way to edit a table is through the *Field Calculator* dialog, which calculates the value of a field for all selected records (or on all records if no records are selected). For example, you might need to set all records to a constant value, perhaps 0.0, or the value of a new field might be the product of two existing fields. Typically, calculations are done when you are *not* in edit mode.

The expression used to define the calculation can be simple or complex. To open the Field Calculator, use a field's context menu (right-click and then select Field Calculator). Note that you can sort the fields in the Fields dialog box

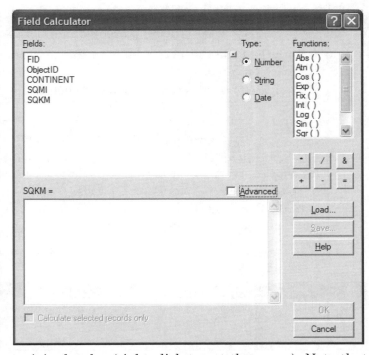

to be ascending, descending or original order (right-click to get the menu). Note that calculator expressions can be copied and pasted, and also saved to an *.cal* file. Below are some examples of common calculation expressions:

"Douglas fir"   set field [Vegetation] to "Douglas fir" -- strings in double quotes

1000.0   set field [Area] to 1000.0

[Area] * 0.000247   convert area in square meters to number of acres in each polygon

[Perimeter] / [Area]   set field [Poly_shape] to the perimeter/area ratio

[First] & " " & [Last]   concatenate fields that contain first & last name into a single field

[FID]   returns the record number

replace([Name], "Colorado", "CO") replaces the abreviation for Colorado

Saving a calculator expression

1. With the Field Calculator dialog open and the desired expression in the box, click on **Save**.

2. Navigate to the desired location and click **OK**.

Turn off annoying warning message

1. When using Field Calculator in regular (non-edit) mode, a warning dialog appears every time you run a calculation (see below).

2. To turn it off, click **Tools --> Options...**, then click on the **Tables** tab.

3. In the middle of the dialog, there is a check-box option "Show warning when calculating field values out edit session" -- check this OFF, then click **OK**.

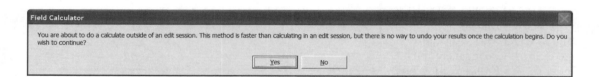

Field Calculator

You are about to do a calculate outside of an edit session. This method is faster than calculating in an edit session, but there is no way to undo your results once the calculation begins. Do you wish to continue?

Yes   No

Note that the Calculate Field dialog (in ArcMap) and the *Calculate Field tool* are very similar, but slightly different. The tool also allows advanced code, but the expression type can be either VBScript or Python code. Also, if there is a selection set on the input table, only the selected features (rows) will be computed. Note that you cannot calculate on a joined field.

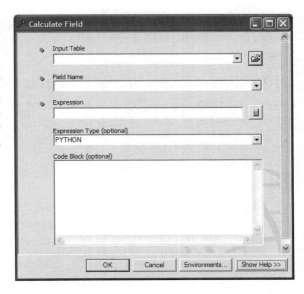

Opening the Field Calculator

ArcToolbox -> Data Management Tools -> Fields -> **Calculate Field**.

6.10.2 Calculate geometry

To compute the geometry of different vector-based features, you can use the *Calculate Geometry* dialog. For points, you can compute the x and y coordinates. For polylines, you can compute the length, x and y coordinates of the center of the polyline, and start or end point of the polyline. For polygons, you can compute the area, perimeter, and x and y coordinates of the centroid. Note that you can use either the coordinate system of the data source or of the data frame. The

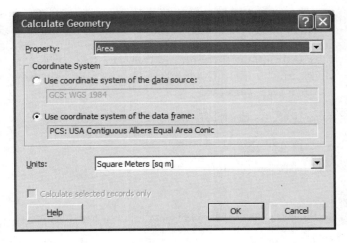

---

values can be computed in a variety of units, such as square miles or hectares.[11] Note that similar to the Field Calculator, right-click on a desired (number) field and select Calculate Geometry.

6.10.3 Common problems with calculator expressions

Occasionally there can be problems with calculator expressions. If you get an error message, then try out the following:

1. Make sure strings are quoted.

2. Numbers cannot have commas, and a value less than 1 should be preceded with a zero (e.g., 0.124, not .124).

3. Dividing by 0 or doing a calculation on a value that is not a number will cause an error. One way to get around these problems is to first query the field to find the records that only contain non-zero values or strings that can be converted by using the query string "<field>.IsNumeric".

4. Make sure that the target field is specified as a data type that is large enough to handle the value—often you'll need a field of type Double rather than Short integer.

6.10.4 Advanced calculator expressions

A powerful feature of the Field Calculator is that, in addition to simple expression, virtually any VB Script function can be called within a more complicated expression. This provides access to a wide range of VB functions and ArcObjects, as well as basic programming statements (e.g., if then-else).[12] There is a range of functions to handle the various data types: date, numeric, text, and shape (Table 6.4), for example, to compute the area of a polygon (which is needed after you alter a feature through an operation such as clip or union, or through interactive editing). To do this, right click on the target field and bring up the Field Calculator. Then, check the "Advanced" box and type the following into the pre-logic text box:

Dim dblX as double

Dim pArea as IArea

Set pArea = [shape]

---

11. Because units are not stored anywhere as metadata, it is good practice to include the units in the field name, so instead of computing a field called "AREA", a field called "AREA_HA" is more descriptive.

12. These functions are documented in the Visual Basic help, under: Visual Basic Language Reference -> Functions.

dblX = pArea.area

The first and second lines set the dimension of a variable to store the area of a polygon (as a numerical value) and a variable to store the shape object (the polygon), respectively. The third line gets the polygon, and the fourth line requests the area of pArea (by the ".area" request), then assigns the area to the variable **dblX**. Finally, in the smaller text box below the field name, enter:

dblX

This last step tells ArcMap to put the value referenced by the variable **dblArea** back into the target field. Note that you cannot access other fields in this line.

Also note that you can save and load these expressions, and you can comment your expressions (e.g., give them a name, describe the logic, etc.) using the single-quote comment character, where everything to the right is not evaluated. Building on this basic idea, you could request a number of properties about a shape object (by replacing the "dblArea = pArea.area" line), to include getting a polygon centroid, or X and Y location of a polygon's centroid.[13]

Another important calculation is the accumulative value of a numeric field (using NUMFIELD and OutValue in the expression in this example). Note that this accumulates using the internal order of the table and does not change with sorting.

Static lastValue as variant

Dim OutValue as Double

If IsEmpty (lastValue) Then

  OutValue = [NUMFIELD]

Else

  OutValue = [NUMFIELD] + lastValue

End If

lastValue = OutValue

---

13. For a helpful set of pre-specified calculator expressions, see Ianko Tchoukanski's EasyCalculate VBScripts, available at: http://www.ian-ko.com.

To compute the rank order (ascending only) of a field, use the Summarize tool and set the field to summarize on (i.e. the "case" field) to be the field of interest. Use the Count field in the resulting summary table to accumulate the rank value.

TABLE 6.4. Listing of VB functions that can be used in the Field Calculator for the date data type.

Function	Returns	Description
Date()	Date	Returns the current system date
DateAdd(<period>, <number>, <date>)	Date	Returns the result of adding or subtracting a given number of time periods ("yyyy"=year, "q"=quarter, "m" = month, "y"= day of year, "d"=day, "w"=week-day, "ww"=week, "h"=hour, "n"=minute, "s"=second. E.g., **DateAdd ("d", 2, Now)** adds two days onto the current day.
DateDiff(<period>, <date1>, <date2>)	Number	Returns the number of time periods between two dates. E.g., **DateDiff ("d", "11/5/2002", "12/31/2002")** adds two days onto the current day.
DatePart(<period>, <date>)	Number	Returns a component of the date or time (e.g., day, second, etc.). E.g., **DatePart ("m", "11/5/2002")** gets the month (11) as an integer two days onto the current day.
DateSerial(<year>,<month>,<day>)	Date	Returns a date specified by year, month, day. E.g., **DatePart (2002, 11, 5)** creates a date specifying the 5th of November 2002.
DateValue (<dateString>)	Date	Returns a date specified by string. E.g., **DateValue (2002, 11, 5)** creates a date specifying the 5th of November 2002. Note that a short cut is: "11/5/2002"
Now()	Date	Returns current date and time (to seconds). E.g., **Now()** returns current time. To get time precise to milliseconds, use Timer.
Timer()	Number (double)	Returns the current number of milliseconds since midnight. E.g., **Timer()**.

TABLE 6.5. Listing of VB functions that can be used in the Field Calculator for the number data type.

Function	Returns	Description
Abs(\<number>)	Number	Returns the absolute value of a number. E.g., **Abs (-1)** equals 1; **Abs (1)** equals 1.
Atn(\<radians>)	Number	Returns the arcTangent of a number in radians. To convert degrees to radians, multiply degrees by pi/180. To convert radians to degrees, multiply radians by 180/pi. E.g., **Atn(1 * (3.1415/180))** equals 0.017451 radians.
CDbl(\<number>)	Number (double)	Returns the number as a type Double, which ranges from -1.79769313486232E308 to 1.79769313486232E308.
CInt(\<number>)	Number (short)	Returns the number as an integer of type Short, which ranges from -32,768 to 32,767.
CLng(\<number>)	Number (long)	Returns the number as an integer of type Long, which ranges from -2,147,483,648 to 2,147,483,647.
Cos(\<radians>)	Number (double)	Returns the cosine of a number in radians, which ranges from -1 to 1.
CSng(\<number>)	Number (float)	Converts a value to a single or floating point type, which ranges from -3.402823E38 to 3.402823E38.
CStr(\<expression>)	Text	Returns a string representation of the expression. E.g., **CStr (10)** returns "10".
Exp(\<number>)	Number (double)	Returns the anti-logarithm of a number, to raise a number e (2.71282818). E.g., **Exp(2)** equals 7.389056..., or e^2.
Fix(\<number>)	Number (integer)	Returns an integer by removing the fractional part returning the next greater whole number. E.g., **Fix (-2.2)** equals -2.
Int(\<number>)	Number (integer)	Returns an integer by removing the fractional part returning the next greater whole number. E.g., **Int (-2.2)** equals -1.
IsNull(\<number>)	Number (boolean)	Returns a boolean flag if the number is Null.

TABLE 6.5. Listing of VB functions that can be used in the Field Calculator for the number data type.

Function	Returns	Description
IsNumeric(<expression>)	Number (boolean)	Returns a boolean flag if the expression is numeric. E.g., **IsNumeric ("wow")** equals FALSE, **IsNumeric(10)** equals TRUE.
Log(<number >)	Number (double)	Returns the natural logarithm of the number. E.g., **Log (0.4)** equals -0.916291...
RGB(<red>, <green>, <blue>	Number (long)	Returns the RGB number for the specified component color values that range from 0 to 255, using the formula: RGB=red + (green * 256) + blue * 65536). E.g., **RGB(0, 255, 174)** returns 11468544.
Rnd ()	Number (double)	Returns a random number. To return a random integer in a range, use: **Int((high - low + 1) * Rnd() + low)**. Call Randomize(<seed>) to reset the random number generator. Using Randomize() uses the system timer and creates a new series of random numbers each time.
Round(<value>, <places>)	Number	Returns a number rounded to the specified number of places. E.g., **Round (10.1234, 0)** returns 10, while **Round(10.1234, 2)** returns 10.12.
Sgn(<number>)	Number	Returns the sign of a number: 1 if positive, 0 if 0, -1 if negative. E.g., **Sgn (-2345)** equals -1.
Sin(<radians>)	Number (double)	Returns the sine of a number in radians.
Sqr()	Number (double)	Returns the square root of a number. E.g., **Sqr(2)** equals 1.1414...
Tan(<radians>)	Number (double)	Returns the tangent of a number.
+	Number	Addition operator. E.g., **1 + 2** equals 3.
-	Number	Subtraction operator. E.g., **2 - 1** equals 1.
*	Number	Multiplication operator. E.g., **2 * 1** equals 2.
/	Number (floating)	Division operator. E.g., **1 / 2** equals 0.5.
\	Number (integer)	Integer division operator. E.g., **1 \ 2** equals 0.

TABLE 6.5. Listing of VB functions that can be used in the Field Calculator for the number data type.

Function	Returns	Description
mod	Number	Modulo operator, returns only the remainder. E.g., **1 mod 2** equals 1.
^	Number	Exponentiation operator, raises a number to the power of the exponent. E.g., **2 ^ 3** equals 8.

TABLE 6.6. Listing of ArcObject and VB methods that can be used in the Field Calculator for the shape data type.

Function	Returns	Description
.Area	Number	Returns the area of a polygon shape in map units. The following lines must be in the pre-logic box: **Dim pArea as IArea** **Set pShape = [shape]** **dblX = pShape.area** In the expression box: **dblX**
.Centroid	Shape (point)	Returns the area-weighted centroid of a polygon (the centroid does not have to fall within the polygon). Replace dblX=pShape.Area (in .Area above) with: **dblX = pShape.Centroid**
.GeometryCount	Number	Returns the number of parts in a shape. **Dim pGeometryCollection As IGeometryCollection** **Dim lngX As Long** **Set pGeometryCollection = [Shape]** **lngX = pGeometryCollection.GeometryCount** In the expression box: **lngX**
.LabelPoint	Shape (point)	Returns the label point of a polygon (this is the same as the centroid if the centroid falls within the polygon, otherwise it is forced to fall in the polygon). Replace dblX=pShape.Area (in .Area above) with: **dblX = pShape.LabelPoint**

TABLE 6.6. Listing of ArcObject and VB methods that can be used in the Field Calculator for the shape data type.

Function	Returns	Description
.PointCount	Number	Returns the number of vertices that comprise a shape. **Dim pPointCollection As IPointCollection** **Dim dblX As Double** **Set pPointCollection = [Shape]** **dblX = pPointCollection.PointCount** In the expression box: **dblX**
.Length	Number	Returns the perimeter of a polygon or length of a polyline. Use the following in the pre-logic box: **Dim pCurve As ICurve** **Dim dLength As Double** **Set pCurve = [Shape]** **dblX = pCurve.Length**
.X	Number (double)	Returns the X coordinate (in map units) of a point. E.g., replace dblX=pShape.area (in .Area above) with: **dblX = pShape.Centroid.X**
.Y	Number (double)	Returns the Y coordinate (in map units) of a point. E.g., replace dblX=pShape.area (in .Area above) with: **dblX = pShape.Centroid.Y**

TABLE 6.7. Listing of VB functions that can be used in the Field Calculator for the string data type.

Function	Returns	Description
&	Text	Concatenates two strings together. E.g., **"Yes" & "!"** equals "Yes!".
Asc(<string>)	Number	Returns the ANSI code of the first character in the string. E.g., **Asc ("a")** equals 97.
Chr(<number>)	Text	Returns the character for the given ASCII code . E.g., **Chr(97)** equals "a".
CStr(<expression>)	Text	Returns a string representation of the input expression. E.g., **CStr (1234)** equals "1234".

TABLE 6.7. Listing of VB functions that can be used in the Field Calculator for the string data type.

Function	Returns	Description
InStr(<search-String>, <find-String>)	Number	Returns the starting position of the findString in searchString, or returns 0 if not found. E.g., **InStr("Colorado", "olo")** returns 2.
LCase(<String>)	Text	Returns the string in all lowercase. E.g., **LCase ("Colorado")** returns "colorado".
Left(<string>,<length>)	Text	Returns the left-most characters defined by length in the input string. E.g., **Left ("Colorado", 4)** returns "Colo".
Len(<string>)	Number	Returns the number of characters in a string. E.g., **Len("Colorado")** returns 8.
LTrim(<string>)	Text	Trims any leading spaces from input string. E.g., **LTrim (" Colorado")** would return "Colorado".
Mid(<string>, <start>, <length>)	Text	Returns the string that begins at start that is a length characters long from the input text. E.g., **Mid ("Colorado", 2, 4)** returns "olor".
Proper	Text	Actually, returning the "proper" form of a string (first character upper case, the rest lower case) can be created using a combination of functions. E.g., the string in the Text field is converted to "proper" form: **UCase (Left([text], 1)) & Right([text], Len([text]) - 1)**
Replace(<string>, <findString>, <replaceString>)	Text	Finds a string in a field and replaces it with a replacement string. E.g., **Replace([Place-Names], "Sakagawea", "Sakakawea").**
Right(<string>, <length>)	Text	Returns the right-most characters defined by length in the input string. E.g., **Right ("Colo-rado", 4)** returns "rado".
RTrim(<string>)	Text	Trims any trailing spaces from input string. E.g., **LTrim ("Colorado ")** would return "Colo-rado".

TABLE 6.7. Listing of VB functions that can be used in the Field Calculator for the string data type.

Function	Returns	Description
Split(<expression>, <delimiter>)	Text	Parses a string into an array using a delimiter. To access the values in an array, simply indicate the position (starting at 0) in parentheses. The following returns "Jones". In the pre-logic expression: **Dim sArray** **sArray = Split("Mr. Jones", " ")** In the assignment expression: **sArray(1)**
StrComp(<string1>, <string2>)	Number	Determines whether string1 is equal to (0), greater than (1), or less than (-1) string2. E.g., **StrComp("Yes", "Yes)** returns 0, while **Str-Comp("Yes","Yes2")** returns -1.
String(<number>, <character>)	String	Returns a string with a single character repeated a specified number of times. E.g., **String(10, "x")** returns "xxxxxxxxxx".
Trim(<string>)	String	Trims any leading or trailing spaces from input string. E.g., **Trim (" Colorado ")** would return "Colorado".
UCase(<string>)	String	Returns the string in all upper case. E.g., **UCase ("Colorado")** returns "COLORADO".
Do...Loop		
Choose(<index>, <choice1>, <choice2>, <choiceN>...)		Use the index value to identify the choice to return. E.g., **Choice([Field], "red", "green", "blue")** returns "red" if the value in the field is 1, etc.
Constants		**vbTab** returns the tab character **vbCr** returns the carriage return character
Switch(<expression1 >, <value1>, <expression2>, <value2>, ...)		For example, you can use this to reclassify values based on a series of ranges: Switch(([Id] >= 0 AND [Id] < 5),1 , ([Id] >=5 AND [Id] < 10), 2, ([Id] >10), 3)

6.11 Chapter review

- Six criteria are needed to judge the suitability of an existing dataset: geographic extent (does it include the desired area?); geographic unit (are the geographic units of adequate resolution for your question?); thematic (does it have the attributes needed?); scale (were the data generated from a map or dataset of adequate scale to allow reasonably precise answers to your questions?); temporal (do the data represent the geographic features during a time that you are interested in?); and metadata (does the dataset have adequate metadata associated with it?)

- Setting the snapping environment is key to generating and editing a topologically correct dataset.

- New datasets are first created in ArcCatalog.

- Attribute values can be computed using the Field Calculator (or Calculate Field tool).

- Length, area, and centroids can be computed using the Calculate Geometry tool.

Acquiring, editing, and creating vector datasets

7   *Raster analysis*

This chapter provides a basic introduction to raster datasets, analyzing raster data, converting between raster and vector, and the analysis environment that controls a number of fundamental aspects of the creation and analysis of raster data. Basic analysis functions that are provided through interfaces in Spatial Analyst are organized by the five fundamental classes of functions—local, neighborhood (focal), zonal, global, and application-specific.

Although Spatial Analyst provides a number of interfaces to access commonly used functions, there is a wide variety of additional functions "under the hood." These functions are accessible through the *Raster Calculator*, which is a dialog where expressions containing functions and operations can be typed and run.

7.1 Raster representation

You may recall from Chapter 2 the comparison of vector and raster data. Raster data typically represent geographic phenomena that varies continuously through space, such as elevation. A raster contains a matrix or grid of *cells* (or *pixels*) that contain a particular numeric value, such as a brightness value or a land cover type.[1] A cell typically is square, and all cells in a raster are the same size. In most raster dataset types commonly used in ArcGIS (Table 7.1) there is one and only one value associated with each cell. Spatial reference information that specifies the geographic or projection coordinates, such as the top-left cell, allow the raster to be georeferenced.

A raster can contain a single *band* (a single matrix or layer of cells) or multiple bands that contain multiple layers of matrices representing the same area. For example, since there is only one elevation value at any location on Earth, then a single band raster can adequately represent elevation. Most satellite or aerial photo imagery is composed of three (or more) bands, such as the red, green, and blue bands, and typically is held in a multi-band dataset.

Each raster band stores a matrix of cells or pixels, which can contain either integer or floating point values. Integer values are whole numbers (e.g., 0, 29, 248) while floating points contain real numbers with a decimal point (e.g., 0.01, 3.14, 1000.0). This is known as the raster *data type*.

Each cell stores a value, and the range of values that can be stored depends on the *data depth* (also known as the pixel or bit depth) of the raster dataset, which is based on binary math (2^n, where n is the bit depth). So, a bit depth of 1 can represent values from 0 to 1, and a bit depth of signed 32 bit can represent values between positive and negative 2.14 x 10^9.

The *spatial extent* of a raster is defined by the number of columns (*m*) and rows (*n*) and the cell size or resolution, totaling *C* cells in the entire spatial extent (Figure 7.1). Note that the spatial extent of a raster is always rectangular in shape. Within the spatial extent, the *NoData* value is used in a raster to signify that the phenomenon of interest does not occur at that location, is outside the study boundary, or that data is missing at that location. Do not confuse NoData with the value 0.0, as 0.0 is valid in raster. NoData values are ignored when computing statistics, and attribute data cannot be associated with them. You can control how different functions behave when they encounter NoData values so that NoData is returned, NoData is ignored and available values are used, or the value is estimated. Locations outside of the extent are considered to have NoData.

Because oftentimes raster files can become quite large, they might be somewhat slow to display. To address this situation, a *pyramid* layer can be created. A pyramid is a reduced resolution layer that provides several stacked layers of the raster data, such that levels in the pyramid contain increasingly coarser resolution.[2] At broad spatial extents, the coarse

---

1. For a thorough introduction to raster data structures, see: Holroyd, F. and S.B.M. Bell. 1992. Raster GIS: Models of raster encoding. *Computers & Geosciences* 18(4): 419-426.
2. Each layer is a down-sampled version at a ratio of 4:1. The reduced-resolution dataset file is usually 8% of the original uncompressed file size.

resolution values are displayed. As you zoom in, finer resolutions are displayed. Pyramids are stored in a reduced resolution dataset file (*.rrd). However, sometimes rasters with pyramids do not display particularly well, especially when zoomed way out.

Creating pyramid files for a raster dataset
ArcToolbox -> Data Management Tools -> Raster -> **Build Pyramids**.
ArcCatalog -> Right-click on the dataset and select Build pyramids.

FIGURE 7.1. Analysis properties in Spatial Analyst. A raster with 5 columns (*m*) and 5 rows (*n*), and total number of cells (C) equals $m \times n = C=25$. Note that there are 4 NoData (*nd*) values (lighter grey), and the valued cells (darker grey) constitute the analysis mask, which contains $C_{nd}=(m \times n)-nd$ cells.

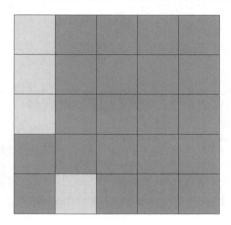

Often multiple rasters are organized using a *raster catalog*, which is a collection of datasets defined in a table format where each record in the table represents an individual raster dataset. Catalogs are often used to manage and display tiled or adjacent datasets, such as a collection of topographic quadrangles for your study area.

TABLE 7.1. Supported raster data formats.

Name	Description
ArcIMS Image Service	An ArcIMS Image Service delivers snapshots of data over the Internet as an image.

TABLE 7.1. Supported raster data formats.

Arc Digitized Raster Graphics (*.img, *.ovr, *.lgg-legend)	Geographically referenced arc-second raster map. Compressed (CADRG).
ArcSDE raster	Raster data stored in an ArcSDE database.
ASCII GRID (*.asc)	ArcINFO ASCII (text) grid format.
BMP (*.bmp, *.bpw)	Windows bitmap images: 1, 4, 8, or 24 bits per pixel. Compressed BMP files are not supported.
BIL, BIP, BSQ (*.bil, *.bip, *.bsq; *.hdr-header; *.clr-colormap; *.stx-statistics)	Single and multi-band images: band sequential (multi-band image), band interleaved by line, band interleaved by pixel. Header file describes layout of image data.
Controlled Image Base (*.cib)	US Department of Defense's Controlled Image Base (CIB) are georeferenced, grayscale images similar to digital orthophoto quads.
Compressed ARC Digitized Raster Graphics (CADRG)	CADRG Image Support extension
DTED (Digital Terrain Elevation Data) (*.dt1, etc)	Created by NIMA (National Imagery and Mapping Agency), level 0, 1, and 2
Enhanced Compressed Wavelet (*.ecw)	ER Mapper's format can compress large images with high quality using wavelet technology.
ER Mapper (*.ers)	ER mapper format
ERDAS (GIS file: *.gis; Imagine file: *.img, *.igw; raw *.raw)	ERDAS Rev 7.3 and 7.4 *.lan and *.gis files
GIF (*.gif, *.gfw)	ArcGIS can create GIF images—high quality, lossless compression that requires an LZW license.
GRID, SDE raster	ESRI format that supports 32-bit integer and 32-bit floating point raster grids. Without Spatial Analyst extension, a GRID is viewed as a single band image and looks for *.clr color map file.
Hierarchical Data Format (HDF)	National Center for Supercomputing Application's Hierarchical Data Format. There is no direct translator currently, but see: http://hdf.ncsa.uiuc.edu/
IDRISI raster (*.rst, *.ref)	Native file format for IDRISI GIS software.
IMPELL (*.rlc)	IMPELL Bitmap format which uses run-length compression used for scanned monochrome images

TABLE 7.1. Supported raster data formats.

Intergraph raster file	Both .CIT or .COT
JPEG (*.jpg, *.jgw)	Standard compression technique for storing full color and gray scale images. Requires JPEG image extension (comes standard)
JPEG 2000 (*.jp2)	Updated standard compression technique for high quality display of large imagery.
MAP (*.map)	PCRaster GIS raster format file.
MrSid (*.sid, *.sdw)	LizardTech's Multi-resolution seamless image database format -- a multi-resolution wavelet-based image format for high compression and fast access.
netCDF	network Common Data Form is a file format commonly used to store multi-dimensional scientific data, particularly climate data (see: www.unidata.ucar.edu/software/netcdf).
NITF	National Image Transfer Format, NITF 2.0 and 2.1.
PCIDSK (*.pix)	PCI Geomatics raster dataset file.
Portable Network Graphics (*.png)	High-quality, lossless compression of graphics—a replacement for GIF. Supports 64-bit color, indexed-color images up to 256.
Sun (*.rs, *.ras, *.sun)	Sun rasterfiles for monochrome, grayscale, pseudocolor, and true color. Uses either 1, 8, 24, or 32 bits per pixel. These support a byte-level run-encoding scheme.
TIFF (*.tif, *.tff, *.tiff, *.tfw)	Tag Image File Format - supports black and white (1 bit), grayscale (4, 8, 16, 24, or 32 bits), pseudocolor (4, 8, or 16), and true colors in compressed or uncompressed format. Multi-band images with 8 bits per band, unlimited number of bands. Requires TIFF 6.0 Image Support extension. *GeoTIFF* 1.0 supported if the file is present. Also supports LZW compression.
USGS DEM (*.dem)	US Geological Survey's digital elevation model (DEM) - a raster grid of elevation values.
XPixMap (XPM, *.xpm)	Used to store color images in ASCII.

7.1.1 GRIDs

A *GRID* is a specific implementation of a raster data structure developed by ESRI. GRIDs have m columns and n rows of cells, and are ordered starting from the origin in the upper-left corner. There are two types of GRIDs: *integer GRIDs* and *real GRIDs*. Integer values are used to represent nominal, ordinal, and ratio data and cells that have the same integer values have the same attributes. Integer GRIDs can also be used to represent continuous phenomena. Values (both integer and real) are stored as 32-bit values. Note that the *Spatial Analyst* extension is needed to conduct analyses on GRIDs, though GRIDs can be displayed and queried in ArcMap without Spatial Analyst.

A GRID is actually comprised of a bunch of files grouped into two separate directories. The first directory is the *INFO* directory, which contains the attribute data. Note that the INFO file is shared by other GRIDs and coverages that are located at the same level in the directory structure. The second directory has the same name as the GRID name and contains a number of files with *.adf (arc data file) extensions. The GRID name cannot be longer than 13 characters and cannot start with a number. The files are as follows:

dblbnd.adf—This stores the rectangular boundary (the spatial extent) of the GRID.

hdr.adf—Stores the type of GRID (integer or floating point), as well as the cell resolution.

log—The log file, which stores the history of commands (in Map Algebra notation), including the date they were processed.

prj.adf—Stores the projection information (note this is a text file and can be opened in a word processor application).

sta.adf—Stores statistics about the GRID, such as minimum, maximum, mean, and standard deviation. There is a corresponding file in the INFO directory that points to the data stored here.

vat.adf—The value attribute table (for integer GRIDs only), which stores the unique cell values and count for each value. There is a corresponding file in the INFO directory that points to the data stored here.

w001001.adf—Stores the cell data.

w001001x.adf—Stores indexes to the values in w001001.adf.

The resolution of large GRIDs (i.e., larger than 1000 x 1000) typically exceeds the resolution of the display so that each pixel on the monitor has more than one GRID cell in it. As a result, the display of these GRIDs can be slow. To speed up display of raster data, you can create what is called a pyramid file. The Source tab on the Layer Properties dialog (shown at right) provides a number of

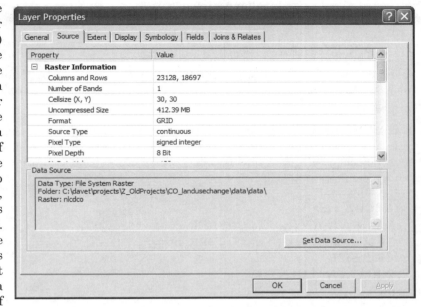

characteristics about a GRID. The GRID type, directory location, name, status (permanent or temporary), and coordinate system are provided in the Data Source box. In the middle of the dialog are listings for the number of rows and columns (10 each in the example), the number of bands (typically 1 for regular GRIDs, but remotely sensed images often have multiple bands), the *x* and *y* cell size (meaning the width and height in map units, not area!), the data type (integer or real), and whether pyramids have been created or not. At the bottom, a number of statistics are provided, including: minimum, maximum, mean, and standard deviation. Also note that the *sum* of all GRID values is displayed in the classification dialog (from the Symbology tab). Note that the Data Source can be changed to another raster (using the Set Data Source button), which allows you to apply the layer properties and legend that you've set up to another dataset.

A GRID attribute table (a.k.a. the Value Attribute Table) contains, at a minimum, two fields: *value* and *count*. The value field contains the values of a GRID, and the count field stores the number of cells in a GRID that have that value. A GRID will not have an attribute table if the GRID is a floating-point type or if the GRID was created from a 1-bit image theme.

7.1.2 Geodatabase raster

Raster datasets can also be stored directly in geodatabases. There are a number of advantages of using this data structure, including managing a large number of datasets within a single geodatabase, larger (up to 1 TB) file sizes, and faster display and processing.

7.1.3 ASCII format

A raster can also be represented simply using text (in ASCII format) in the following format. This format is often used as a way to pass raster data between ArcGIS and other programs.[3]

The ASCII file needs to contain header information using a set of keywords, followed by cell values in row-major order, as shown below. Note that in ArcGIS rasters typically are georeferenced to the lower-left corner of the lowest left cell, though you can use the cell center as an option.

```
<NCOLS xxx>
<NROWS xxx>
<XLLCENTER xxx | XLLCORNER xxx>
<YLLCENTER xxx | YLLCORNER xxx>
<CELLSIZE xxx>
{NODATA_VALUE xxx}
row 1
row 2
row n
```

For example, the following text would specify the ASCII text for the simple raster shown in Figure 2.9. Cell values are delimited by spaces and make sure that the number of columns and number of rows are specified correctly, with a return character at the last line.

```
NCOLS 10
NROWS 9
XLLCORNER 1000
YLLCORNER 1000
CELLSIZE 1
NODATA_VALUE -9
-9 -9  1  1  0  1  0  1 -9 -9
-9 -9  1  1  2  2  2  1  1 -9
-9  1  1  1  2  2  2  2  3  3
 1  1  1  1  2  2  2  2  3  3
 0  1  1  1  1  2  3  3  3  3
```

---

3. Such as FRAGSTATS.

```
0  0  0  1  1  1  1  1  1  1
0  2  2  3  3  3 -9  4  4  4
0  2  2  3  3  3  3  4  4  4
0  2  2  2  4  4  4  4  4  4
```

> ### *Importing ASCII raster data*
> ArcToolbox -> Conversion -> To Raster -> **ASCII to Raster**.

7.1.4 Images

Image data, which is also considered a raster dataset, includes remotely sensed satellite images, scanned aerial photographs, and Digital Raster Graphics (digital topographic quads). *Georeferenced images* have an associated header or world file that tells software where to place the image in space. For example, Digital Raster Graphics (scanned, georeferenced images of topographic maps) are typically used as background maps, with spatial data drawn on top of them. Images do not contain attribute data about the features they show, so you cannot query them as you can GRID data. Most common image formats are supported in ArcGIS, such as TIFF, JPEG, and GIF. See Table 2.12 for an overview of supported raster data formats

Most image data formats have a companion file that is called a *world file*, which contains specifications so that the image can be georeferenced. ArcGIS will use these specifications to transform the image to geographic coordinates. Commonly, a world file is a text file with six parameters listed on each line, like the following of a world file for an image with 2.438 m x 2.438 m cell width and projected in UTM coordinates:

2.43839999999
0.00000000000
0.00000000000
-2.4383999999
500001.2191999999
4358189.6539999999

These values correspond to the following parameters (in order): x-scale, the pixel width in the x direction (in map units); a rotation term about the y-axis, in degrees; a second rotation term, the y-scale pixel width, and the x and y coordinates of the centroid of the upper-left pixel.

7.1.4.1 Digital Raster Graphic

Topographic quadrangles from the US Geological Survey have been made electronic in a form called *Digital Raster Graphic* (DRG). This is an image that is georeferenced, and has 3 bands for red, green, blue portions of the spectrum.

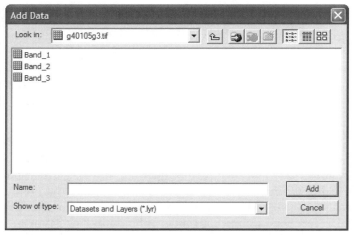

7.2 Symbology

Rasters are displayed using symbology that is defined similarly to feature datasets. As with feature data, the symbology of choice depends on the data type that the raster represents. The *Unique Values* option is used for nominal data, to display land cover categories, for instance. The *Discrete Color* option is also used for nominal data (and integer rasters), but it is more efficient in displaying when a

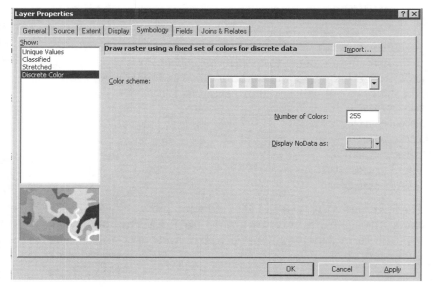

raster contains a large number of unique values because it does not calculate how many unique values exist. The *Classified* option is used for quantitative data, such as elevation.

The *Stretched* option can also be used for quantitative data. This option applies a contrast stretch to the values, which is designed to maximize the contrast based on different distributions. Stretch works by "mapping" the values found in the raster to the 0 to 255 found in the color maps. There are five types of stretches: none, custom, standard deviations (default), histogram equalize, and min-max. The None option will set the minimum value to the beginning of the color ramp and the maximum value to the end of the color ramp. To apply a *Custom* stretch, use the Histogram button and establish breakpoints by clicking in the graph. If raster statistics are not calculated, you will need to re-calculate them using the *Calculate Statistics* tool.

Calculate raster statistics

ArcToolbox -> Data Management Tools -> Raster -> **Calculate Statistics**.

Some raster layers that are created using Spatial Analyst functions will automatically have a pre-defined legend (color and labels) applied to them when generated in ArcMap. A good example of a pre-defined legend is for an raster that was generated using the Aspect tool (right).

Another interesting difference in raster symbology is the ability to display the *raster resolution*, which is the ratio of screen pixels to dataset pixels at the scale the raster is currently being displayed. A ratio of <1 means that each screen pixel is representing only a portion of the raster cell (zoomed in), while a ratio of >1 means that each screen pixel is showing only one of many raster values (zoomed out).

☐ ☑ Aspect of elevation
    <VALUE>
  ☐ Flat (-1)
  ■ North (0-22.5)
  ■ Northeast (22.5-67.5)
  ☐ East (67.5-112.5)
  ■ Southeast (112.5-157.5)
  ■ South (157.5-202.5)
  ■ Southwest (202.5-247.5)
  ■ West(247.5-292.5)
  ■ Northwest (292.5-337.5)
  ■ North (337.5-360)

7.3 Analysis environment

Raster datasets that have already been created can be displayed in ArcMap. This is a great start, but a next step is to generate new rasters by performing some sort of analysis. To do analysis on raster datasets, though, you will need to have the Spatial Analyst extension. Although the toolbar for the Spatial Analyst provides a number of menu items to access analytical operations, there are many more for which you will need to access through ArcToolbox (as a tool) or through Raster Calculator (more on that later). Also note that it is best to have raster (and vector) layers in the same projection system. If the coordinate system of a raster layer is different than the data frame coordinate system (in

ArcMap), then the layer is on-the-fly projected using an approximation of the projection transformation. This transformation can introduce error, so to ensure high-quality results, the raster layers should be projected into the same coordinate system as the data frame. Generally speaking, the errors introduced by the approximation are minimal for spatial extents smaller than a couple of degrees.

There are a number of analysis properties or options that can be controlled when conducting analysis on a raster dataset. The first of these specifies the directory where new rasters will be located. By default, the working directory is set to the system's temporary directory (usually c:\temp). Both temporary and permanent GRIDs will be saved there by default. Because analysis with rasters often requires a number of steps to get a final map, Spatial Analyst automatically creates *temporary* GRIDs by default. Temporary GRIDs can be made *permanent* in two ways. First, each desired GRID can be made permanent through its context menu (right click on a layer, then select Make Permanent). Second, all temporary GRIDs can be made permanent at once by saving the map document. Also, a permanent GRID will be created if a specific name (and path) of a GRID is provided when using a function.[4] Note that because a lot of raster files are typically generated during analysis, managing these files is particularly important.

A second parameter in the Analysis Environment that can be set is the *analysis mask*. This parameter allows analysis to be performed only on certain cells within the analysis extent. The NoData cells in the *mask GRID* will carry through to any GRID created subsequently. Note that in addition to raster datasets, feature datasets can be used as the mask layer.[5]

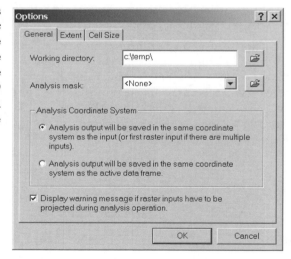

---

4. Recall from earlier in the book that GRID names cannot exceed 13 characters, and both the name and the directory path can contain only alphanumeric characters and the underscore ("_") character. Unpredictable errors can occur when a GRID has a hyphen ("-") and/or space in the name or path.
5. However, a temporary raster is generated on-the-fly that represents the feature data.

7.3.1 Analysis extent

The *analysis extent* determines the spatial extent or geographic coverage of a raster. It is specified through the four *x, y* coordinates of a rectangle. By default, the analysis extent is set to be the *intersection of inputs*, which sets the extent of the output rasters to the extent made by the intersection of the input rasters. You also have the option of "snapping" the extent to that of an existing raster so that all subsequent layers will share the lower-left corner and cell size (recommended). The *snap extent to* option is especially useful when resampling layers.

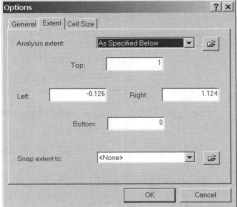

The analysis extent can be set to the following:

Same as Display—Sets the extent of output rasters to the current display extent. When working with really large data sets, numerous rasters, or complicated functions, you may want to set the extent to a small portion of the full extent so that processing is faster. First, zoom into a small portion of the overall extent, and then set the extent to *Same as Display*. Create your test rasters, and after you confirm that the output raster has worked as expected using the trial extent, reset the extent and rerun the analysis.

Union of Inputs—Sets the extent of output rasters to the union of all input layer extents.

Intersection of Inputs—Sets the extent of output rasters to the intersection of all input layer extents.

As Specified Below—Sets the extent by entering geographical coordinates for the top, bottom, left, and right of the extent.

Same As <layer>—Sets the extent to the extent of the selected layer. This is frequently used to create rasters that cover the same extent as some existing layer.

7.3.2 Cell size

The *cell size* or *resolution* of the output raster can be specified using the cell size option. Cell size is the width (or height) of a cell—not the area—and is measured in map units specified by the coordinate system. The default cell size is set to the largest cell size of the inputs, the assumption reflecting that the output map is only as good as the coarsest resolution input raster. There are, however, some instances where you might want to have the cell size smaller than the maximum, or specify your own size. However, realize that no new data is created, rather, cell values are interpolated. When converting a feature dataset to raster, the default cell size is calculated to get at least 250 columns and rows.

The following options allow you to specify how the cell size of output rasters will be set:

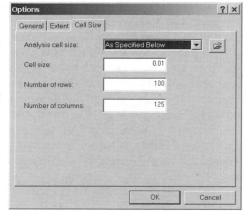

Minimum Of Inputs—Sets the cell size to the size of the smallest found in the input raster layers.

Maximum of Inputs—The largest cell size of the input raster layers.

As Specified Below—The size you input. Note that the number of rows and columns is automatically updated when you type in the cell size. You can also enter either the number of rows or columns and the cell size is automatically calculated as well.

Same As <layer>—Sets the cell size to be the same as the selected layer.

Setting the analysis environment in Spatial Analyst

1. Add the Spatial Analyst extension by selecting **Tools -> Extensions...**, then checking the Spatial Analyst box.

2. Add the Spatial Analyst toolbar by selecting **View -> Toolbars -> Spatial Analyst**.

3. From the Spatial Analyst toolbar, select **Options.**

4. Select the desired tab: General, Extent, or Cell Size.

7.4 Functions

There are five classes of functions (sometimes called *tools*) that operate on raster data, grouped by the way they handle space: *local, neighborhood* (aka *focal*), *zonal, global,* and *application-specific*.[6] Spatial Analyst provides direct interfaces to many of these functions through easy-to-use dialogs available from the Spatial Analyst toolbar. Many other functions are available through the Raster Calculator, which is discussed at length below.

7.4.1 Local functions

Local functions calculate output GRID values based on the values from multiple rasters at the same location. That is, the output value for each cell is a function of the values of one or more input rasters *at that same location* only. The values of neighboring cells do not have any influence on the output value. You can visualize local functions by thinking of a shish kabob: spear your stack of rasters with a skewer and then perform a function on the pierced cells (and repeat on all cells). A NoData value is returned in the output raster for any cell that has a NoData value in any input raster.

7.4.1.1 Cell statistics

There are five types of local functions that handle the values at a single location in different ways. First, often some statistic is needed that is calculated from a number of input rasters. For example, the 10-year average (mean) precipitation could be computed on a stack of rasters depicting precipitation from 1990 to 2000. A variety of *cell statistics* can be computed on two or more raster layers.[7] The statistics available are: majority, maximum, mean, median, minimum, minority, range, standard deviation, sum, and variety (see Table 7.2).

---

6. Berry, J.K. 1987. Fundamental operations in computer-assisted map analysis. *International Journal of Geographical Information Systems* 1(2):119-136. Actually, the first paper that characterized cartographic modeling was: Tomlin, C.D. and J.K. Berry. 1979. A mathematical structure for cartographic modeling and analysis. *Proceedings of the 39th Symposium*, American Congress on Surveying and Mapping, Falls Church, Virginia, 269-283.
7. Up to 48 input GRIDs.

Computing cell statistics
ArcToolbox -> Spatial Analyst Tools -> Local -> **Cell Statistics**.
- OR -
1. From the Spatial Analyst toolbar, select **Cell Statistics.**
2. Select the desired layers and add them to the Input Rasters list. Click on the Folder button to open a GRID that is not in the Layers list.
3. Select the type of statistic from the drop-down list.
4. Set the location of the output raster.

TABLE 7.2. Cell statistics available with examples of returned values for a stack of rasters at one location, with values: 3, 4, 2, 2, 3, 2, and 4.

Statistic	Returned value	Comments
Majority	2	Value that appears most often, tie results in NoData value
Maximum	4	Maximum value
Mean	2.857	Always returns a floating-point GRID
Median	3	
Minimum	2	
Minority	NoData	Value that occurs least often, tie results in NoData
Range	2	Maximum - minimum
Standard deviation	0.899	Always returns a floating-point GRID
Sum	20	
Variety	3	

Second, the values at a single location can be combined to find unique combinations of values. The *Combine* function combines two or more raster layers on a cell-by-cell basis. For example, if you wanted to "overlay" a raster representing soil types and a raster representing vegetation types to explore the relationship between soils and vegetation. Unique combinations of the input values are given a unique index value, which is assigned to the cells of the output layer. The original value of the input raster dataset is added to the attribute table, one field per input layer (Figure 7.2).

Combining rasters
ArcToolbox -> Spatial Analyst Tools -> Local -> **Combine**.

FIGURE 7.2. Example of combine function, illustrating *Combine ([G1], [G2])*. **Combining G1 (left) with G2 (left center) creates a new raster (right center) with values indexing unique combinations of G1 and G2. The attribute table (right) has fields with original values of G1 and G2 (download color figures from <u>www.consplan.com</u>).**

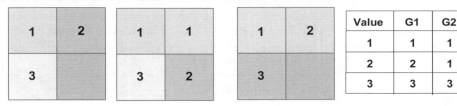

Third, the values at a single location in a stack of rasters can be compared to a specified criteria and the number of occurrences that the condition is met can be sent to an output raster. For example, imagine that you had twelve rasters each representing the monthly precipitation amount for a given year, and you wanted to determine the number of months that exceeded 100 mm of precipitation. There are three tools that can be used that examine the number of times the value is less than, equal to, or greater than the conditional value.

Counting the occurrences that a location meets a condition
ArcToolbox -> Spatial Analyst Tools -> Local -> **Equal to Frequency**.
ArcToolbox -> Spatial Analyst Tools -> Local -> **Greater Than Frequency**.
ArcToolbox -> Spatial Analyst Tools -> Local -> **Less Than Frequency**.

Fourth, the values at a single location can be examined to see which meets a specified criteria, and then the value that meets the criteria can be assigned to the output raster (rather than the number of occurrences). There are two tools that do this. The *Popularity* tool determines from the list of values at a location the value that is the nth most popular (where n is an integer that specifies the condition/place). The *Rank* tool orders the list of values from smallest to largest and assigns the value to the output raster that is in the nth place.

Getting the value that meets a condition

ArcToolbox -> Spatial Analyst Tools -> Local -> **Popularity**.

ArcToolbox -> Spatial Analyst Tools -> Local -> **Rank**.

Fifth, the values at a single location can be examined to see which meets a specified criteria, and then the position (of the raster in the list of rasters) that meets the criteria can be assigned to the output raster (rather than the number of occurrences or the value). The *Highest Position* tool assigns the value in the output raster to be the position of raster that contains the maximum value for the input rasters, while the Lowest Position tool assigns the position of raster that contains the minimum value for the input rasters.

Getting the position that meets a condition

ArcToolbox -> Spatial Analyst Tools -> Local -> **Highest Position**.

ArcToolbox -> Spatial Analyst Tools -> Local -> **Lowest Position**.

7.4.1.2 Reclassification

Although individual input values can be grouped so that they display with similar symbols, there is often the need to create new values to reflect new groupings. The *reclassification* function allows cell values from an input raster to be replaced with new values. Often, reclassification is done to group a number of values into a few categories or classes (e.g., slopes that range from 0 - 5%=1, 5 - 10%=2, 10 - 20%=3, and 20 - 45%=4). Occasionally it is used to reassign classes on single values based on new information or a different set of assumptions (e.g., 1=2, 2=2, 3=3, 4=5) or to isolate the locations of a particular value (or range of values). Note that often reclassing data changes the data type. For example, reclassing slope

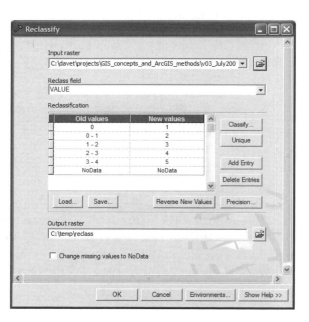

values (ratio data) into categories (1 to 4) results in ordinal data. The input raster to the reclass function can be both real and integer rasters, but it returns only an integer raster. If the first raster in the table of contents is a single-valued raster, then a warning message may occur when bringing up the Reclassify dialog

To reclass a raster, use the *Reclassify* interface. A NoData value can be output by typing in "NoData" instead of a numerical value, or all input values that are not expressly listed in the dialog (the missing values) can be changed to NoData. Output classes can be specified by classifying the data (similar to classifying a legend) or by loading in a predefined reclass (a.k.a. *remap*) table that is stored as an INFO table. Note that because the option to change missing values to NoData is *not* saved in a reclass table, it is recommended to explicitly assign NoData values to the "missing values" rather than to rely on checking the NoData box.

Reclassifying a raster

ArcToolbox -> Spatial Analyst Tools -> Reclass -> **Reclassify**

- OR -

1. From the Spatial Analyst toolbar, select **Reclassify...**.

2. Specify the Input raster from the drop-down list.

3. Specify the reclass field from the second drop down list.

4. Set the desired "old values" through using the Unique button (if nominal data), through the Classify button (if quantitative data), or by clicking on the values and entering the desired values (must be in the form of "x - x", with a space, hyphen, space). Multiple entries can be selected (using shift-select) and deleted.

5. Save the remap table for documentation and later use.

6. Specify output raster name and location.

7. Click **OK**.

Although the same concept of reclassifying data applies to feature-based datasets, there is not a straightforward reclassification method for feature datasets. One way to reclassify feature attribute data is to use a combination of queries to get a desired selected set (e.g., all Lucodes value between 40 and 49) and then calculate the reclassed value in a new field (e.g., [Newlucode] = 4). Another method that works when reclassing nominal data is to create a summary table by summarizing on a field (e.g., [Lucode]). Then, add a reclass field onto the summary table and calculate the new values, then join the summary table back to the attribute table.

7.4.1.3 Math, conditional, and overlay

A whole range of mathematical, conditional, and overlay functions are provided as tools in Spatial Analyst. This includes standard math functions such as multiplication and division, but also trigonometric, logical, and bitwise operations. A comprehensive list of these is provided in Table 7.4. Note that for most situations where a mathematical formula is required it is easier to use the Raster Calculator and/or Map Algebra tools (described below).

Mathematical functions on a raster
ArcToolbox -> Spatial Analyst Tools -> Math -> **tool.**

7.4.2 Neighborhood functions

Neighborhood (or *focal*) functions create an output raster that is a function of the input value at a location *and* the values in the cells surrounding a location, specified by a *neighborhood*. Neighborhood functions "pass" the same size and shaped neighborhood over the entire raster. That is, they move the neighborhood window over whole raster, visiting each cell. They are often used to smooth or filter a raster by using the neighborhood values, or to compute the local variety of different land cover types, for instance. Note that the size of the neighborhood is typically defined to correspond to the functional aspect of interest. For instance, if a mammal has a one-hectare home range, then often habitat is averaged using a one-hectare neighborhood.

There are two ways that these neighborhoods are moved across a raster. Typically, a *focal neighborhood* operator places a *neighborhood* with respect to the *processing cell*, computes the new value and assigns it to the output GRID at the location of the processing cell, then slides the neighborhood over one cell (and continue down to the next row after all cells in that row are completed). That is, the focal operation is computed for each and every cell in the input raster. As the neighborhood is moved across the raster, the neighborhoods *overlap*. The number of neighborhoods N_f in a focal placement is:

$$N_f = C$$

where C is the number of cells in a GRID.

In contrast to focal neighborhood movement, *block neighborhood* movement moves the neighborhood across in a non-overlapping fashion. That is, block operators place a neighborhood with respect to the processing cell, compute the new value and assign it to *all* cells in the output raster that fall underneath the neighborhood's minimum bounding rectangle, and then the neighborhood is lifted up and placed adjacent to the previous neighborhood (so the neighborhoods do not overlap). The resulting raster typically has the same number of cells as the original. The difference between the focal and block placement methods is relatively small when the window or neighborhood is small (e.g., 3x3) but grows larger when bigger neighborhoods are used (e.g., >10x10).

The number of neighborhoods N_b in a block operation is:

$$N_b = C/B$$

where B is the number of cells in a block neighborhood.

7.4.2.1 Neighborhood shape

There are five *neighborhood shapes* available: rectangle, circle, annulus, wedge, and irregular (this last option is available only through the Raster Calculator).

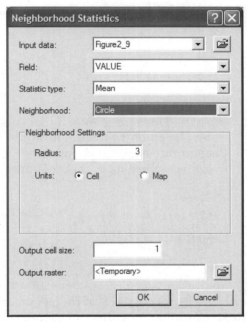

Rectangle—The most common neighborhood shape is the rectangle (usually a square, e.g., 3x3). To simulate the four adjacent neighbors (rook's or von Neumann's case) use width and height values of 2. To get the eight adjacent and diagonal neighbors (queen's or Moore's case), use width and height values of 3. The *x, y* location of the *processing cell* (sometimes called the *focal cell*)—where the resultant value will be placed—is computed with respect to the upper-left corner of the neighborhood, by:

$$x = (w+1)/2$$

$$y = (h+1)/2$$

where w is the width and h is the height of the rectangle. If w or h is even, then the location is computed by truncation.

Circle—The size of the circle is specified by a radius value. Any cell whose center is within the radius value will be processed. (See Table 7.3 for a listing of the number of cells in the neighborhood of a given radius).

Annulus—You can specify a neighborhood such that cells immediately adjacent to the processing cell are not included, but cells slightly further away are included in the neighborhood. The inner radius specifies the area where cells will not be processed, while all cells that fall between the inner and outer radius will be processed. (This is also known as a "doughnut" neighborhood.)

Wedge—The wedge neighborhood allows you to specify a neighborhood that has a directional component. The start and end angle are specified in degrees (integer or floating point values) running from 0 to 360.

Irregular—The irregular neighborhood allows you to specify a neighborhood through a simple text file (called a *kernel*, a space-delimited file that depicts the cells that will be considered in the neighborhood. For example, only the diagonal cells are specified in the kernel below. Note that the first line indicates the number of columns and rows in the kernel file.

3 3

1 0 1

0 0 0

1 0 1

Weight—This also allows an irregular neighborhood, but you can also specify a weight to be placed on the value at a given location in a neighborhood. This allows many image-processing functions to be computed. For example, only the diagonal cells are weighted according to their distance in the kernel below.

3 3

0.71 1.0 0.71

1.0 0 1.0

0.71 1.0 0.71

Computation time of focal operators typically increases rapidly (roughly exponentially) with the increasing size of the neighborhood. The length of processing time is dependent on the number of cells in the neighborhood, not the shape (or complexity) of the neighborhood.

TABLE 7.3. **The number of cells in a circular neighborhood.**

Radius (cells)	Area (# of cells)	Area (true circle)	Error
1	5	3.14	159.2%
2	13	12.5	103.5%
3	29	28.27	102.6%

GIS Concepts and ArcGIS Methods

TABLE 7.3. The number of cells in a circular neighborhood.

Radius (cells)	Area (# of cells)	Area (true circle)	Error
4	49	50.26	97.5%
5	81	78.53	103.1%
6	113	113.09	99.9%
7	149	153.93	96.8%
8	197	201.05	98.0%
9	253	254.46	99.4%
10	317	314.15	100.9%
15	709	706.83	100.3%
20	1257	1256.60	100.0%
30	2821	2827.35	99.8%
40	5025	5026.40	100.0%
50	7845	7853.75	99.9%

7.4.2.2 Neighborhood statistics

Computing *neighborhood statistics* can be accomplished similar to Cell Statistics, through a dialog interface provided by Spatial Analyst. The following statistics can be computed for an annulus, circle, rectangular, or wedge neighborhood: majority, maximum, mean, median, minimum, minority, range, standard deviation, sum, and variety. This interface uses the focal (not block) method of moving the neighborhood across the input layer. Note that neighborhood statistics can be computed using a point layer as an input as well (only selected points are used). To compute density surfaces based on a specific number of points or for linear features, see the discussion on calculating density surfaces in the section on global functions.

Computing neighborhood statistics
ArcToolbox -> Spatial Analyst Tools -> Neighborhood -> **Block Statistics**
ArcToolbox -> Spatial Analyst Tools -> Neighborhood -> **Focal Statistics**
- OR -
1. From the Spatial Analyst toolbar, select **Neighborhood Statistics.**
2. Select the desired layer.
3. Select the field that contains the values.
4. Select the type of statistic from the statistics drop-down list.
5. Select the neighborhood type and settings.
6. Change the default output cell size, if desired.
7. Specify the location of the output raster.

7.4.2.3 Filters

Occasionally a neighborhood analysis is conducted to improve the quality of raster data by smoothing out or filtering spurious data, or perhaps by enhancing certain aspects of an image. These types of neighborhood analysis are called *filters*. A *low pass filter* smooths data and reduces local variation by computing the mean value of a 3 x 3 neighborhood (aka a *kernel*), by multiplying the following weights times the input raster values, then finding the weighted average:

1 1 1

1 1 1

1 1 1

A *high pass filter* accentuates the difference in values among neighbors. This is useful to sharpen edges between objects (it is often called an edge enhancement filter) such as between a road and its surroundings. This filter also uses a 3 x 3 weighted neighborhood:

-0.7 -1.0 -0.7

-1.0 6.8 -1.0

-0.7 -1.0 -0.7

Filtering a raster
ArcToolbox -> Spatial Analyst Tools -> Neighborhood -> **Filter**

7.4.2.4 Point and line statistics

The point and line statistics functions use a neighborhood, but rather than using a raster as input, they are applied to point and line features (vector data model). Unlike first converting the features to a raster, and then applying the *Focal Statistics* tool, the *Point Statistics* tool is applied directly to the points so that all points are used, and are not "lost" when two or more points fall within the same cell. Also, this tool is similar to computing the *kernel density*, but points are simply in or our of the neighborhood and are not weighted by distance from the center of the neighborhood. The *Line Statistics* tool is applied directly to polyline features.

Computing point and line statistics

ArcToolbox -> Spatial Analyst Tools -> Neighborhood -> **Line Statistics**
ArcToolbox -> Spatial Analyst Tools -> Neighborhood -> **Point Statistics**

7.4.3 Zonal functions

Recall that in the raster model, a *zone* represents a feature that is relatively homogenous, such as a vegetation patch or a political administrative unit like a state or district. A zone is composed of one or more cells that have the same (integer) value, and these cells are often contiguous but can also be disconnected or non-adjacent. A *region* is also composed of one or more cells that have the same value, but the cells must be contiguous. Thus, a zone can be composed of one or more regions. Zones represent areal features in a raster. For example, the cells that represent each of the 50 United States would have a separate value, and the raster attribute table would contain 50 records, one for each state.

A *zonal* function produces an output grid where the value of each cell depends on the value of the input raster at that location and the association of that value with other cells of the same value across the input raster. The number of zones equals the number of classes, not the number of regions. Even if more than one region has the same value, the number of zones remains equal to the number of unique values. Cells that are in the same zone often are adjacent to one another, but can be at any, often disjoint, location in the raster. The layer that defines the zones is called the zone layer and can be either an integer raster or a feature theme. Usually a zonal function will use the *zone* layer to specify the cells from the *value* layer to use when calculating a statistic.

7.4.3.1 Region group

How does one create a raster of unique zones? The *region group* function assigns a unique value to a group of contiguous cells that have the same value. Recall that a region differs from a zone in that a *region* is a group of contiguous cells, while a *zone* can be composed of disconnected cells. For example, to find the regions (patches) of a classified vegetation image, the *region group* tool would be used.

However, there are a couple of different ways to define contiguity with neighboring cells. A common method is to use only the four orthogonal neighbors (a.k.a. rook's or Von Neumann's case). Another method is to use both the four orthogonal and four diagonal neighbors (a.k.a. queen's or king's or Moore's case) are considered. The *excludedValue* specifies the value to be used that breaks connectivity in a region.

7.4.3.2 Zonal statistics

One of the main uses of zonal functions is to compute a summary statistic for each zone in the *zone* layer using the cell values from the *value* layer. Only an integer raster can be input as a *zone* layer. The output of this function is a table containing all of the summary statistics. For *value* rasters of integer type, you can compute the area, minimum, maximum, range, mean, standard deviation, sum, variety, majority, minority, and median value. For *value* rasters of floating-point type, you can compute area, minimum, maximum, range, mean, standard deviation, and sum.

For example, zonal statistics can be used to determine which state is the "highest" in the US. This can be computed by using the *Zonal Statistics* interface provided by the Spatial Analyst. Note that the zone dataset can be either a feature or raster layer. Colorado turns out to be the highest state in the nation, averaging 2,094 m. Wyoming is the second highest (1,957 m) and Utah is third (1,843 m).

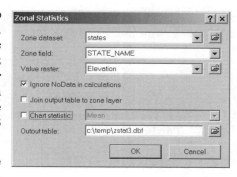

The standard use of this tool is to assign the resulting statistic value to the output raster. In addition, you can generate a table that provides a summary of all statistical values for each zone using the *Zonal Statistics as Table* tool. This table can then be joined back to the zonal features if needed.

Computing zonal statistics

ArcToolbox -> Spatial Analyst Tools -> Zonal -> **Zonal Statistics.**

- OR -

1. From the Spatial Analyst toolbar, select **Zonal Statistics....**

2. Set the Zone Dataset to the layer that defines the zones to be summarized.

3. Select the zone field.

4. Set the Value raster to be the raster's values that will be summarized.

5. Check the options if you wish to ignore NoData, to join the summary output table to the Zone Dataset, or to create a chart.

6. Set the Output table name and click OK.

7.4.3.3 Zonal geometry

The *Zonal Geometry* tool can be used to compute the area, perimeter, thickness, or centroid of each zone input. The value returned for the area is computed as the number of cells in a zone times the cell size and is in map units. The perimeter is computed as the sum of the lengths of the boundaries of each connected region in a zone (both external and internal boundaries are counted). The units are in map units. The *thickness* is the distance of the deepest point within a zone. This is computed by finding the radius of the largest circle that can be fit within a region. Similar to zonal statistics, you can also compute a table that summarizes the geometry for each zone using the *Zonal Geometry as Table* tool.

Computing zonal geometry
ArcToolbox -> Spatial Analyst Tools -> Zonal -> **Zonal Geometry.**
ArcToolbox -> Spatial Analyst Tools -> Zonal -> **Zonal Geometry as Table.**

7.4.4 Global functions

Global functions manipulate values on an entire raster all at once. There is a wide variety of types of global functions, but the most commonly-used ones help to analyze distance, density, interpolation, hydrology, and generalization (which are discussed in detail below). A few additional sets of tools provide operations to analyze groundwater, multi-variate imagery, raster creation, and solar radiation.

7.4.4.1 Distance

Distance is a fundamental factor in controlling the spatial relationships between different geographic features. Indeed, the *First Law of Geography* states that "Everything is related to everything else, but near things are more related than distant things."[8] Because of the importance of distance in GIS, there are a number of ways to calculate distance on raster data, and Spatial Analyst provides interfaces to four of the most common methods: straight line, allocation, cost weighted, and shortest path.

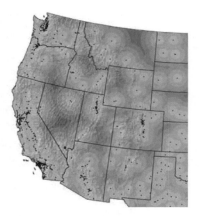

Straight-line distance (a.k.a Euclidean or "as the crow flies") measures the distance, D_e, from a location to the nearest feature of interest. Distance is measured from the center of each cell to the center of the nearest cell representing some feature of interest, and uses the Pythagorean theorem to compute the Euclidean distance. Distance from features is typically used when conducting a suitability analysis. For example, the distance from cities (yellow to red) could be used as an indicator of the relative *remoteness* in the western US. So, to "get away from it all," one might be inclined to find those red areas (see right) that are furthest away from cities (and so much

---

8. Tobler, W.R. 1970. A computer model of simulating urban growth in the Detroit region. *Economic Geography* 46: 234-240.

of Nevada is fairly remote). Note that the output raster is a surface of real-valued distances.

Related to straight-line distance is the notion of the Euclidean *direction* GRID, which provides the compass direction pointing back to the nearest feature of interest. This directional information might be useful when one wants to return from the isolated areas. Also note that in addition to finding the distance from features of interest, the particular feature that is closest can be identified for each location in a cell, which is known as *allocation*. This function is often used to locate the "service area" of a store, for example. The tesselations created by allocation zones can also be converted into polygons that are called *proximity regions*, area of influence polygons, or *Thiessen* or *Voronoi* polygons (Figure 7.3). These allocation polygons have been used in a wide variety of applications, from determining mathematical surfaces to interpolating precipitation averages.[9] Spatial Analyst provides interfaces to compute distance, direction, and allocation rasters.

FIGURE 7.3. The author succumbing to a Thiessen polygon in Death Valley, California (note old ArcINFO t-shirt!).

---

9. Thiessen, A.H. 1911. Precipitation averages for large areas. *Monthly Weather Review* 39: 1082-1084.

Calculating straight-line distance

ArcToolbox -> Spatial Analyst Tools -> Distance -> **Euclidean Distance.**

- OR -

1. From the Spatial Analyst toolbar, select **Distance -> Straight line...**.

2. Select the layer to compute the distance from. This is typically a point or line feature layer (selected features are used). If you input a raster layer, distance is computed from *all* valued (but not NoData) cells.

3. Input a maximum distance (if desired) in map units. Cells beyond this distance will be given the NoData value.

4. Set the output cell size.

5. Check the Create direction and/or Create allocation options if you wish.

6. Specify the Output raster name.

7. Click **OK**.[a]

---

a. Note: a common reason for the "Error in opening or reading VAT" is that the input layer (e.g., representing point or linear features) is not in the same projection as the data frame's coordinate system—try projecting the feature layer to the same coordinate system.

Calculating allocation zones

ArcToolbox -> Spatial Analyst Tools -> Distance -> **Euclidean Allocation.**

- OR -

1. From the Spatial Analyst toolbar, select **Distance -> Allocation...**.

2. Select the layer to compute the allocation zones around (selected features are used).

3. Set the output cell size.

5. Specify the Output raster name.

6. Click **OK**.

GIS Concepts and ArcGIS Methods

A second approach to computing distance is to recognize that there may be geographic conditions that affect how far a particular location is from another, from a functional perspective. Restating the First Law of Geography slightly: some equidistant things are closer than others. That is, it is likely that some equidistant locations may take longer to get to than others. This is often the case when one thinks about how "far" away a location is in terms of the time it takes to get there rather than straight-line distance. Returning to the *remoteness* example, some remote locations in wilderness areas take much longer to access, and remoteness changes dramatically by the mode of travel (e.g., driving or walking). For example, the speed with which one can hike depends largely on the steepness of a road or trail. One estimation of the relationship between a hiker's velocity in km/hr (*V*) and slope in degrees (*S*) is:

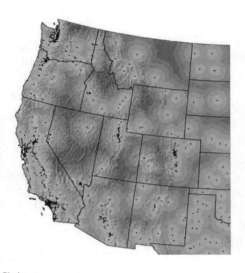

$$V = 6e^{\angle 3.5 \times abs(\tan(S/57.29578) + 0.05)}$$

so that on flat terrain a typical hiker averages 5.04 km/hr.[10] So, how can we reflect these geographic conditions when computing distance?

Cost weighted distance incorporates such factors that influence movement across a surface. Cost weighted distance computes distance in terms of cost units and accumulates these units at locations away from features of interest. For example, because mountainous areas are more difficult to access, our measure of remoteness should reflect this and hence some of the interior ranges of the west have a higher level of remoteness. To compute cost weighted distance, two input rasters are needed: the *source* raster that defines the features of interest (all non-NoData values); and the *cost* raster that contains the cost (or impedance) to travel across a location, for all cells. In the hiker example, the source raster would mark the trailhead location, while the cost raster would specify the cost based on some function (like the one above) of slope.

The cost weighted distance algorithm utilizes graph theory by placing a node at the center of each cell connected by a link to each of the eight neighboring cells. The accumulative cost of a link (*a*) is computed by averaging the costs of two adjacent cells (c_1 and c_2):

10. From Tobler, W. 1993. *Three presentations on geographical analysis and modeling.* Technical report 93-1, National Center for Geographic Information and Analysis, University of California, Santa Barbara; based on empirical values estimated by Imhof, E. 1950. *Gelaende und Karte*, Rentsch, Zurich.

$a = (c_1 + c_2)/2$ (for orthogonal links) and $a = (\sqrt{2(c_1 + c_2)})/2$ (for diagonal links)

Using an iterative process, the averaged cost is accumulated in steps away from the source cells (see Figure 7.4). This results in the cost distance D_c being computed by:

$$D_c = D_e a$$

Note that cost weighted distance is equivalent to straight-line distance if all cells in the cost raster equal 1. Also, allocation and direction rasters can be created that reflect the cost weighted surface.

FIGURE 7.4. An example of computing one-way travel time from trailheads to all locations within Yosemite National Park, California. Accessibility computed here reflects trail slope[11] and is weighted by off-trail slopes (download color figures from www.consplan.com).

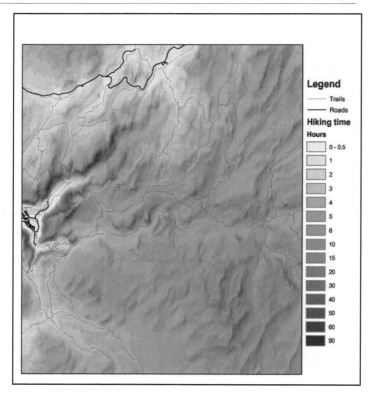

11. Computed using data from van Wagtendonk, J. W., and J. M. Benedict. 1980. Travel time variation on back-country trails. *Journal of Leisure Research* 12(2): 99-109

Calculating cost weighted distance

ArcToolbox -> Spatial Analyst Tools -> Distance -> **Cost Distance.**

- OR -

1. From the Spatial Analyst toolbar, select **Distance -> Cost weighted...**.

2. Select the layer to compute the distance from. This is typically a point or line feature layer (selected features are used). If you input a raster layer, distance is computed from *all* valued (non-NoData) cells.

3. Select the cost raster.

4. Input a maximum distance (if desired) in map units. Cells beyond this distance will be given the NoData value.

5. Set the output cell size.

5. Check the Create direction and/or Create allocation options if you wish.

6. Specify the Output raster name.

7. Click **OK**.

Computing shortest paths

ArcToolbox -> Spatial Analyst Tools -> Distance -> **Cost Path.**

- OR -

1. From the Spatial Analyst toolbar, select **Distance -> Shortest path...**.

2. Set the Path to: layer that specifies the source location(s).

3. Select Cost distance raster: to the desired cost-weight raster.

4. Select the Cost direction raster.

5. Select the path type.

6. Specify the Output raster name.

7. Click **OK**.

The *shortest path function* is used to find the least-cost path or route that is guaranteed to be the cheapest cost to travel between two locations. The shortest path is often used to help plan new construction, to identify where to locate a new road or trail, for example. To compute the shortest path in Spatial Analyst, first cost-distance and cost-direction rasters (using the cost weighted distance method) must be created. The *destination layer* specifies a source, or set of sources, from which a path will be found to a destination. There are three possible *path types* to control the number of paths created. *For Each Cell* finds a path to each cell in each zone defined in the destination layer. *For Each Zone* finds the one least-cost path from the destination to each zone. *Best Single* finds the shortest or least-cost path for all zones. The output for the shortest path function is a feature dataset (line type).

Another distance tool that incorporates a few more factors that influence distance measurements is called *path distance*, which is computed by:

$$D_p = D_s ahv$$

- D_s, surface distance between cells in map units that adjusts distance as a function of ground slope;
- a, cost associated with friction or impediments;
- h, cost adjustment that incorporates horizontal factors relative to the direction of travel (e.g., wind direction);
- v, cost adjustment related to vertical factors relative to the direction of travel to incorporate uphill or downhill travel.

Let's use the example of understanding hiking time to understand path distance. The friction factor a would most likely account for the vegetation types that would modify the relative ease or difficulty of hiking. We could assume that a dirt road or trail has been cleared of (most) impediments so that $a=1.0$. Hiking off-trail is more challenging, depending largely on the vegetation types, so that cells or locations that are dominated by grass $a=1.1$, for shrubland $a=1.5$, and for dense forest with some fallen trees $a=2.0$.[12] Next, a horizontal factor such as wind direction might influence hiking speed. That is, imagine in that the study area is dominated by strong winds from the west such that hiking into the wind (westward) causes one to slow down by 50%, so that $h=2.0$. In contrast, hiking to the east means a wonderful wind at your back and so $h=0.8$, while $h=1.0$ during hiking northward or southward. Finally, as was discussed earlier, hiking is more challenging depending on slope, so steeper slopes cause a slowing in travel velocity. Unlike the way that cost weights reflected difficulty of travel related to slope in the cost distance tool, with the path distance tool slope can be computed relative to the direction of travel. So, hiking *up* a 5% grade might have a $v=2.0$, but $v=0.8$ when hiking *down* a 5% grade (one would likely assume that $v=1.0$ for horizontal surface). Note also that the cost factor a can reflect

---

12. How does one determine these weighting coefficients? Good question! So far, there is very little empirical data to base this on. In the meantime, using a pairwise comparison method such as the Analytic Hierarchy Process helps to provide some rigor and a measure of "internal consistency". See: Saaty, T.L. 1980. *The Analytic Hierarchy Process*. McGraw Hill, NY, NY.

---

a number of factors, such as overall elevation (higher elevations have less oxygen in the atmosphere so hiking velocity would slow) in addition to friction due to vegetation type.

Calculating path distance

ArcToolbox -> Spatial Analyst Tools -> Distance -> **Path Distance.**

7.4.4.2 Density

Typically, continuous *density surfaces* are created to "smooth" or spread out counts located at points so that concentrations or "hot spots" can be more readily identified. An underlying assumption is that the process or geographic phenomena being mapped is continuous in nature. For example, a density surface representing population is often used to visualize where urban concentrations are located. Density surfaces can be created from both point and line layers. Essentially, density for each raster cell is computed by determining the features (e.g., cities) within a given neighborhood (typically defined by a circle), summing the value of interest (e.g., population in 2000) for those features, and then computing the average number of occurrences per square unit area (e.g., square miles).

There are two density methods: simple and kernel. The *simple density* method calculates density by summing the values of a *population field* for all features found within the search radius or neighborhood, and then dividing by the neighborhood area. The density values can be expressed in a variety of units (roughly from largest to smallest): mi^2, km^2, acres, hectares, yds^2, ft^2, in^2, m^2, cm^2, and mm^2. Note that using larger areal units will result in smaller density values, and that because the values are specific to the areal units used, it is best to include the units in the raster name to explicitly record the units of the raster values.[13] The *kernel density* method calculates density similarly to the *simple* method, but a smoothly curved surface (based on a quadratic kernel function) is fit through each sample point, resulting in a smoother output.[14] The value is weighted highest at the center and diminishes with increasing distance from the center. The search radius (in map distance units) determines the distance to search for points from each cell in the output raster layer. The default radius equals 1/30 of either the width or height of the extent, whichever is smaller. However, it is best to provide a radius that corresponds

---

13. Unfortunately there is no way to record the units that the raster value represents. However, units could be stored in the raster's metadata in the *entity attribute* section.
14. The kernel function is described in: Silverman, B.W. 1986. *Density Estimation for Statistics and Data Analysis.* New York: Chapman and Hall. (p. 76, equation 4.5).

---

to the spatial scale of the process or phenomenon under study. Larger radii smooth or average the values, while smaller radii result in "peakier" surfaces.

Calculating a density surface

ArcToolbox -> Spatial Analyst Tools -> Distance -> **Kernel Density.**

ArcToolbox -> Spatial Analyst Tools -> Distance -> **Point Density.**

- OR -

1. From the Spatial Analyst toolbar, select **Density...**.

2. Select the input feature layer (typically a point feature, but it can also be a line feature type).

3. Select the "population" field (should represent counts).

4. Select the density type, either Simple or Kernel.

5. Specify the search radius (in map units).

6. Set the area units of the output raster.

7. Specify the cell size.

8. Specify the output raster filename and location.

9. Click **OK**.

Often a map showing the density of linear features, such as *road density* or *stream density*, is needed. For example, a number of studies have found that in the Great Lakes region of the US (Wisconsin and Minnesota), wolves (*Canis lupus*) do not persist in areas with road densities greater than about 0.5 km/km². Some of these studies, however, have computed road density by summing the total length of roads in each county, then dividing by the area of each county.[15] If the distribution of roads is heterogeneous within a county (e.g., many roads near a city, few in the

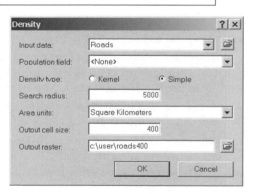

countryside), then the average road density in a county may be misleading. Ideally, road density is computed using a focal operator because the analytical unit (the area that is used to compute the denominator of the density) can be controlled by specifying the neighborhood size so that it is meaningful to the process or organism under study. This

---

15. Mech, L.D. 1989. Wolf population survival in an area of high road density. *American Midland Naturalist* 121:387-389. Thiel, R.P. 1985. Relationship between road densities and wolf habitat suitability in Wisconsin. *American Midland Naturalist* 113:404-407.

type of computation can be accomplished using the *Density* interface in Spatial Analyst (the *linestats* function can also be used in Map Algebra).

Computing road density

ArcToolbox -> Spatial Analyst Tools -> Distance -> **Line Density.**

- OR -

1. From the Spatial Analyst toolbar, select **Density...**.
2. Set the Input Data to the line layer with roads.
3. Leave the population field as <none>.
4. Set the Density type to be Simple.
5. Set the search radius (the circle radius).
6. Set the Output cell size.
7. Set the name of the output GRID.
8. Click **OK**.

7.4.4.3 Surface analysis

We have long examined the intricacies of Earth's surface to understand topographic relief and variation and how these influence other geographic phenomena. Powerful GIS methods have been developed to manipulate and analyze elevation data that represent surfaces through digital terrain models (DTMs) or digital elevation models (DEMs).

DEMs represent surfaces by "posting" an elevation at equal-spaced locations, usually at the center of every GRID cell. A wide variety of data sources for DEMs are available. For instance, the US National Imagery and Mapping Agency developed the Digital Terrain Elevation Data (DTED), a 30 arc-second resolution (Level 0).[16] GTOPO30 provides global coverage at 30 arc second (roughly 1 km) resolution and is composed of a variety of different sources, including DTED and US Geological Survey (USGS) DEMs. If the source of the 1 km data was finer resolution (e.g., 90 m), then instead of using the average or the center cell, the average of the dominant geomorphic feature (ridge or valley) was used.[17] In the United States, the USGS provides DEMs at varying scales: 7.5' (~10 m and ~30 m) and 1° (3 arc-second: ~90 m).[18] At the fine resolution, a number of methods have been used to create DEMs from aerial photographs, including an automated photogrammetric system known as the Gestalt Photo Mapper II that estimated elevations in "patches," manual profiling using photogrammetric stereomodels that recorded postings along successive

---

16. DTED is available from: http://www.fas.org/irp/program/core/dted.htm.
17. US Geological Survey, 1996. GTOPO30 documentation. http://edcdaac.usgs.gov/gtopo30/README.html.
18. USGS DEMs: http://edc.usgs.gov/glis/hyper/guide/usgs_dem.

east-to-west and west-to-east terrain profiles, and interpolation of digital line graph (DLG) hypsographic (i.e. contour lines) and hydrographic lines. The USGS found the last method produces the most accurate DEMs and is their preferred method for production. More recently the USGS has embarked on the National Elevation Dataset (NED), which is a seamless, edge-matched dataset that provides standardized and pre-processed DEMs for large expanses (i.e. broader than a single quadsheet).[19] Most recently, a joint effort between the National Imagery and Mapping Agency and the National Aeronautics and Space Administration has produced the Shuttle Radar Topography Mission (SRTM), whose goal is to map 80% of the world at 1 arc-second (~30 m) resolution using radar interferometry.[20] Also, surfaces are commonly represented using as a series of postings from LIDAR (Light Detection and Ranging) methods or as Triangular Irregular Networks as well.[21]

There are two types of errors found in DEMS: systematic and random. Systematic errors are relatively common in the "older" DEMs. These are usually visible as "seams," such as abrupt changes or *slivers* of missing data at map sheet boundaries (e.g., at the border of two quad sheets,) or *stripes* introduced by the method used to produce the DEM. Random errors are very difficult to spot visually in a DEM, but they rear their ugly heads when using DEM's particular surface analyses, such as watershed basin delineation. The most common types of random errors are artificial pits and peaks.[22] *Pits* are cells that are surrounded by higher elevation values, though some of these may be natural (e.g., in a karst landscape). Artificial pits cause breaks in hydrologic drainage. *Peaks* are cells that are surrounded by cells of lower value.

The Spatial Analyst extension provides interfaces to six of the most common surface analysis methods: contours, slope, aspect, hillshade, viewshed, and cut/fill (see Figure 7.5 for examples of these at different resolutions). Also, note that *any* raster data with ratio values can be analyzed using these methods, so that surfaces representing phenomena other than elevation can be analyzed.

19. Gesch, D., M. Oimoen, S. Greenlee, C. Nelson, M. Steuck, and D. Tyler. 2002. The National Elevation Dataset. Photogrammetric Engineering & Remote Sensing 68(1), available online at: www.asprs.org/asprs/publications/pers/2002journal/january/highlight.html
20. http://srtm.usgs.gov/.
21. Kumler, M.P. 1994. An intensive comparison of triangulated irregular networks (TINs) and Digital Elevation Models (DEMs). *Cartographica* 31(2):1-99.
22. Mark, D.M. 1988. Network models in Geomorphology. In: Modeling in Geomorphologic Systems. John Wiley. Also see Mark, D.M. 1983. Automated detection of drainage networks from digital elevation models. *Proceedings of the Sixth International Symposium on Automated Cartography* 2: 288-295.

FIGURE 7.5. Examples of surface functions at different resolutions (top to bottom: 90 m, 30 m, and 10 m) for Redstone Canyon, west of Fort Collins, CO, USA. Left to right, the images show elevation (white higher), hillshade, slope (red steeper, green flatter), and aspect (north red, east yellow, south turquoise, west blue, and flat in gray) (download color figures from www.consplan.com).

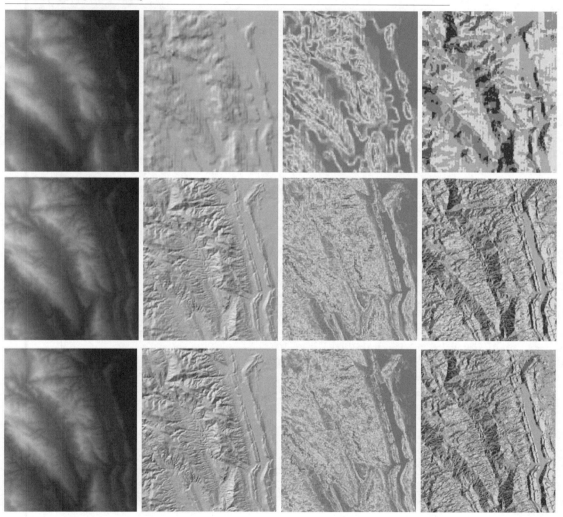

Contours represent points of equal elevation (technically, contours are for above sea level elevations, while bathymetric contours or *isobaths* are used for below-sea level). Often the term contour is used synonymously with the more general *isoline*, which connects points of equal value. Isolines not only show elevation, but they are also used to display numerous other types of data, such as isobars (pressure) and isohyets (precipitation). Spatial Analyst interpolates from a smooth surface, it does not merely connect lines to the center of cells with the same value.

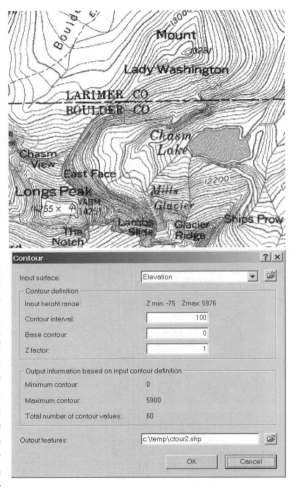

Contours have long been used to visualize topographic relief: steep hillsides are shown in contours with little space between them, while flat areas have widely spaced contours. The *base contour* establishes the lowest contour and all contours build from it. The *contour interval* defines the vertical distance between contours—the smaller the interval, the more detailed the portrayal of topography. However, if the interval is too small, then the resulting map is too messy and will be difficult to read. It might be helpful to make use of ArcMap's ability to display layers at different scales so that as one zooms in, the contour layer with smaller intervals is shown.

Contour lines can also be created interactively by using the *contour tool* ( ) on the Spatial Analyst toolbar. ArcGIS finds the contour for the value at that location for the top-most visible GRID.

Creating a contour layer

ArcToolbox -> Spatial Analyst Tools -> Distance -> **Contour.**

- OR -

1. From the Spatial Analyst toolbar, select **Surface analysis -> Contour.**...
2. Select the input raster that contains the elevation values.
3. Specify the contour interval.
4. Specify the base contour elevation.
5. Set the Z factor to convert vertical units (e.g., m to ft).
6. Enter the name of the output polyline shapefile.
7. Click **OK**.

Although contour maps remain very useful, a newer method that is used frequently to help readers visualize surfaces is the *hillshade* map. Hillshade maps represent data from an *orthographic* perspective. The *azimuth* is the angle of the light source (e.g., the sun) using 0° and 360° as north, increasing clockwise. The default value is 315° (northeast). Hillshade maps are customarily created using an azimuth that is in the north (between 0° to 90° and 270° to 360°). Because we generally read maps with north at the top and because light comes

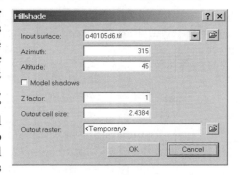

from above, we perceive ridge and canyon features correctly. If the light source was from the south (or we flipped the hillshade map 180°), we would perceive ridges to be canyons and vice versa. The altitude or *zenith* defines how high the sun is in the sky; the higher the value, the flatter the hillshade looks, and only areas with steep relief will cast shadows. In contrast, low altitude values will accentuate relief. A zenith of 45° is commonly used. Typically, hillshades are displayed using a dark to light gray color ramp so that high values have lighter colors (this is the reverse of most other graduated color legends).[23] Hillshade maps are often used as the base, with another layer draped on top and the *transparency* set so the topographic relief can be seen. Because both the direction of the sun (azimuth) and its height in the sky (zenith) need to be defined, many different hillshade GRIDs can be created for the same surface, each highlighting different aspects of

23. Schruben, P. 1999. *Color shaded relief map of the coterminous United States.* USGS Open-file Report 99-11. http://pubs.usgs.gov/openfile/of99-011/index.html

the terrain. It is also useful for analysis, for example, to determine the number of hours of direct sunlight for a particular location. There are also techniques to do simultaneous hillshading.

Two types of blemishes are common in hillshade maps. The first is a fine-scale horizontal striping caused by an defect in the process used to create many DEMs—typically by semi-automatic profiling of stereo-pairs of aerial photographs. The elevation values are recorded consecutively in an east-west direction, and, as a result, the elevation values in different E-W rows were recorded from the opposite direction. That is, the systematic sampling results in stronger autocorrelation within, as compared to between, rows. A second blemish occurs at quadsheet boundaries, where an abrupt discontinuity in elevation is noticeable. Both of these types of blemishes can be reduced by using advanced filtering methods.[24]

Creating a hillshade raster

ArcToolbox -> Spatial Analyst Tools -> Distance -> **Hillshade.**

- OR -

1. From the Spatial Analyst toolbar, select **Surface analysis -> Hillshade....**
2. Select the input raster that contains the elevation values.
3. Specify the azimuth (in degrees, north is 0, clockwise).
4. Specify the altitude (in degrees, 90 is straight overhead).
5. Check the model shadows box if make shadow cells = 0.
6. Set the Z factor to convert vertical units (e.g., m to ft).
7. Enter the output cell size.
8. Enter the name of the output raster.
9. Click **OK**.

In addition to using contours or hillshades to visualize topographic features, three-dimensional modeling can provide oblique perspectives using the *3D Analyst* extension (Figure 7.6).

---

24. For details on removing striping from DEMs, see: Russell, E. and H. Ochis. 1996. *Mitigation methods for systematic errors in USGS DEMs.* www.ctmap.com/gis_journal/filtering_wp.pdf.

FIGURE 7.6. Redstone Canyon, Colorado viewed from the southeast (looking northwest).

Slope can be derived directly from an elevation raster. Slope is the maximum rate of change at all locations on a GRID or TIN layer. Slope is calculated by fitting a plane at a location using a 3x3 window to average the maximum slope. Therefore, slope is resolution dependent.[25] If the value of one of the 3x3 cell is NoData, the center cell's elevation value is substituted in the missing cell when calculating slope. Although

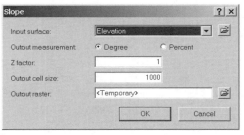

---

25. Burrough, P.A. and R.A. McDonnell, 1998. *Principles of Geographical Informational Systems*. Oxford University Press.

any raster layer can be input, calculation of slope assumes a continuous phenomenon (ratio data).

Slope is found using the *rise* (vertical distance) over *run* (horizontal distance), and is expressed in degrees ($S°$), where:

$$S° = \tan\theta = \frac{rise}{run}$$

or in percent (S'), where:

$$S' = \frac{rise}{run} \times 100 \quad.$$

When the z (elevation) units of a raster are not the same as the coordinate system (x,y) units, a *z-factor* must be used to account for the unit change. For example, if a raster is in UTM meters but elevation values are in feet, then use a z-factor of 0.3048. Note that slope (the maximum rate of change at a location) cannot be used directly for the slope of linear features, such as streams, roads, or trails, because the direction of the linear feature does not have to coincide with the direction of the steepest slope (i.e. the "fall line"). Rather, only those cells that fall on the linear feature can be used when calculating slope.

Creating a slope raster

ArcToolbox -> Spatial Analyst Tools -> Distance -> **Slope.**

- OR -

1. From the Spatial Analyst toolbar, select **Surface analysis -> Slope....**
2. Select the input GRID that contains the elevation values.
3. Specify the whether you want the output in degrees or percent.
4. Set the Z factor to convert vertical units (e.g., m to ft).
5. Enter the output cell size.
6. Enter the name of the output GRID.
7. Click **OK**.

Related to slope is *aspect*, which is the direction of maximum slope. Output values are expressed in degrees, with 0° and 360° at north, increasing clockwise. Cells that are flat are assigned a value of -1. If the input surface is a raster, then aspect is calculated using a 3x3 window. If the input surface is a TIN, then cells are assigned the aspect of the

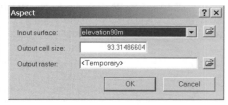

triangle its center falls in. The default legend for an aspect raster is optimized to show the 360° nature of aspect. Also note that aspect is a *cyclical* data type. Often the average aspect is needed, and one way to get around the cyclical data is to convert it to N-S values and not differentiate E-W directions. That is, if an aspect is greater than 180°, then the normalized aspect equals the aspect -180°.

Creating an aspect raster

ArcToolbox -> Spatial Analyst Tools -> Distance -> **Aspect.**

- OR -

1. From the Spatial Analyst toolbar, select **Surface analysis -> Aspect...**.

2. Select the input GRID that contains the elevation values.

3. Enter the output cell size.

4. Enter the name of the output GRID.

5. Click **OK**.

A *viewshed* is composed of the places that are viewable from a given location (Figure 7.7). Viewsheds are important when siting features such as cell towers or buildings, or for understanding amenity (view) values. A viewshed can be calculated from either a single position or a number of positions, defined by an *observation* theme with either point or line features. That is, from an observation point, you can identify the locations that are visible.

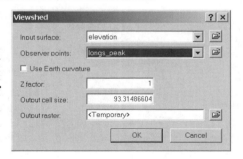

A number of options can be specified for each of the observation points. These settings must be defined in the *observation* layer's (observer points) attribute table, not interactively through a series of dialogs. The value in the *spot field* in the attribute table of the observation table is used for the elevation value. The elevation value is interpolated (bilinear) from the input raster if the field is not in the table. An observation point is excluded from the analysis if the value of the nearest cell is NoData.

The value in the *Offseta field* specifies a vertical distance (in surface units) to be added to the elevation value of the observation point. This value is added to either the *Spot* or interpolated elevation value (it must be positive). By default, a value of 1 is added if the *Offseta* field does not exist. The value in the *Offsetb* field specifies a vertical distance to be added to the elevation values to each cell in the input raster. By default, a value of 0 is added if the *Offsetb* field does not exist.

The values in the *Azimuth1* and *Azimuth2* fields specify the beginning and ending horizontal angles of the scan. The scan proceeds in a clockwise direction from angle 1 to angle 2. If these fields do not exist, a full 360° scan is implemented. The values in the *Vert1* and *Vert2* fields define the upper and lower limit of the scan, respectively. Default values are 90° and -90°.

FIGURE 7.7. Areas on the northern Colorado Front Range where Longs Peak (lower left cross) can be seen are shown in green (download color figures from <u>www.consplan.com</u>).

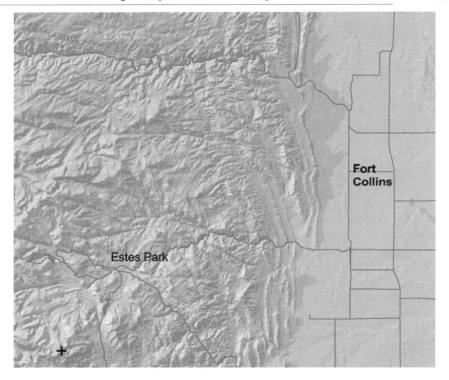

You can also limit the search distance from each point by specifying a short and far search radius in the *Radius1* and *Radius2* fields. Locations closer than the short radius will not be visible in the output raster but can block the visibility beyond that location. Locations beyond the far radius are excluded from the analysis. The default values are 0 and infinity, respectively. By default, the distances are three-dimensional line-of-sight distances. You can use planimetric distances by inserting a negative sign in front of the distance values.

GIS Concepts and ArcGIS Methods

Creating a viewshed raster

ArcToolbox -> Spatial Analyst Tools -> Distance -> **Viewshed.**

- OR -

1. From the Spatial Analyst toolbar, select **Surface analysis -> Viewshed...**.

2. Select the input raster that contains the elevation values.

3. Select the layer (point or line) that contains the observations.

4. Check the box if you wish to account for Earth's curvature.

5. Enter the Z factor (to convert units).

6. Enter the output cell size.

7. Enter the name of the output raster.

8. Click **OK**.

The differences between two surfaces, in terms of area and volume, can be computed by cut and fill analysis. Most often this operation is used for planning construction projects, but it is useful in other applications as well, such as examining population growth patterns, changes in river geomorphology, or lake sedimentation.[26]

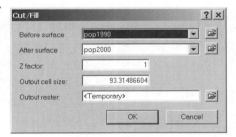

Cut and fill analysis

ArcToolbox -> Spatial Analyst Tools -> Distance -> **Cut/Fill.**

- OR -

1. From the Spatial Analyst toolbar, select **Surface analysis -> Cut/fill...**.

2. Select the input raster of the "before" surface, and "after" surface.

4. Enter the Z factor (to convert units).

5. Enter the output cell size.

6. Enter the name of the output raster.

7. Click **OK**.

---

26. For a detailed description of cut and fill operations, see: Price, M. 2002. Deriving volumes with ArcGIS Spatial Analyst. ArcUser (October-December):52-55. www.esri.com/news/arcuser/1002/files/volumes.pdf

7.4.4.4 Interpolation

Often geographic data are sampled at various locations, rather than a complete census, because of time or money constraints. To create a surface from sampled data, that is to estimate the values at all non-sampled locations, one needs to *interpolate*. There is a variety of interpolation methods, but all make use of the First Law of Geography, that things closer together tend to be more similar than those farther away. Spatial Analyst provides ready-access to three methods: inverse distance weighted (IDW), spline, and kriging. Which method should you use? It depends, mostly on the assumptions that you can make with a given dataset. It is best to assess the accuracy of the model chosen, either through cross-validation[27] or through tests against a set of "test points." To illustrate the differences between these methods and the results they provide, we'll use an example dataset of 509 elevation test points, randomly selected from a 30 m DEM (Figure 7.8). Because we know the "truth" for the rest of the elevations, we can assess the accuracy of the interpolation methods. Although any point layer with integer or real values can be input, interpolation assumes that the geographic phenomena represented by the surface values is *continuous*.

FIGURE 7.8. **Elevation with "x"s showing the 509 sampled locations.**

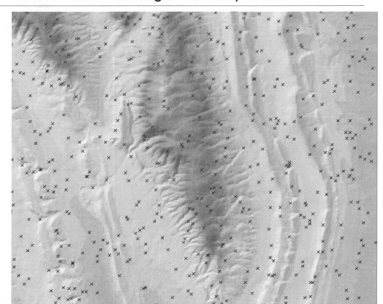

27. Note that the Geostatistical Analyst extension provides a flexible interface to explore the accuracy of different models.

The inverse distance weighted (IDW) method assumes a distance decay function using a linearly weighted set of sample points, so that the influence of a point declines with increasing distance from that point. Therefore, points closer to the processing cell have greater weight than those farther away. The interpolation algorithm uses either a specified number of nearest points or all points within a given radius. The power parameter affects the rate of decline in influence with distance. As the power parameter value approaches 0 (but is not less than), the influence of distant points increases. As the value increases, the influence of distant points decreases. Reasonable results can be

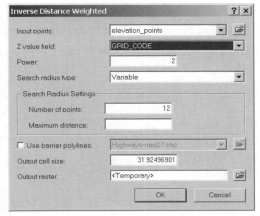

obtained using values from 0.5 to 3. The default value is 2. A *barrier* layer (of line feature type) can be specified to break the limit of search for sample points using linear features.[28] The nearest neighbor method is typically used when the phenomenon exhibits the behavior that more distant locations have less influence. Neighbors can be specified by using either a fixed or variable search radius. Fixed neighborhoods use all points that are found within a given radius (though a minimum number of points can be required as well). Variable search neighbors use the nearest n neighbors, where n is specified (and a maximum distance can be defined as well). The *barrier* theme is useful when there are geographic features, such as ridges, cliffs, rivers, highways, or some feature that interrupts the continuous distribution of the phenomenon of interest.

The *root mean square error* (RMSE) is typically used to compute error in surfaces (Figure 7.9). RMSE is the square root of the average squared difference between the estimated value (x) and the "true" value (x_0):

$$\mathit{RSE} = \sqrt{\left(\sum (x \angle x_0)^2 \right)/n} =$$

where n is the number of points (also usually randomly selected).

28. Phillip, G.M. and D.F. Watson. 1982. A precise method for determining contoured surfaces. *Australian Petroleum Explanation Association Journal* 22: 205-212; Watson, D.F. and G.M. Phillip. 1985. A refinement of Inverse Distance Weighted interpolation. *Geo-Processing* 2:315-327.

FIGURE 7.9. IDW-interpolated surface (left), with error surface (right—darker blues show overestimation, light cyan and yellow show little error, while darker reds show underestimation). The RMSE was 21.5 m (download color figures from www.consplan.com).

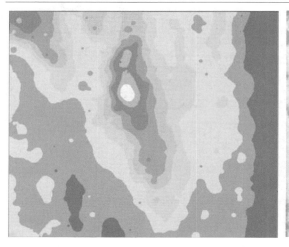
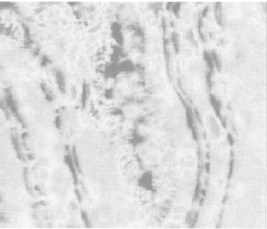

Interpolating using IDW

ArcToolbox -> Spatial Analyst Tools -> Interpolation -> **IDW.**

- OR -

1. From the Spatial Analyst toolbar, select **Interpolate to raster -> Inverse distance weighted...**.

2. Select the input layer that contains the points.

3. Select the field that contains the "elevation" values.

4. Set the Power factor (typically 0.5 to 3).

5. Specify the search radius type as Variable or Fixed.

6. If Variable, then specify the number of points in a neighborhood and the maximum distance. If fixed, then enter the search radius (in map units) and the minimum number of points needed.

7. Check the box to use barrier polylines, and specify the polyline shapefile.

8. Enter the output cell size.

9. Enter the name of the output GRID.

10. Click **OK.**

The *spline* interpolation algorithm fits a two-dimensional, minimum-curvature surface through the sample points using a mathematical function (Figure 7.10). The resulting surface passes exactly through the input points. This method is best for surfaces that exhibit smooth, gentle variations, such as water table heights or precipitation. It is not appropriate for surfaces that have abrupt changes (use the IDW with a barrier theme). You have the option of using a *regularized* method, which produces a smooth surface by using the specified weight parameter to define the weight of

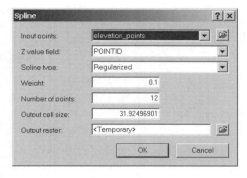

the third derivative in the curvature minimization equation. Higher values produce a smoother surface, and typically range from 0.0 to 0.5. The *tension* method produces a "stiffer" surface and uses the specified weight parameter for the tension weight and the specified number of points to establish the number of points required during local approximation. The greater the weight, the coarser the surface, and typical values range from 1 to 10. The greater the number of sample points required, the smoother the resulting surface.

FIGURE 7.10. Spline-interpolated surface (left), with error surface (right—darker blues show overestimation, light cyan and yellow show little error, while darker reds show underestimation). The RMSE for the spline surface is 21.2 m.

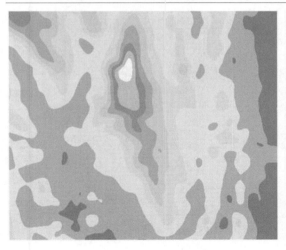
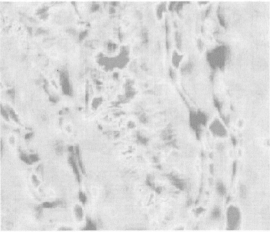

Interpolating using spline

ArcToolbox -> Spatial Analyst Tools -> Interpolation -> **Spline.**

- OR -1. From the Spatial Analyst toolbar, select **Interpolate to raster -> Spline....**

2. Select the input layer that contains the points.

3. Select the field that contains the "elevation" values.

4. Specify the spline type: Regularized or Tension.

6. Specify the weight and number of points in a neighborhood.

7. Enter the output cell size.

8. Enter the name of the output raster.

9. Click **OK**.

Kriging is an interpolation method that includes the autocorrelation of the values of the input points (Figure 7.11). It is similar to IDW in that the surrounding measures are weighted, but kriging also utilizes the spatial arrangement of the weights. The interface allows ordinary and universal kriging and a number of common semivariogram models: spherical, circular, exponential, Gaussian, and linear. Importantly, kriging allows the creation of a surface of predicted variance. There are number of books that discuss kriging methods in detail.[29]

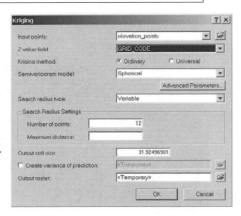

---

29. See: Bailey, T.C. and A.C. Gatrell. 1995. *Interactive spatial data analysis*. Prentice Hall; Isaaks, E.H. and R.M. Srivaastava. 1989. *Applied geostatistics*. Oxford University Press; O'Sullivan, D. and D.J. Unwin. 2002. *Geographic Information Analysis*. John Wiley and Sons.

GIS Concepts and ArcGIS Methods

FIGURE 7.11. Kriging-interpolated surface (left), with error surface (right—darker blues show overestimation, light cyan and yellow show little error, while darker reds show underestimation). For this model, the RMSE was 33.1 m.

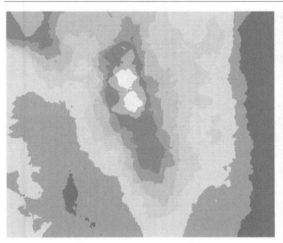 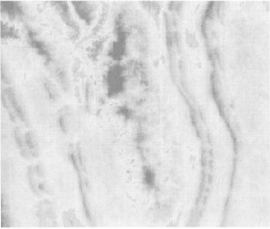

Interpolating using kriging

ArcToolbox -> Spatial Analyst Tools -> Interpolation -> **Kriging.**

The *Natural Neighbor* interpolation method interpolates values using the closest subset of points and applies a weight to them based on the proportionate area. Thiessen (or Voronoi) polygons are first formed around every point in the input feature layer, and then used as the weights.[30]

Interpolating using natural neighbors

ArcToolbox -> Spatial Analyst Tools -> Interpolation -> **Natural Neighbors.**

---

30. Sibson, R. 1981. A brief description of natural neighbor interpolation", Chapter 2 in *Interpolating multivariate data*. John Wiley & Sons, NY, NY. pp. 21-36.

Trend analysis is often used to differentiate broad-scale from local-scale spatial patterns using a global polynomial interpolation. The *Trend tool* fits a smooth surface to the input sample points. The polynomial order can range from simple (1st) to complex (up to 12th order). Rarely does it make sense to use orders beyond the 2nd or 3rd order. There are two types of regression that can be used: linear and logistic. *Linear regression* fits a least-squares surface to the set of input points, and is most applicable to understanding the pattern of continuous (or real-valued) data such as elevation or precipitation. *Logistic regression* generates a continuous probability surface from binary (0/1, presence/absence) type of data.

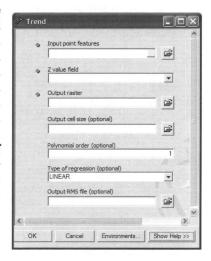

Interpolating using trend analysis

ArcToolbox -> Spatial Analyst Tools -> Interpolation -> **Trend.**

A final interpolation method is one that generates a "hydrologically-correct" surface from point, line, and polygon data. This is a method that uses an iterative finite difference interpolation technique and is specifically designed to use elevational data from contours.[31]

Interpolating from contour lines

ArcToolbox -> Spatial Analyst Tools -> Interpolation -> **Topo to Raster.**

7.4.4.5 Hydrologic analysis

The Hydrology tools enable you to analyze surface hydrology to better understand the movement of water across a surface and to identify watersheds and drainage systems. An excellent example of this processing has been done by the US Geological Survey's Earth

---

31. This method is described more fully in: Hutchinson, M.F. 1993. Development of a continent-wide DEM with applications to terrain and climate analysis. In *Environmental modeling with GIS*, Goodchild, M.F. et al. (eds.). pp. 392-399. Oxford University Press, NY, NY.

Resources Observation and Science group to produce the Elevation Derivatives for National Applications (EDNA) datasets (Figure 7.12).[32]

FIGURE 7.12. The data flow or processing steps used to generate the Elevation Derivatives for National Applications datasets (Source: http://edna.usgs.gov).

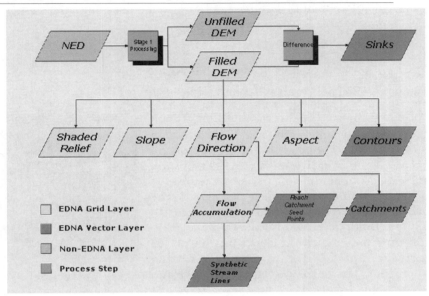

A simplified approach to extract hydrologic information from a digital elevation model can be accomplished using the following steps (and illustrated by Figure 7.13):

1. Create a "hydrologically conditioned" raster by filling in the small imperfections in a DEM (called *sinks* or "pits").

2. Compute the direction of flow from each cell to its adjacent cells.

3. Identify the drainage network (often called the synthetic stream network) using flow accumulation.

4. Generate watersheds for the drainage network.

A *sink* is a cell in a DEM whose elevation is lower than all of its eight adjacent neighbors. Real-world features that are "true" sinks are places like Lake Pyramid in Nevada[33]

---

32. Also, the US Geological Survey's National Hydrology Dataset and its NHDPlus has been produced using some related methods. Also see the Functional Linkage of Watersheds and Streams ArcGIS tools (www.nrel.colostate.edu/projects/starmap).

33. This is called a terminal or closed basin (also called an endorheic basin).

because there is no outflow of water, rather all water flows into the lake. But for most applications using a DEM, a sink is an artifact that can be created due to relatively coarse resolution of elevation data or the rounding of elevation heights. These artifacts disrupt the presumed flow of water across a surface and/or down a stream channel. To remove a sink, the *Fill* tool is used. Typically the Fill tool is run in an iterative fashion, trying incrementally larger fill or "z-limit" values that specify the maximum depth of a sink that will be filled.

Conditioning a DEM using Fill

ArcToolbox -> Spatial Analyst Tools -> Hydrology -> **Fill.**

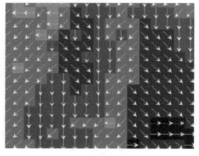

The next step is to compute the direction of flow from a cell to one of its eight adjacent neighbors.[34] The direction of flow is determine by computing the direction of the steepest descent from a cell (rise / run). The *Flow Direction* tool is used to compute this, and the output raster uses a binary coding scheme such that flow to the east = 1, southeast = 2, south = 4, southwest = 8, west = 16, northwest = 32, north = 64, and northeast = 128. Using an eight direction algorithm works fairly well for most applications, but additional artifacts can be introduced such that flow paths (i.e. streams, overland flow paths) can get caught in a "groove". These artifacts are well explored and discussed in the hydrologic literature.[35]

With the flow direction determined, the accumulated flow can be computed to help identify the location of the stream network using the *Flow Accumulation* tool. If a stream network has been generated strictly from a DEM, it is called a *synthetic stream network*. Typically a threshold value is applied to select cells that have a "high" accumulated flow that are likely to be streams (e.g., EDNA uses a threshold of 5,000 cells that are 0.22 ha in size).[36]

---

34. Jenson S.K. and J.O. Domingue. 1988. Extracting Topographic Structure from Digital Elevation Data for Geographic Information System Analysis. *Photogrammetric Engineering and Remote Sensing* 54 (11): 1593-1600.

35. For a starting point, try: Tarboton, D.G., R.L. Bras, and I. Rodriguez-Iturbe. 1991. On the Extraction of Channel Networks from Digital Elevation Data. *Hydrological Processes.* 5: 81-100.

36. The *Flow Length* tool can be used to compute the length of flow paths.

This threshold value is, however, arbitrary and is typically not adjusted regionally or even locally to adjust to different precipitation/evapotranspiration regimes. However, one could implement this by specifying an input weight raster that is optional, which would likely be generated to reflect either aspect or solar insolation. Otherwise, there are a variety of methods for "burning in" the blue-line hydrology into the DEM. To generate a polyline feature that represents the river network that was generated synthetically, use the *Stream to Feature* tool.

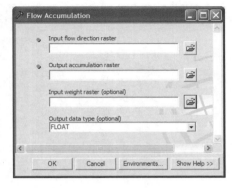

Computing flow accumulation and river network

ArcToolbox -> Spatial Analyst Tools -> Hydrology -> **Flow Accumulation, Stream to Feature**

The last step is to create a raster that represents the delineation of all drainage basins. The Basin tool identifies ridge lines between basins by following the flow direction to find all possible contiguous sets (or regions) that belong to the same drainage basin. The *Watershed tool* is similar to the Basin tool, but it relies on having a set of outlets or *pour points* specified (typically from the synthetic stream network or blue-lines).

Computing basins and watersheds

ArcToolbox -> Spatial Analyst Tools -> Hydrology -> **Basin, Watershed**

FIGURE 7.13. Data layers from the EDNA hydrologic process (Source: http://edna.usgs.gov): hillshade, filled DEM, flow direction and accumulation, watersheds, and synthetic streams.

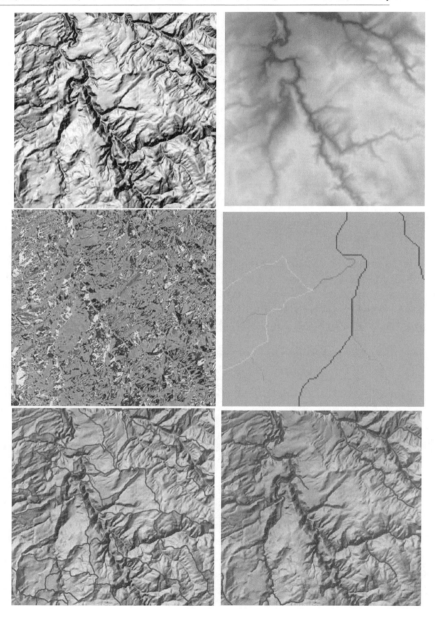

7.4.4.6 Generalization

A common need in raster analysis is to clean up a raster and remove unwanted artifacts. For example, removal of specks or "salt and pepper," which are small (often just a single cell) regions (Figure 7.14). Typically these specks are regarded as noise and are removed by a focal filter. For example, fine-grained (30 m resolution) land cover maps (e.g., USGS National Land Cover Dataset[37]) created from remotely sensed images often have specks in them, yet to make a more generalized map of land cover, we may want to remove them. Because these are nominal values (land cover classes), they can be removed using a specialized *Majority Filter* tool.

This filter replaces the center cell with the majority value of the eight surrounding cells (note that four orthogonal cells could be used as well). To require that the majority be at least half of the neighboring cells, the replacement threshold of HALF. If there is not a clear majority (i.e. a tie), or if the majority does not meet the half constraint, then a NoData is assigned to the center cell. Typically these NoData values are simply replaced with the original values. One difference between Majority Filter and *Focal Statistics* (using the MAJORITY statistic) is that Majority Filter does not use the center cell.

FIGURE 7.14. Example of generalizing a land cover map (left) using MajorityFilter with EIGHT neighbors (left center), FocalMajority using 3x3 neighbors (right center), and Nibble to replace yellow linear feature (right).

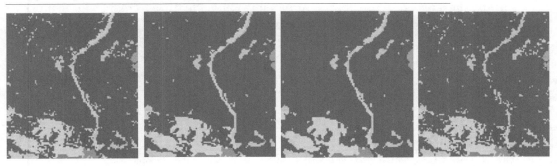

---

37. http://landcover.usgs.gov/natllandcover.html

7.5 Raster/vector conversions

In the late 1970s and early 1980s, a hotly debated issue in the field of GIS was the particular advantages and disadvantages of one data model over another. One of the catchy (but misleading) adages that emerged from these debates was: "raster is faster, but vector is corrector."[38] But in actuality, *both* data models are useful for different purposes and so conversion routines between data models were developed. Spatial Analyst allows you to easily convert data between vector and raster data formats. However, conversion between formats can result in loss of information and can be problematic. Generally, using finer resolution produces better results, but the trade-off is that file sizes grow exponentially with increasing resolution.[39]

7.5.1 *Vector to raster*

Any feature layer can be converted to a GRID. For point features, a cell is assigned the value of the point that is found within the cell. If two or more points intersect a single cell, the cell is assigned the value of the first point that is processed (in processing order[40]). For example, in the diagram to the right, the cell that has two points located within it (1 and 2) at the bottom is assigned a value of 1, but the cell on the right that has two points (also a 1

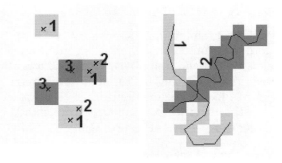

and 2) is assigned the value of 2. Increasing the raster resolution decreases the likelihood that a cell will share two or more points. After converting a feature to raster data, sum the count field to determine the number of cells, which should equal the number of points in the feature attribute table (if there are no multiple-point cells). Cells that do not have any points are assigned the NoData value.

There are eight methods that are used to assign cell values for point features if more than one point falls within a cell:

---

38. Chrisman, N. 1997. *Exploring Geographic Information Systems.* John Wiley & Sons. (page 117). Also see: Peuquet, D.J. 1984. A conceptual framework and comparison of spatial data models. *Cartographica* 21: 66-113.

39. Also, beware that finer resolution can result in over-estimation of linear and polygon perimeter distances of raster zones and features. See: Theobald, D.M. 2000. Correcting linear and perimeter measurement errors in raster-based data. *Cartography and Geographic Information Science* 27(2): 111-116.

40. Features are processed in the same order as the feature ID value.

- MOST_FREQUENT - the value in an attribute that has the most frequent occurrence will be assigned to the output raster;
- SUM - the sum of the attribute values for all the points within the cell will be assigned;
- MEAN - the mean of the attribute values for all the points within the cell will be assigned;
- STANDARD_DEVIATION - the standard deviation will be assigned;
- MAXIMUM - the maximum of the attribute values will be assigned;
- MINIMUM - the maximum of the attribute values will be assigned;
- RANGE - the range (maximum minus minimum) of the attribute values will be assigned;
- COUNT - the number of points within a cell will be assigned to the output raster.

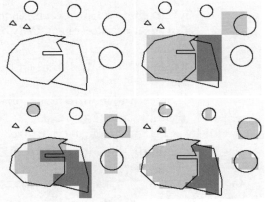

For line features, cells are assigned values based on the line that intersects any cell (see above). This is similar to Bresenham's algorithm[41], where any cell that is intersected by the line is "turned on." Similar to points, if there are two or more lines that cross a cell, the cell value is assigned the value of the feature that is first encountered during processing.

There are three methods that are used to assign cell values for polygon features: centroid, dominant, and most important.[42]

- The *center method* assigns the value of the polygon found at the center of a grid cell. This is called *CELL_CENTER* in the Polygon to Raster tool.

- The *dominant method* assigns the value of the polygon that occupies the largest portion of a cell area. This method is called *MAXIMUM_AREA* in the Polygon to Raster tool. A similar method is to combine features with common attributes when determining the largest area, which is called *MAXIMUM_COMBINED_AREA*.

- The *most important method* assigns the value of the polygon based on some specified ranking or weighting of polygon values.

41. Foley, J.D. and A. van Dam. 1984. *Fundamentals of Interactive Computer Graphics*. Addison-Wesley.
42. Chou, Y.H. 1997. *Exploring Spatial Analysis in Geographic Information Systems*. Santa Fe, New Mexico: Onword Press.

An advantage of using the centroid method is that small features (in relation to the cell size) are not systematically excluded, which happens with the dominate method. This is the default method that ArcGIS uses (called *Cell center*). Notice in the graphic above that polygon features are *only* converted to raster if the center of a cell falls within a polygon.

A number of factors should be considered when determining the appropriate cell size during vector to raster conversion. First, consider the minimum mapping unit (MMU) or smallest polygon size. Setting the cell size to one-half the width of the MMU may be reasonable *if* the source polygons are a regular, compact (circular or square) shape. But to resolve long, narrow features such as riparian zones along a river, the cell size should be one-half the width of the *narrowest* polygon. For all three feature types, cells that do not intersect a feature are assigned the NoData value.

Converting features to raster

ArcToolbox -> Conversion Tools -> To Raster -> **Point to Raster, Polygon to Raster,** or **Polyline to Raster**.

- OR -

1. From the Spatial Analyst toolbar, select **Convert -> Features to raster...**.

2. Select the feature layer to be converted (selected features are used).

3. Specify the output cell size.

4. Specify the output raster filename and location.

5. Click **OK**.

7.5.2 Raster to vector

Raster can also be converted back to vector format, and Spatial Analyst allows you to select the resulting feature type. When creating point features, a point will be created at the center of each cell for all non-NoData valued cells. For linear features, a polyline is created that links the center of all contiguous, same-valued cells. For polygon features, a polygon is built from regions of cells (same-valued, contiguous). For linear and polygon features, you have the option of using a generalization algorithm based on the Douglas-Peucker algorithm[43] to automatically smooth the "jagginess" of the resulting features. Note that only integer rasters can be converted from raster to feature.

---

43. Douglas, D.H. and T.K. Peucker. 1973. Algorithms for the reduction of the number of points required to represent a digitized line or its caricature. *Canadian Cartographer* 10(2):110-122.

Converting raster to features

ArcToolbox -> Conversion Tools -> From Raster -> **Raster to Point, Raster to Polygon,** or **Raster to Polyline**.
- OR -
1. From the Spatial Analyst toolbar, select **Convert -> Raster to features...**.
2. Select the raster layer to be converted (selected values are used). If a layer is not available in the list, make sure it is an integer GRID.
3. Specify whether generalization should be used or not.
4. Specify the output feature filename and location.
5. Click **OK**.

7.5.3 Image-GRID conversion

Although images and GRID data are both in raster format, the data values can be accessed only in a GRID. Occasionally you may want to convert a GRID to an image file so that it displays faster, is a smaller file size, or so that it can be used in another software program. The formats that are supported are: BMP, GIF, GRID, IMAGINE, JPEG, JPEG2000, PNG, TIFF, or geodatabase raster. GRIDs can be exported to images using the Export function. To convert an image to a GRID, the Image-to-GRID routine in ArcToolbox is used (requires ArcInfo license).

Converting raster to other image format

ArcToolbox -> Conversion Tools -> From Raster -> **Raster to Other Format (multiple).**

7.6 Advanced raster processing and map algebra

The format and rules of these functions are based on *map algebra*, which is a "language" that defines the syntax, functions, and variables for combining layers. Map algebra treats entire maps as variables and operations on maps are analogous to traditional mathematical opera-

---

tions.[44] The *Raster Calculator* not only provides access to additional functions, it also allows more complex expressions to be built. Moreover, lists of map algebra "models" can be saved to word processing files to document your work and provide models for others to use.

Map algebra statements contain functions and operators. Functions (e.g., **sin(<inGrid>)**) require an input(s) to be specified and their parameters separated by commas. Parameters can be additional datasets, keywords, or numbers. Operators (e.g., +, /, etc.) are generally placed between raster datasets, and spaces between the operand and datasets are mandatory. In general, functions are processed in left-to-right order. However, many functions have a *precedence order* that modifies this left-to-right processing. The best way to ensure that Spatial Analyst processes the statement according to your desires (and understanding) is to explicitly set precedence using parentheses.

7.6.1 Raster Calculator

The *Raster Calculator* provides an interface in which map algebra expressions can be entered. The dialog provides a list of the raster layers currently included in ArcMap (upper left), a number of buttons for often-used operations (upper right), and an *expression text box* where map algebra expressions or statements are formed (lower). The output raster created after an expression is evaluated is automatically added to ArcMap after processing. Raster datasets can be accessed from the raster calculator a number of ways. If the raster data set is 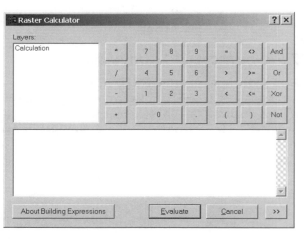 listed as a layer, then the layer name must be enclosed by brackets ([ ]). For example:

[Calculation] * 1

Other datasets (permanent rasters, feature datasets, tables) that have not been added to ArcMap can be accessed by specifying the entire path and filename:

c:\temp\roads * 2

---

44. Berry, J.K. 1987. Fundamental operations in computer-assisted map analysis. *International Journal of Geographical Information Systems* 1(2):119-136

By default, the resulting output raster is created as a temporary raster in the working directory. Permanent rasters can be created directly by explicitly assigning an output raster name:

c:\temp\roads2 = c:\temp\roads * 1

By default, the values in the *Value* field in the raster's attribute table are used in the calculations.[45] If your expression grows very long, or if you would like to break it into multiple parts on different lines to make it more readable, use the *line continuation* character ("~"):

con ([Calculation] > 4, ~

    [Calculation2], ~

    [Calculation3])

Multiple lines of map algebra expressions can be processed as well, enabling you to build complex models.[46] Output raster names must be enclosed by brackets so that they can be accessed later in the statement. However, do not confuse the temporary output rasters created (on the left of the equal sign) with layers in ArcMap. Each line in a multi-line expression must be separated by a carriage return. Also, the dialog box can be dragged downward to enlarge the expression text box, and the font of the expression text box can also be changed for easier reading.[47]

[R1] = rand()

[b_w] = con ([R1] > 0.5, 1, 0)

If you are unclear what parameters are used for a given function, the *usage* of a function can be obtained quickly by typing in the function name (e.g., REGIONGROUP), highlighting it, then right-clicking and selecting **Usage**. Usage describes a function's inputs, e.g., focalsum(). Options that are enclosed with "<>" are required. Those enclosed with "{}" are optional. There are many types of options: conditions, expressions, values, keywords, input rasters, and output rasters. For example, the simple usage for focalsum() is:

FocalSum(<grid>, {DATA | NODATA})

---

45. In older versions of ArcGIS, other fields in the attribute table (e.g., Count) could be accessed using what is known as "<grid>.<item>" notation (no spaces before or after the period). Now use the Lookup tool.

46. Starting at ArcGIS v8.2.

47. This is also a nice feature, as brackets and parentheses were remarkably difficult to distinguish in the Map Calculator dialog in ArcView v3.x. Try: Courier, 10 pt., regular, which seems to work well.

where <grid> is a required input raster and the DATA or NODATA parameter is optional (e.g., FocalSum([G1]) is valid). Note that default values are used if they are not explicitly specified. Because there are a variety of neighborhoods that can be specified for focal functions, there are some additional ways to use FocalSum:

FocalSum(<grid>, <RECTANGLE>, <width>, <height>, {DATA | NODATA})

FocalSum(<grid>, <CIRCLE>, <radius>, {DATA | NODATA})

FocalSum(<grid>, <ANNULUS>, <inner_radius>, <outer_radius>, {DATA | NODATA})

FocalSum(<grid>, <WEDGE>, <radius>, <start_angle>, <end_angle>, {DATA | NO-DATA})

FocalSum(<grid>, <IRREGULAR>, <kernel_file>, {DATA | NODATA})

FocalSum(<grid>, <WEIGHT>, <kernel_file>, {DATA | NODATA})

Parameters like <RECTANGLE> distinguish the neighborhood type, while <width> is a required number value (e.g., FocalSum ([G1], RECTANGLE, 3, 3)).

Sometimes the usage defines a <condition> or <expression>. For example, the usage for con() is: con(<condition>, <trueExpression>, <FalseExpression). A condition must equal true or false, while full expressions can be simple or complicated:

con ([G1] > 0, 1, 0)

con ([G1] > 0, sin([G1]), log([G1]))

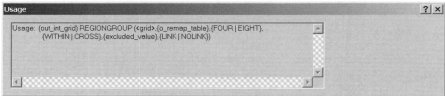

Recent map algebra expressions can be accessed as well by right-clicking in the text box, then selecting *recent expressions*. Copy the expression(s) that you are interested in, then paste it into the text box. It is good practice, however, to paste the expressions that

you ultimately used into a word processor document to save for later use, because these expressions are not saved with the map document file.

7.6.2 Integer and floating-point math

When you are calculating values using integer rasters, you need to be careful about your assumptions of how Spatial Analyst handles decimal places. First of all, Spatial Analyst *truncates* decimal points, rather than rounding. For example, if you calculate the following (in Map Calculator):

(2 / 3)

the resulting integer raster would have a value of 0, not 1. Furthermore, the decimal places cannot be accessed by multiplying a raster by a factor of 10, as in the following:

((10 / 3) * 1000)

This results in a raster with a value of 3000, not 3333. The consequence of this is that your everyday mathematical equation, such as: $y=(4/3)*3$, is not calculated the way we might expect. For instance, y should equal 4, but:

((4 / 3) * 3)

equals 3! In other words, the values are not simply truncated at the end of the calculation, but throughout the equation! To force Spatial Analyst to utilize the decimal places, you will need to call *Float()* for every part of an equation that uses integer rasters, but should use real-value computation. For example:

((float(4) / 3) * 3)

will result in a value of 4, but the following will result in a value of 3:

((4 / 3) * float (3))

7.6.3 Advanced map algebra expressions

As discussed above, Spatial Analyst provides access to a number of commonly used functions through dialog interfaces. These dialogs gather the input parameters from the user, and then process the request. The exact same requests could be accomplished directly through the Raster Calculator. Returning to the focal averaging example, finding the mean habitat value within a 1000 m radius could be found with:

Focalmean ([Habitat], CIRCLE, 1000)

As was asserted earlier, there are numerous additional functions that may be useful. Now that we know about map algebra and the Raster Calculator, we can explore these functions in detail.

7.6.3.1 Local

In addition to statistical operators, there are a wide variety of additional local operators, including mathematical and logical operators (arithmetic, bitwise, boolean, combinatorial, logical, and relational), conditional, and reclassify. A couple of the more commonly used local functions are described in detail below. The most powerful and most commonly used conditional function is *Con*. Con essentially allows "if-then" logic and has three components: **Con(<condition>, <true>, <false>)**. For example, imagine you wanted to create a map to locate areas that are not so steep (>15) they preclude development. Two categories are needed: OK to develop (1), and too steep to develop (0). Con could be used to do this:

con([slope] > 15, 1, 0)

Note that NoData values could be used in place of the 0s if you do not specify the <false> parameter:

con([slope] > 15, 1)

Con statements can also be imbedded to incorporate more complex logic, for example, to add the constraint that development must be 100 m or further away from water:

con([slope] > 15, ~

    con([d2water] > 100,~

        1,~

        0), ~

  0)

When using the reclassify function through the Raster Calculator, text-based remap tables can be used in addition to INFO remap tables. For example, the remap table (slope1.txt) for the slope example above would look like:

    0 5 : 1
    5 10 : 2
    10 20 : 3
    20 45 : 4

and would be called from the Raster Calculator using:

Reclass ([slope], slope1.txt)

There are a few *built-in variables* (called scalars) that can be accessed in the Raster Calculator that are quite useful: **$$COLMAP** (column number), **$$ROWMAP** (row number), **$$NCOLS** (number of columns), **$$NROWS** (number of rows), **$$CELLSIZE** (cell size in map units), **$$XMAP** (x map coordinate at center of processing cell), **$$YMAP** (y map coordinate at center of processing cell), **$$WX0** (minimum x value), **$$WX1** (maximum x value), **$$WY0** (minimum y value), and **$$WY1** (maximum y value).

These variables can be used in expressions to create a wide variety of GRIDs. For example, to identify column and row locations, beginning with 0,0 in the top-left corner, use:

[column] = $$colmap

[row] = $$rowmap

To compute a GRID where the value of the cell is the x and y locations, use:

[x] = $$xmap

[y] = $$ymap

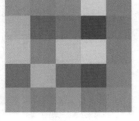

Another use of these variables is to create a GRID where every cell has a unique integer value (here shown by unique colors at right), in row-major (moving from left to right: 0, 1, 2, 3, 4; continuing at the next row: 5, 6, 7, 8, 9; etc.) (see Figure 7.15):

$$COLMAP + ($$ROWMAP * $$NCOLS)

To create a GRID with unique values in row-prime, or *boustrophedon*[48], ordering (left to right: 0, 1, 2, 3, 4; continuing at the next row right to left: 9, 8, 7, 6, 5; etc.), use:

$$COLMAP + ($$ROWMAP * $$NCOLS) + ~

(($$ROWMAP MOD 2) * (($$NCOLS - 1) - ($$COLMAP * 2)))

Note that sections in the US Public Land Survey System follow a row-prime order.

An interesting hierarchical raster ordering scheme is attributed to Guy Morton's work at IBM in the 1960s, known as the Morton or "N" (or "Z") order (note that the Morton ordering in Figure 7.15 is a "backwards N" order).[49] To create a GRID with Morton order values (1 to 4) at a given level of resolution, use:

(($$COLMAP mod 2) * 2) + ($$ROWMAP mod 2) + 1

---

48. Boustrophedon is derived from a Greek adverb that means "like an ox turning" or "as a field is plowed"—*The Concise Oxford Dictionary of Linguistics*. 1997. Oxford University Press.

49. A comparison of these ordering schemes is provided in: Goodchild, M.F. and A.W. Grandfield. 1983. Optimizing raster storage: an examination of four alternatives. In *Proceedings of AutoCarto 6*, Ottawa, Canada. Pgs. 400-407.

Also note that by converting these unique-valued GRIDs into polygons (without generalization), a *fishnet* or mesh of squares (as polygons) can be created.

To compute a *checkerboard* pattern of alternative values, use:

($$colmap + $$rowmap) mod 2

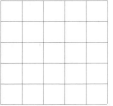

FIGURE 7.15. A comparison of raster ordering methods: row-major (top left), row-prime (top right), Morton or "N" ordering (bottom left), and Morton hierarchical addressing (bottom right). (Download color figures from www.consplan.com).

0	1	2	3	4	5	6	7
8	9	10	11	12	13	14	15
16	17	18	19	20	21	22	23
24	25	26	27	28	29	30	31
32	33	34	35	36	37	38	39
40	41	42	43	44	45	46	47
48	49	50	51	52	53	54	55
56	57	58	59	60	61	62	63

0	1	2	3	4	5	6	7
15	14	13	12	11	10	9	8
16	17	18	19	20	21	22	23
31	30	29	28	27	26	25	24
32	33	34	35	36	37	38	39
47	46	45	44	43	42	41	40
48	49	50	51	52	53	54	55
63	62	61	60	59	58	57	56

0	2	8	10	32	34	40	42
1	3	9	11	33	35	41	43
4	6	12	14	36	38	44	46
5	7	13	15	37	39	45	47
16	18	24	26	48	50	56	58
17	19	25	27	49	51	57	59
20	22	28	30	52	54	60	62
21	23	29	31	53	55	61	63

111	113	131	133	311	313	331	333
112	114	132	134	312	314	332	334
121	123	141	143	321	323	341	343
122	124	142	144	322	324	342	344
211	213	231	233	411	413	431	433
212	214	232	234	412	414	432	434
221	223	241	243	421	423	441	443
222	224	242	244	422	424	442	444

A comprehensive list of local operators and functions is provided in Table 7.4.

7.6.3.2 Neighborhood functions

There are a few additional focal functions that are not available directly through the neighborhood statistics dialog, including block functions (see Table 7.5). Also, in addition to annulus, circular, rectangular, and wedge neighborhoods, *irregular* neighborhoods can be used in Map Algebra expressions. Irregularly shaped neighborhoods are created by directly specifying the cells in a neighborhood that will be processed through a *kernel* file. Typically, the kernel file is used simply as a mask to include or exclude particular neighboring cells. For example, the following kernel file (i.e. irr4x4.txt) specifies a 4x4 neighborhood.

```
4 4
0 1 1 1
1 1 1 0
1 1 1 0
0 1 1 0
```

An example expression that would use an irregular neighborhood is:

Focalmean ([Habitat], IRREGULAR, irr4x4.txt)

This neighborhood is used only as a mask, however. Using an additional keyword WEIGHT, the neighborhood values will be multiplied times the cell values, which is similar to *spatial convolution filtering*.[50] This is useful for spatial filtering and image processing. For example, a high-pass filter (e.g., high.txt) that enhances edges looks like:

```
3 3
-0.7 -1.0 -0.7
--1.0 6.8 -1.0
-0.7 -1.0 -0.7
```

and would be called using:

Focalmean ([Habitat], WEIGHT, high.txt)

Another interesting use of focal functions is to implement *cellular automata* (CA) models. A CA model is typically computed using a 2-D array of regular cells where the state of a cell at time t is defined by a set of transition rules that govern local behavior of each cell using the cell's neighboring values. One of the most popular CAs is John Conway's *Game of Life*.[51] This modeling approach is a natural for GRID processing with focal functions[52], and a number of GIS implementations of Life have been developed using map algebra

---

50. Jensen, J.R. 1996. *Introductory digital image processing: A remote sensing perspective.* Prentice-Hall.

51. Gardner, M. 1972. The fantastic combinations of John Conway's new solitaire game "Life."*Scientific American* 233(4):120-123.

52. Theobald, D.M. and M. Gross. 1994. EML: A modeling environment for exploring landscape dynamics. *Computers, Environmental, and Urban Systems* 18(3): 193-204.

expressions.[53] On the next page is an elegant, single-line expression, that, when used iteratively, implements the rules, assuming an initial GRID *G0*:[54]

[G1] = abs(focalsum([G0]) * 2 - [G0] - 6) <= 1

7.6.3.3 Global and application functions

There are a number of advanced global and application-specific functions, and below a few of the more commonly used functions are described (see Table 7.6 for a complete listing of global functions).

Earlier, *cost-weighted distance* was used to compute a *remoteness* surface for the western US. A significant refinement to the previous method used to compute remoteness is to recognize that we travel in different modes: via planes, trains, and automobiles, as well as by boats, buses, bicycles, on horseback, and on foot as well. Ideally then, a distance surface might reflect these different modes of travel, at least the most likely modes. Building on the earlier example of remoteness, let's use the average speed of car travel along different road types, for example: 70 mph on Interstates, 55 mph on highways, and 40 mph on secondary roads; and the average speed of walking given different slopes: 4 mph on flat ground, 3 mph on 1-3°, 2 mph on 3-5°, 1 on >5°. Because we want to express cost in terms of the time it takes to move across a single cell, we'll convert these values to km per hour (corresponding to 1 km cells). Finally, we'll use the inverse (number of hours it takes to cross one cell). The result is a map of remoteness, expressed in hours to access a location from a city, that formalizes our assumption that places closer to large cities are less remote (Figure 7.16).

Computing travel time from cities via car and feet

1. Reclass road type to number of hours it takes to drive across one cell (ROADS).

2. Reclass the slope to the number of hours it takes to walk across 1 cell (Reclass of Slope of Elevation).

3. Compute the cost weight GRID:

con (isnull ([ROADS]), 1.0 / [Reclass of Slope of Elevation], 1.0 / [ROADS])

4. Run the cost weighted distance routine, calculating distance from Cities, using the cost weight GRID just created.

---

53. For example: Wagner, D.F. 1997. Cellular automata and geographic information systems. *Environment and Planning B* 24:219-234.

54. This was created by Bill Huber, 2000. For more information, go to the ESRI ArcScripts web site and search for "Life": http://arcscripts.esri.com/details.asp?dbid=D2AE23B0-71D5-11D4-943200508B0CB419

FIGURE 7.16. Remoteness in the western US (1 km resolution). Isolated areas (dark green) are further from cities (crosses), defined in terms of travel time via automobile along major roads (interstates shown in black) and then by walking from roads. (Download color figures from www.consplan.com).

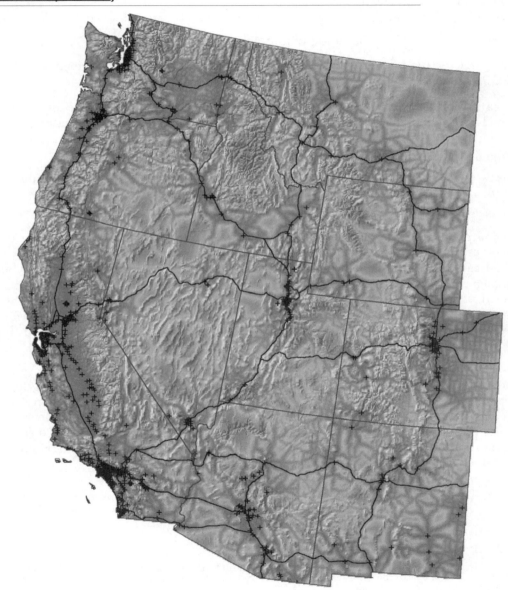

7.6.4 Randomization

Often raster datasets are used as covariates in a statistical model, and so a common task is to obtain the raster values' particular locations. Raster values (e.g., [G1], [G2], [G3], etc.) can be *sampled* at particular locations using a point (e.g., points.shp) or raster layer:

c:\temp\samplesG123 = Sample (c:\temp\points.shp, [G1], [G2], [G3])

The output textfile (space delimited) provides a listing of the point number, *x,y* location, and GRID values.

Typically, random location points are created using a *simple random sample* (SRS)[55] method with feature-based techniques. In a spatial context, a SRS is typically generated by:

- find a minimum bounding rectangle of the desired study area;
- draw a random value from a uniform distribution from 0 to 1, normalize it to the x axis, and created an x value and do the same for the y axis;
- test to see if the new *x,y* location falls within the study area.

One characteristic of the SRS method is that it often results in distribution of random values that have clusters of points or "voids" of points (simply by chance). A slightly more sophisticated method to generate a spatial sample design is to use a spatially-balanced approach that attempts to "spread out" the points to avoid clustering and voids. This is the general approach taken in the *Create Random Points* tool. Rather than using the full extent of the minimum bounding rectangle, the population frame is subset into triangles based on a polygon's vertices. Points are randomly allocated to each of these triangles (area-weighted).

This tool allows the *population frame* (the possible spatial locations from which random points can be drawn from) to be defined by a spatial extent (simple rectangle), to a polygon(s) feature class, or to a polyline(s) feature class. If a feature class is used to define the sampling frame (Constraining Feature Class is specified), then you have the option of specifying a constant number of random points desired for each feature (e.g., 100 points) or a variable number of points per feature that is specified through an attribute field associated with either the polyline or polygon feature class.

---

55. Note that there are a variety of other alternatives, including spatially-balanced sampling: Theobald, D.M. et al. 2007. Using a GIS to generate spatially-balanced random survey designs for natural resource applications. *Environmental Management* 40(1): 134-146.

Random points can also be created in continuous space using raster functions, which provide an easy means to specify *inclusion rates* for different zones so that sampling intensity varies across the study area according to some stratification or desire to sample some areas more or less intensely. The first step is to determine the cell resolution, which should be consistent with the spatial precision that is important for a particular process. It also determines in an indirect way the minimum distance between two random points. If the cell size is too large, then using the center of the randomly selected cells may create a systematic bias. If the cell size is too small, then two points may be too close to one another and would be overly clustered (not well balanced). Second, create a raster that reflects the study area, where all locations within the study are 1 and locations outside

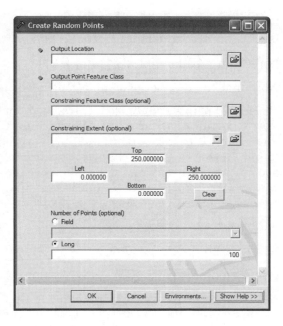

(including exclusion zones within the spatial extent) are NoData. The analysis mask is set to the study area raster. Note that the total number of cells in the study area (at a given resolution) is listed in the count field in the attribute table of the study raster. Third, compute a threshold value (t):

$$t = s/C$$

where s is the number of desired random points and C is the number of cells in the study area. Fourth, find the cell values of a random raster with values ranging from 0.0 to 1.0 (uniformly distributed) that are less than the threshold t. The resulting raster contains the sample locations, which can then be converted to a point feature dataset. For example, if we wanted 100 random points from a 100 x 100 raster, then $t = 100/10000=0.01$:

[r] = rand()

con ([r] < (0.01), 1)

We can also incorporate the number of desired sample locations (i.e. 100) and the number of cells in the study area directly as:

[study] = 1

[study_sum] = zonalsum ([study], [study])

con ([r] < (100.0 / [study_sum]), 1)

Note that the number of sample cells needs to be entered as a floating-point value.

These 100 points could also be stratified, for example, so that 10 quadrats (from a 10x10 raster) are first selected, and then 10 points within each selected quadrat are found. In this case, first change the cell size so that there are 10 x 10 columns and rows, then create a new study raster ([studyq]) and random raster ([rq]) using the coarser cell size. Then, select the quadrats:

[studyq] = 1

[study_sumq] = zonalsum([studyq], [studyq])

[qpts] = con ([rq] < (10.0 / [study_sumq]), 1)

Now, reset the analysis environment so that the cell size is back to 100x100. Next, substitute the quadrat points raster in place of the study area raster, and recall that we want 100 points total:

[studyqpts] = 1

[study_sumq] = zonalsum ([studyqpts], [studyqpts])

[rpts] = con ([rq2] < (100.0 / [study_sumq]), 1)

One of the difficulties with this method, you may have noticed from the graphic on the previous page, is that although it is likely that the desired number of points will be created using this methodology, the exact number is not guaranteed since we are drawing from a distribution of numbers. A straightforward way to address this limitation is to tweak the threshold value slightly to get the exact number of points for that given distribution of random points.

Now, imagine the situation where there are three different zones that require different numbers of samples, perhaps reflecting different geology or land cover types, where the number of points desired for zone 1 = 10, zone 2 = 70, and zone 3 = 20. First, the number of points would need to be converted to a raster; we'll call it: [ZonePts]. Also noticed that there is a "hole" in the middle—this is our exclusion zone where no random points can be located. Following our logic above (creating a study mask raster of 1), use:

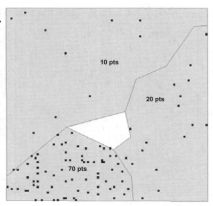

[study_sum] = zonalsum([zonePts], [study1])

con ([r] < ([zonePts] / [study_sum]), 1)

TABLE 7.4. Local operators and functions available through the Raster Calculator.

Group	Usage	Example	Comments
Arith-metic	+ (addition)	G1 + G2	If G1 = 2 and G2 = 3, then G3 = 5
	- (subtraction)	G1 - G2	If G1 = 2 and G2 = 3, then G3 = -1
	* (multiplication)	G1 * G2	If G1 = 2 and G2 = 3, then G3 = 6
	/ (division)	G1 / G2	If G1 = 2 and G2 = 3, then G3 = 0.666. DIV and "/" are equivalent.
	MOD (Modulo)	G1 MOD G2	Returns the integer remainder. If G1 = 7 and G2 = 2, then G3 = 1. Use FMOD to calculate the remainder between two floating point GRIDs.

TABLE 7.4. Local operators and functions available through the Raster Calculator.

Bitwise	!! (exclusive OR)	G3 = G1 !! G2	If G1 = 5 and G2 = 3 (Bitwise G1 = 000000101 and G2 = 00000011), then G3 = 6 (00000110).
	&& (AND)	G3 = G1 && G2	If G1 = 5 and G2 = 3 (Bitwise G1 = 000000101 and G2 = 00000011), then G3 = 1 (00000001).
	<< (left shift)	G1 << G2	If G1 = 1 (0001) and G2 = 2, then it results in a value of 4 (0100). G2 specifies the number of places to shift.
	>> (right shift)	G1 >> G2	If G1 = 7 (0111) and G2 = 1, then it results in a value of 3 (0011). G2 specifies the number of places to shift.
	^^ (complement)	G2 = ^^G1	If G1 = 5 (00000101) then G2 = -6 (11111010) .
	| | (OR)	G3 = G1 | | G2	If G1 = 5 and G2 = 3 (Bitwise G1 = 000000101 and G2 = 00000011), then G3 = 7 (00000111).
Boolean	! (Exclusive OR)	G1 ! G2	Any value other than 0 is TRUE, 0 is FALSE.
	& (AND)	G1 & G2	If the values of both G1 and G2 not 0, then G3 = 1, otherwise 0. The values of floating-point GRIDs are truncated to integer before operation is performed.
	^ (complement)	G2 = ^G1	If G1 is TRUE, then G2 = FALSE, and vice versa.
Combi-natorial	CAnd	G3 = G1 CAnd G2	G3 is a unique value for each unique combination where G1 and G2 are non-zero (TRUE) values.
	Combine(<GRID, ..., GRID>)	G3 = combine (G1, G2)	Combine creates a new unique number for each unique combination of input GRIDs, and the value of each cell is listed in the output GRID's attribute table.
	COr	G3 = G1 COr G2	G3 is a unique value for each unique combination where G1 or G2 are non-zero (TRUE) values.
	CXor	G3 = G1 CXor G2	G3 is a unique value for each unique combination where G1 xor G2 are non-zero (TRUE) values.

TABLE 7.4. Local operators and functions available through the Raster Calculator.

Condi-tional	Con(<condi-tion>, <TrueEx-pression>, <FalseExpres-sion>)	G3 = con(G2 > G1, 1, 0)	Implements if-then-else logic, so that if the value of G2 > G1, then output value equals 1, otherwise 0.
	Pick(<Index-GRID>, <GRID, ..., GRID>)	G5 = Pick(G1, G2, G3, G4)	Uses the value of an input GRID as an index to select which GRID's values will be output. I.e., if G1 = 1, then G1 values will be output, etc.
	SetNull(<condi-tion>, { GRID | number })	G3= Set-null(G1 > 2, G2)	If G1 > 2, then G3 = NoData, otherwise G3 = G2.
	Test(<GRID>, <logicalExpres-sion>)	G3 = test(G1, "value > 2")	Tests or "thresholds" a single GRID based on a conditional statement, so that if the value of G1 > 2 then the output value equals 1, otherwise 0.
Logical	Diff	G3 = G1 DIFF G2	If G1 is different than G2, then G3 = G1, else G3 = 0.
	<GRID	num-ber> In {<list>}	G3 = G1 IN {<list>}	If value in G1 is in a list of values, then G3 = value. E.g., G3 = G1 IN { 0, 1, 2}.
	Over	G3 = G1 OVER G2	If G1 is non-zero, then G3 = G1, else G3 = G2.

TABLE 7.4. Local operators and functions available through the Raster Calculator.

Mathe-matical	Abs (<GRID | number>)	G3 = Abs(G1)	If G1 = -1, then G3 = 1; if G1 = 1, then G3 = 1.
	Ceil (<GRID | number>)	G3 = Ceil(G1)	Returns the next highest integer value. If G1 = 1, then G3 = 1; if G1 = 1.1, then G3 = 2.
	Exp (<GRID | number>)	G3 = Exp(G1)	Calculates the base e (natural) exponent. If G1 = 0.1, then G3 = 1.1.
	Exp10 (<GRID | number>)	G3 = Exp10(G1)	Calculates the base 10 exponent. If G1 = 1, then G3 = 10.
	Exp2 (<GRID | number>)	G3 = Exp2(G1)	Calculates the base 2 exponent. If G1 = 1, then G3 = 2.
	Float(<GRID | number>)	G3 = Float (G1)	Converts values to floating-point values.
	Floor(<GRID | number>)	G3 = Floor (G1)	Returns the next lowest integer value. If G1 = 1, then G3 = 1, if G1= 1.1, then G3 = 1.
	Int (<GRID | number>)	G3 = Int(G1)	Truncates floating-point to integer. If G1 = 1.1, then G3 = 1; if G1 = 1.7, then G3 = 1. To round the number, then use: Int(G1+0.5)
	IsNull(<GRID>)	G3 = IsNull(G1)	Returns 1 if the value in G1 is NODATA. This is often used with Con, e.g., G3=con(IsNull(G1), 99, G1) replaces NODATA cells with 99.
	Ln (<GRID | number>)	G3 = Ln(G1)	Calculates the natural log. If G1 = 2, then G3 = 0.7.
	Log10 (<GRID | number>)	G3 = Log10(G1)	Calculates the base 10 log. If G1 = 2, then G3 = 0.3

TABLE 7.4. Local operators and functions available through the Raster Calculator.

Mathe-matical	Log2 (<GRID | number>)	G3 = Log2(G1)	Calculates the base 2 log. If G1 = 2, then G3 = 1.0
	LPos(<GRID, ..., GRID>)	G4 = LPos (G1,G2,G3)	Finds position of GRID in list with lowest value. E.g., G4=2 if G1=3, G2=2, G3=4.
	Majority(<GRID, ..., GRID>)	G4=Major-ity(G1,G2,G3)	Returns the majority value in list of GRIDs.
	Max(<GRID, ..., GRID>)	G4=Max(G1,G2,G3)	Returns largest value in list of GRIDs
	Mean(<GRID, ..., GRID>)	G4=Mean(G1,G2,G3)	Returns mean value in list of GRIDs.
	Med(<GRID, ..., GRID>)	G4=Med(G1,G2,G3)	Returns median value in list of GRIDs.
	Min(<GRID, ..., GRID>)	G4=Min(G1,G2,G3)	Returns smallest value in list of GRIDs.
	Minority(<GRID, ..., GRID>)	G4=Minor-ity(G1,G2,G3)	Returns most infrequent value in list of GRIDs.
	Pow	G3=Pow(G1,G2)	Raises value in G1 to the power of value in G2.
	Range(<GRID, ..., GRID>)	G4=Range(G1,G2,G3)	Returns the range (max - min) value in list of GRIDs.
	Rank(<GRID, ..., GRID>)	G4=Rank(2,G1,G2,G3)	Returns the value at a given rank order-ing. If G1=2, G2=5, and G3=1, then G4=2.
	SetNull(<condi-tion>, <GRID | number>)	G3=Set-Null(G1,G2)	If G1 is TRUE, then G3=NO DATA, else G3=G2.
	Sqr(<GRID | number>)	G2= Sqr(G1)	Squares a GRID (raises the values to the 2nd power).
	Sqrt(<GRID | number>)	G2= Sqrt(G1)	Computes the square root of the values in G1.
	Std(<GRID, ..., GRID>)	G4=Std(2,G1,G2,G3)	Returns the standard deviation of the val-ues in list of GRIDs.
	Sum(<GRID, ..., GRID>)	G4=Range(G1,G2,G3)	Returns sum of values in list of GRIDs
	UPos(<GRID, ..., GRID>)	G4 = UPos (G1,G2,G3)	Finds position of GRID in list with highest value. E.g., G4=2 if G1=3, G2=2, G3=4.
	Variety(<GRID, ..., GRID>)	G4=Range(G1,G2,G3)	Returns variety (the number of different values) in a list of GRIDs.

TABLE 7.4. Local operators and functions available through the Raster Calculator.

Reclas- sify	Reclass(<GRID>, <remapTable>, {DATA | NODATA}, {InField}, {Out- Field})	G2 = Reclass (G1, remap1.txt)	Reclassifies G1 based on classes specified in a remap table (e.g., remap1.txt).
	Slice(<GRID>, TABLE, <remapTable>, {InField}, {Out- Field}, {InMin}) Slice(<GRID>, EQAREA, <NZones>, {Base- Zone#}, {InMin}, {InMax}) Slice(<GRID>, EQINTERVAL, <NZones>, {Base- Zone#}, {InMin}, {InMax})	G2 = Slice (G1, table, slice.txt)	Changes ranges of values.
Rela- tional	<> (not equal to)	G2 = G1 <> <num>	If G1 does not equal <num>, G2 = 1, else G2 = 0. E.g., G2 = G1 ^= . Same as "^=" or "NE".
	== (equal to)	G2 = G1 == <num>	If G1 equals <num>, then G2 = 1, else 0. This is used to differentiate "=" which is the assignment operator.
	<= (less than or equal to)	G3 = G1 <= G2	If G1 <= G2, then G3 = 1, else G3 = 0.
	<> (not equal to)	G3 = G1 <> G2	If G1 <> G2, then G3 = 1, else G3 = 0.
	> (greater than)	G3 = G1 > G2	If G1 > G2, then G3 = 1, else G3 = 0.
	>= (greater than or equal to)	G3 = G1 >= G2	If G1 >= G2, then G3 = 1, else G3 = 0.
	< (less than)	G1 < G2	If G1 < G2, then G3 = 1, else G3 = 0. Note: For all conditional operators, the result- ing GRID will always have values of 0, 1, or NODATA. If any of the input GRIDs has a value of NODATA, the output will equal NODATA.

TABLE 7.5. Focal functions available through the Raster Calculator.

Usage	Description
BlockMajority() BlockMax() BlockMean() BlockMedian() BlockMin() BlockMinority() BlockRange() BlockStd() BlockVariety()	Computes the statistic in the function name, using the cells defined in the *block* neighborhood. The options below apply to each function, except the WEIGHT option, which does not apply to majority, max, min, minority, and variety. BlockMean(<GRID>, <RECTANGLE>, <width>, <height>, {DATA | NODATA}) BlockMean(<GRID>, <CIRCLE>, <radius>, {DATA | NODATA}) BlockMean(<GRID>, <ANNULUS>, <inner_radius>, <outer_radius>, {DATA | NODATA}) BlockMean(<GRID>, <WEDGE>, <radius>, <start_angle>, <end_angle>, {DATA | NODATA}) BlockMean(<GRID>, <IRREGULAR>, <kernel_file>, {DATA | NODATA}) BlockMean(<GRID>, <WEIGHT>, <kernel_file>, {DATA | NODATA})
FocalMajority() FocalMax() FocalMean() FocalMedian() FocalMin() FocalMinority() FocalRange() FocalStd() FocalSum() FocalVariety()	Computes the statistic in the function name, using the cells defined in the *focal* neighborhood. The options below apply to each function, except the WEIGHT option, which does not apply to majority, max, min, minority, and variety. FocalMean(<GRID>, <RECTANGLE>, <width>, <height>, {DATA | NODATA}) FocalMean(<GRID>, <CIRCLE>, <radius>, {DATA | NODATA}) FocalMean(<GRID>, <ANNULUS>, <inner_radius>, <outer_radius>, {DATA | NODATA}) FocalMean(<GRID>, <WEDGE>, <radius>, <start_angle>, <end_angle>, {DATA | NODATA}) FocalMean(<GRID>, <IRREGULAR>, <kernel_file>, {DATA | NODATA}) FocalMean(<GRID>, <WEIGHT>, <kernel_file>, {DATA | NODATA})

TABLE 7.5. Focal functions available through the Raster Calculator.

LineStats(<LINES>, {item}, {CellSize}, {Statistic}, {Radius})	Computes a statistic using linear features as input. The item name options are: RAND_INT, RAND_FLOAT, or NONE. The statistic options are: MIN, MAX, MEAN, RANGE, MIDRANGE, MEDIAN, MAJORITY, MINORITY, VARIETY, or LENGTH.
PointStats(<POINTS>, {item}, {cellsize}, {statistic}, {neighborhood})	Computes a statistic using point features as input. The item name options are: RAND_INT, RAND_FLOAT, or NONE. The statistic options are: MIN, MAX, MEAN, RANGE, MIDRANGE, MEDIAN, MAJORITY, MINORITY, VARIETY, or NPOINTS. The neighborhood options are: {CIRCLE, {radius}	RECTANGLE, {width}, {height}, {angle}	ELLIPSE, {axis1}, {axis2}, {axis1_angle}	RINGS, {radius1}, {radius2}, ...	WEDGES, {radius1}, <from_angle1>, <to_angle1>, {radius2}, {from_angle2}, {to_angle2}, ...	POLYGON, <vertex_file>}

TABLE 7.6. Zonal functions available through the Raster Calculator.

Usage	Description
ZonalArea(<GRID>)	Calculates the area of each zone of the input GRID, and outputs a GRID with the corresponding zone area in each cell.
ZonalCentroid(<GRID>)	Creates an output GRID with the centroid cell for each zone (all other cells are NoData).
ZonalGeometry (<GRID>, {GeometryType}, {MaxThickness})	Calculates an aspect of the geometry of zones, based on the GeometryType keyword: AREA, PERIMETER, THICKNESS, ELLIPSE, and ALL.
ZonalFill(<ZoneGRID>, <WeightGRID>)	Creates an output GRID with values filled in using minimum value.
ZonalMajority(<ZoneGRID>, <ValueGRID>)	Outputs a GRID whose cell values contain the majority value found in a given zone.
ZonalMax(<ZoneGRID>, <ValueGRID>, {DATA | NODATA})	Outputs a GRID whose cell values contain the maximum value found in a given zone.
ZonalMean(<ZoneGRID>, <ValueGRID>, {DATA | NODATA})	Outputs a GRID whose cell values contain the mean value found in a given zone.
ZonalMedian(<ZoneGRID>, <ValueGRID>, {DATA | NODATA})	Outputs a GRID whose cell values contain the median value found in a given zone.

TABLE 7.6. Zonal functions available through the Raster Calculator.

ZonalMin(<ZoneGRID>, <ValueGRID>, {DATA | NODATA})	Outputs a GRID whose values contain the mean of the <ValueGRID> for the zones defined in <ZoneGRID>.
ZonalMinority(<ZoneGRID>, <ValueGRID>, {DATA | NODATA})	Outputs a GRID whose cell values contain the minority value found in a given zone.
ZonalPerimeter (<GRID>)	Outputs a GRID whose cell values contain the perimeter of a given zone.
ZonalRange(<ZoneGRID>, <ValueGRID>, {DATA | NODATA})	Outputs a GRID whose cell values contain the range value found in a given zone.
ZonalStats(<ZoneGRID>, <ValueGRID>, {StatisticName}, {DATA | NODATA})	Computes the statistic using values from <ValueGRID> for the zones defined in <ZoneGRID>. Valid statistic names are: MAJORITY, MEAN, MIN, MAX, RANGE, SUM, STD, VARIETY, MINORITY, MEDIAN, ALL, EXTREME (returns Min and Max), MOMENT (returns Mean and Std). If no statistic name, then returns MEAN, MIN, and MAX.
ZonalStd(<ZoneGRID>, <ValueGRID>, {DATA | NODATA})	Outputs a GRID whose cell values contain the standard deviation found in a given zone.
ZonalSum(<ZoneGRID>, <ValueGRID>, {DATA | NODATA})	Outputs a GRID whose cell values contain the sum of values found in a given zone.
ZonalThickness(<GRID>, {MaxThickness})	Outputs a GRID whose cell values contain the thickness value found in a given zone.
ZonalVariety(<ZoneGRID>, <ValueGRID>, {DATA | NODATA})	Outputs a GRID whose cell values contain the number of different values found in a given zone.

TABLE 7.7. A comprehensive listing of global functions available through the Raster Calculator.

Group	Usage	Comments

TABLE 7.7. A comprehensive listing of global functions available through the Raster Calculator.

Distance	CostAllocation(<SourceGRID>, <CostGRID>, {OutAccumCost-GRID}, {OutBacklinkGRID}, {MaxDistance}, {ValueGRID})	For each cell, the value of the output GRID is the allocation zone from the sources using <SourceGrid> across a weighted surface using <CostGrid>.
	CostBackLink(<SourceGRID>, <CostGRID>, {OutAccumCost-GRID}, {OutBacklinkGRID}, {MaxDistance}, {ValueGRID})	Finds the neighbor on the least-cost path from a cell to a set of course cells.
	CostDistance(<SourceGRID>, <CostGRID>, {OutAccumCost-GRID}, {OutBacklinkGRID}, {MaxDistance}, {ValueGRID})	Computes the cost weighted distance from each source cell specified in <SourceGRID>, reflecting the impedance values of <CostGRID>.
	CostPath(<FromCellGRID>, <AccumCostGRID>, <Backlink-GRID>, {BYCELL | BYZONE | BYLAYER})	Creates a GRID with the least-cost paths from <From-CellGRID> to closest source defined in <AccumCost-GRID>.
	Corridor(<AccumGRID1>, <AccumGRID2>)	For each cell, it sums the accumulative cost GRIDs.
	EucAllocation(<SourceGRID>, {OutDistGRID}, {OutDirGRID}, {MaxDistance}, {ValueGRID})	Computes the zone of the closest (straight-line) source cell.
	EucDirection(<SourceGRID>, {OutDistanceGRID}, {OutDirection-GRID}, {MaxDistance}, {Value-GRID})	Computes the direction of each cell from the closest source cell.
	EucDistance(<SourceGRID>, {OutDistanceGRID}, {OutDirection-GRID}, {MaxDistance}, {ValGRID})	Computes the distance of each cell from the closest source cell.
	PathDistance(<SourceGRID>, {CostGRID}, {SurfaceGRID}, {HorizFactGRID}, {HorizFact-Parm}, {VertFactorGRID}, {Vert-FactorParm}, {OutBacklinkGRID}, {OutAllocateGRID}, {MaxDist}, {ValGRID})	Computes the least-cost distance from a source cell.

TABLE 7.7. A comprehensive listing of global functions available through the Raster Calculator.

Generalize	Aggregate (G1, <CellFactor>, <Statistic>, { EXPAND | TRUN-CATE }, {DATA | NODATA})	Resamples a GRID to coarser resolution using sum (default), minimum, maximum, mean, or median value of input cells covered by the square spatial extent of the output cell, defined by the *cell factor*. The cell size of the new grid equals the original cell size times <cellFactor>. The extent of the new grid is smaller if TRUNCATE (if the number of rows or columns is not divisible by <cellFactor>). If DATA, then any of the input values are NODATA, then the output grid's values are NODATA. The following <statistic> types are valid: MAX, MEAN, MEDIAN, MIN, SUM. This request should only be used on continuous (ratio) data (use resample for nominal data).
	BoundaryClean(<GRID>, {NOSORT | DESCEND | ASCEND |}, { TWOWAY | ONE-WAY })	Cleans the boundary between zones by expanding and shrinking the boundary. Priority is set by: NOSORT (no sorting by size, but zones with larger values have higher priority); DESCEND (descending order by size); or ASCEND (ascending order by size). The cleaning process is done only once if ONE-WAY, otherwise it is done twice, with the second pass reversing the priority. Can only be done on integer grids.
	Expand (<GRID>, <NCells>, LIST, <ValueList>)	Expands zones in <GRID> listed in <ValueList> by <NCells>.
	MajorityFilter(<GRID>, {FOUR | EIGHT}, {MAJORITY | HALF})	Filters values in <GRID> using a majority statistic. This is similar to FocalMajority, but you can require that at least half the cells are the same value with HALF.
	Nibble (<GRID>, <MaskGRID>, {ALL | DATAONLY})	Replaces the cells of <GRID> if the cells in <MaskGRID> are NoData, and the replacement values are the nearest neighbors. If DATAONLY, then only neighbors with non-NoData values are used.
	Shrink(<GRID>, <NCells>, LIST, <ValueList>)	Shrinks zones of <GRID> defined in the <ValueList> by <NCells>. <GRID> must be integer.
	Thin(<GRID>, {POSITIVE | DATA}, {NOFILTER | FILTER}, {ROUND | SHARP}, {thickness})	Thins linear features in <GRID>. All non NoData values are thinned. Boundaries are smoothed if FILTER; right-angled corners are preserved if SHARP. Thickness defines the maximum thickness of linear features in map units.

TABLE 7.7. A comprehensive listing of global functions available through the Raster Calculator.

Geometric transformation	Flip(<GRID>)	Flips<GRID> in the Y direction (top to bottom).
	Merge(<GRID>, ..., <GRID>)	Merges <GRID>s. When the cells overlap, the priority is determined by their order.
	Mirror(<GRID>)	Flips<GRID> in the X direction (Left to right).
	Mosaic(<GRID>,..., <GRID>)	Mosaics <GRID>s, but overlapping cells are averaged to create a smooth transition. Do not use this on GRIDs with nominal values.
	Resample (<GRID>, {CellSize}, {NEAREST | BILINEAR | CUBIC | SEARCH })	Creates a new GRID with the specified resolution <CellSize> using nearest neighbor (for nominal data), bilinear interpolation, cubic convolution, or SEARCH (extended nearest neighbor).
	Rotate(<GRID>, <Angle>, {NEAREST | BILINEAR | CUBIC })	Rotates <GRID> clockwise about the lower-left corner by <Angle> in degrees, using nearest neighbor, bilinear interpolation, or cubic convolution.
	Shift(<GRID>, <XMin>, <YMin>, {CellSize})	Creates new GRID that is shifted by x,y (in map units) with cells that are <CellSize>.
	Warp(<GRID>, <LinkFeature | LinkFile>, {Order}, {NEAREST | BILINEAR | CUBIC }, {FORWARD | BACKWARD}, {OutCellSize})	Transforms all cells according to a polynomial transformation, achieving the best overall fit within the points specified in <Link...>.

TABLE 7.7. A comprehensive listing of global functions available through the Raster Calculator.

Ground-water	DarcyFlow(<HeadElevGRID>, <PorosityGRID>, <Thickness-GRID>, <TransmissivityGRID>, {OutDirectionGRID, OutMagnitudeGRID})	Computes groundwater volume balance using Darcy's Law.
	ParticleTrack(<FlowDirGRID>, <FlowMagGRID>, <x,y>, {StepLength}, {Time}, {OutTrack-Coverage})	Computes the path of a particle through a velocity field
	PorousPuff(<TrackFile>, <Porosi-tyGRID>, <ThicknessGRID>, <Mass>, {time}, {longDispersivity}, {DispersRatio}, {RetardFactor}, {DecayCoeff})	Calculates distribution of mass per volume of a solute.
Hydrologic	Basin (<DirectionGRID>)	Delineates all drainage basins with spatial extent using <DirectionGRID>.
	FlowAccumulation(<Direction-GRID>, { WeightGRID })	Accumulates the number of cells above a cell that would flow into or contribute runoff into it. <DirectionGRID> has flow direction values, <WeightGRID> assigns weight to each cell.

TABLE 7.7. A comprehensive listing of global functions available through the Raster Calculator.

Hydrologic	FlowDirection(<GRID>, {ODrop-GRID}, {NORMAL | FORCE})	Calculates the flow direction in <>. If ODrop-GRID is specified, then an optional GRID that shows the ratio of the maximum change in elevation is output. All cells on the edge of the surface will flow away if FORCE.
	FlowLength(<DirectionGRID, {WeightGRID}, {DOWNSTREAM | UPSTREAM})	Calculates the accumulated flow length to each cell. The impedence to move through a cell is specified by WeightGRID. Length is calculated from the top of the drainage down to the cell if DOWNSTREAM.
	FocalFlow(<GRID>, {Thresh-Value})	Determines which of the eight neighboring cells flow into the center cell. The Thresh-Value is added to the center cell's value. Because there is a possibility that all neighboring cells are greater, the value is encoded in a binary scheme, where, starting to the right of center and working clockwise, are the values 1, 2, 4, 8, 16, 32, 64, and 128.
	Sink(<DirectionGRID>)	Computes the pits or sinks in <DirectionGRID>. Usually Sink is used to pre-process data to remove spurious artifacts in the data.
	SnapPour(<GRID | Point>, <AccumGRID>, {SnapDistance})	Snaps pour points to highest flow accumulation.
	StreamLink(<NetGRID>, <DirectionGRID>)	This is used to identify stream sections, and assigns a unique value for each section of raster linear network.
	StreamOrder(<NetGRID>, <DirectionGRID>, { STRAHLER | SHREVE })	Assigns a stream order to stream segments of <GRID>, using Shreve ordering (adds segments downslope when two segments intersect, their magnitudes are added) or Strahler (stream order increases downstream only when streams of the same order intersect).
	StreamShape(<NetGRID>, <DirectionGRID>, {NOWEED | WEED})	Converts a GRID representing a stream network to a polyline shapefile. This uses <DirectionGRID> to aid in vectorizing cells. If WEED, then generalization using Douglas-Peucker algorithm is used.
	Watershed(<DirectionGRID, <SourceGRID>)	Creates a GRID that represents watersheds or basins using <DirectionGRID>, from all non-NoData values in <SourceGRID>.

TABLE 7.7. A comprehensive listing of global functions available through the Raster Calculator.

Surface	Aspect (<GRID>)	Computes the direction of maximum change in surface <GRID>, in degrees (0 North, increasing clockwise).
	Contour(<GRID>, <INTERVAL>, <InterVal>, { base })	Creates isolines for the input< GRID>, starting at base, and incrementing every <InterVal>. This returns a polyline shapefile.
	Curvature(<GRID>, {Out-ProfCurve}, {OutPlanCurve}, {Out-Slope}, {OutAspect})	Computes the 2nd derivative of a surface <GRID> by fitting a 4th order polynomial through each cell. Convex upward are positive values, convex are negative.
	CutFill	Not implemented at v8.2.
Surface	Hillshade(<GRID>, {Azimuth}, {Altitude}, {ALL | SHADE | SHADOW }, {ZFactor})	Computes illumination of surface <GRID>, with source at <Azimuth>, and zenith or Altitude. ALL considers both local illumination angles and shadows; SHADE does not consider shadows; SHADOW finds only shadows and returns 0s (shadow), 1 (not shadow).
	Slope (<GRID>, {DEGREE | PER-CENTRISE}) Slope (<GRID>, {ZFactor}, {DEGREE | PERCENTRISE})	Computes slope of <GRID> using ZFactor of 1.0 and returns values in DEGREES or PERCENTRISE.
	Visibility (<GRID>, <Feature>, {POINT | LINE}, {FREQUENCY | OBSERVERS})	Computes the visibility on a surface <GRID> from source location <Feature>. FREQUENCY records the number of times a cell can be seen from input points (<17). OBSERVERS records whether the observation point can be seen from that cell.

7.7 Chapter review

- A raster dataset typically represents geographic phenomena that vary continuously through space.

- A raster contains a matrix or grid of *cells* that contain a single numeric value, such as a brightness value or a land cover type.

- There are five classes of functions that operate on raster data: *local, neighborhood* (aka *focal), zonal, global,* and *application-specific.*

- A *zone* is composed of one or more cells that have the same integer value, and these cells are often contiguous but can also be disconnected or non-adjacent. A *region* is also composed of one or more cells that have the same value, but the cells must be contiguous.

- Spatial Analyst allows you to easily convert data between vector and raster data formats, but conversion can result in loss of information. Generally, using finer resolution produces better results, but the trade-off is that file sizes grow exponentially with increasing resolution.

8   *Single-layer analysis*

In this chapter, basic analytical techniques are described that operate on a single map of either feature or raster type. Most often, simple summary statistics are computed for feature attributes. But various aspects of features themselves are computed as well, such as area, length, and shape, and the relationship between features, such as average distance between features. Proximity analysis buffers features to examine how relationships change with distance. Finally, features are occasionally transformed from one type to another to facilitate spatial analysis.

8.1 Geoprocessing basics

Although up until now the term Geoprocessing has been mentioned, it really has not been fully explored. *Geoprocessing* is the broader framework in ArcGIS that includes applying an operation (with a tool) to manipulate some GIS datasets. The result of an operation is an output dataset. The Arc-Toolbox is the central repository for the tools (or operations).

With the flexibility and power of the variety of tools is that users can easily create many new datasets, so that data management becomes quite an important skill. One recommended way to track your work is to track your actions in ArcGIS by opening up a text editor and typing in notes as you go along through your work session.

8.1.1 Auto-documentation through History

A very useful capability of ArcGIS is the auto-documentation of much of its processing through the ArcToolbox History toolbox and the *Results tab* in ArcToolbox. Anytime you use a tool in an ArcGIS session, it is recorded as a "result" and captured in the *History toolbox*. The information includes not only what tool was used, what inputs (i.e. datasets, parameters, etc.), and any associated messages that provides information about when it was executed, how long it took, etc.

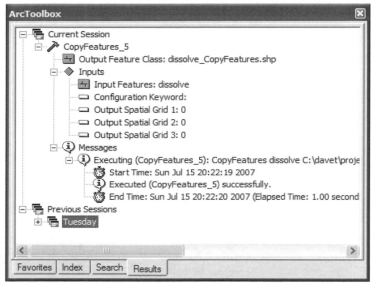

And, because all the information required to re-run the tool is captured, you can easily open the tool (right-click) and re-run the tool with the settings already specified. This is great stuff. Not only to document your work sessions but to allow you to re-do your work quickly and efficiently. Access the History toolbox through ArcCatalog. In addition to placing information in the history toolbox, information about geoprocessing history is placed automatically into the metadata of the output dataset. This can be accessed through ArcCatalog and the metadata for a given dataset. Look for the *Geoprocessing History* link in the metadata record

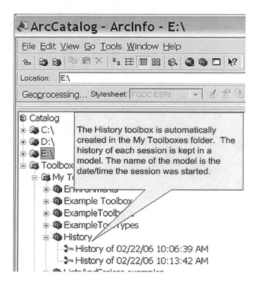

The History toolbox is automatically created in the My Toolboxes folder. The history of each session is kept in a model. The name of the model is the date/time the session was started.

8.1.2 Batch geoprocessing

There are situations where you might want to run the same tool a number of times using slightly different parameters. This is called *batch processing*. For example, imagine you wanted to create a series of polygon features that were the result of buffers around cities at incremental distances, say 1000, 2000, and 3000 meters. To open a tool in batch mode, simply right-click on the tool and select Batch (double-clicking on it opens it). Then, simply fill out the rows to specify the parameters for a given tool. Note that you can create a blank row (by clicking on the plus sign) and then can select and copy/paste between lines.

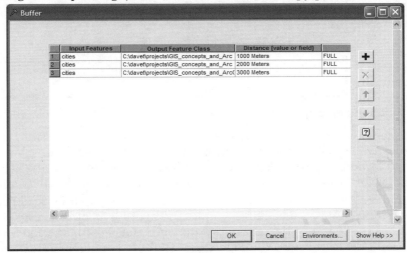

8.2 Summarizing attributes

A basic way to analyze data is to compile statistics for selected features of a map. This allows you to answer questions such as: How many total acres do the Great Lakes occupy? How many miles of interstate highway are there in the western US? How many people are there along the forest fringe in the western US?

8.2.1 Basic statistics

Probably the most common way to analyze geographic features is to compute basic statistics. For example, how many people are there in United States in 2000? What is the average population by county? Many statistics can be computed for the attributes of selected features in a layer, but typically the following are used: count, minimum,

---

maximum, sum, mean, and standard deviation. For example, the arithmetic mean value ($\bar{X}$) is computed by:

$$\bar{X} = \sum_{i=1}^{n} x_i / n$$

where x represents the attribute of interest and n is the number of data points (features or records). Note that you can select the text inside the

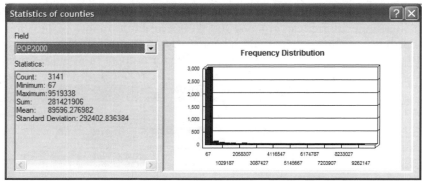

statistics so that you can copy and paste into a spreadsheet or text report document.

There are three ways to compute statistics in ArcGIS. First, in ArcMap, the *Selection Statistics* dialog can be opened without first specifying the layer or attribute field. This dialog allows differences between layers to be easily compared by selecting layers from the drop-down list. Note that only layers that have some selected features are available through the dialog,[1] and that statistics can be performed only on numerical fields that are listed in the field drop-down list. For example, the average population by US county in 2000 equals 87,631. The Selection Statistics dialog is not modal, so you can change the feature selection (either through the Select by Attributes dialog or interactively on the map) and the statistics will be dynamically updated. The second method, also in ArcMap,

---

1. If none of the layers have selected features, then the menu is greyed out. Note that this is inconsistent with the rest of the ArcMap interface that assumes that no features being selected is the same as if all features are selected.

is to compute statistics directly on a field from a particular attribute table. Statistics can also be computed from the attribute table when opened through ArcCatalog.

Calculating statistics for tables using Statistics

1. In ArcMap, open the attribute table that contains the field to be analyzed by right-clicking on the desired layer and selecting Open Attribute Table.

2. Right-click on the field that contains the values to analyze and select Statistics....

3. The results of the various statistics of the selected records are listed in the lower-left box.

4. Close the dialog when finished.

Calculating statistics for layers using Selection Statistics

1. In ArcMap, select Selection-->Statistics.

2. Select the layer to compute the statistics on.

3. Select the field from the selected layer to compute statistics on.

4. Close the dialog when finished.

8.2.1.1 Weighted statistics

When using count values (e.g., population) collected in analytical units that vary broadly in size, it may be more appropriate to weight the values by the area or length of the collection unit. The *weighted mean* ($\bar{X}$) is computed by:

$$\bar{X} = \sum_{i=1}^{n} w_i x_i / \sum_{i=1}^{n} w_i$$

where w is the weight and x is the value of interest (e.g., population). For example, the area-weighted mean population in 2000 by county is 106,561.9. This makes more sense for computing area for counties, particularly because the minimum and maximum county

---

area differs by nearly five orders of magnitude! Other statistics (such as standard deviation) can be computed in a similar fashion.

Calculating area-weighted mean

1. In ArcMap, open the attribute table.

2. Add a field called Weighted of type Double.

3. Calculate the Weighted field to equal the attribute of interest times the [Area] field, e.g., [Area] * [Pop2000].

4. Compute the sum of the Weighted field and write it down.

5. Compute the sum of the field that was used to weight, e.g.,: [Area], and write it down.

6. Divide the sum of the Weighted field by the sum of the area field.

8.2.2 Summarize

Another common way to analyze data is to summarize attribute data based on unique occurrences of a value within a field containing any type of data (i.e. qualitative as well as quantitative). When you summarize an attribute table, ArcMap creates a new table that counts the occurrences of each value of a field from the selected set of records. Each record in the new table contains at least two fields: the first lists the unique values found in the selected field and the second lists the number of records that have this value. These tables can be related, though the relationship may be one-to-one or many-to-one.

Also, additional numerical fields can be selected to summarize using a statistical method, including: minimum, maximum, mean, standard deviation, sum, and variance. A typical use of this function is to identify all unique values that occur

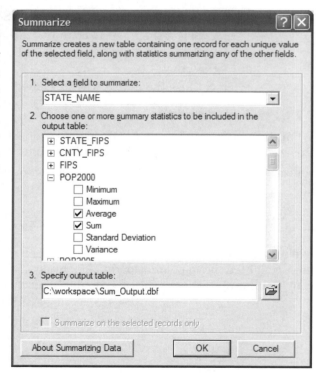

in a field that contains nominal or class data. For example, if you wanted to find the number of land cover polygons and the total area of the polygons by land cover type, you would summarize on the "type" field by making it active (e.g., Lucode). Then, you can add a statistic by selecting on the "area" field, selecting the "Sum" statistic and adding it to the table. Note that the field you are summarizing on (the active field) is not available for other statistics.

Summarizing data is a convenient way to filter or preprocess data to discover possible data entry or logical errors in a dataset before you invest a lot of time creating maps and computing statistics. For example, summarizing a field that represents nominal values is a quick way to determine all classes represented in an attribute table, and often data entry errors can be discovered. A summary table can also be created from an attribute table, then joined back to the attribute table to calculate various proportions, differences from average values, etc. For example, if you want to calculate the proportion of the total class area occupied by each polygon, you would first create the summary table, then relate the tables based on the class code field ("Lucode"). Then, add another field in which to calculate the proportion (e.g., [Area] / [Total area in Class]). Note that in order to combine adjacent features (dissolving the shared boundaries), you need to use the *Dissolve tool*.

Summarizing attribute data
ArcToolbox -> Analysis -> Statistics -> **Summary Statistics**.

8.2.3 Using Summarize to generate descriptive statistics

Let's illustrate how to use the Summarize tool to generate a table of descriptive statistics, which is a fairly common task in environmental assessments. I acquired a vegetation dataset from the National Park Service for Rocky Mountain National Park (RMNP), which contains 36,158 polygons for 46 different vegetation types. To compute the composition of the park by vegetation cover type, first summarize the attribute table on the unique vegetation type (i.e. "COMMON_MAP" field) and calculate the average, sum, and standard deviation of the HECTARES field.

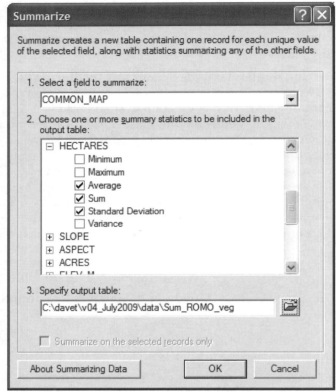

Second, sum the total area of all polygons (172983.26 ha) by right-clicking on the HECTARES field and selecting Statistics... Finally, add a new field (i.e. "Pcnt", DOUBLE) and calculate it to be:

([Sum_HECTARES] / 172983.2625) * 100

This provides a nice summary table (below) that shows that the dominant vegetation type in the park is *Sub-alpine Mixed Conifer*, covering about 24% of the park. Also, the iconic aspen vegetation that draws many visitors to the park in the fall occupies less than 1% (*Riparian Aspen* 0.21% and *Upper Montane Aspen* 0.59%). The Count field provides a count of the number of polygons ("patches") of each cover type (i.e. 320 and 1,349 respectively), while the Average field provides some indication as to the distribution of aspen-dominated patches (i.e. 1.2 ha and 0.8 ha, respectively).

However, one of the challenges of using basic descriptive statistics is that they can be misleading for data that are not normally distributed. So, let's examine the distribution of the aspen patches. To do this, extract the attributes for just the *Riparian Aspen* polygons by using Select by Attributes ("COMMON_MAP" = 'Riparian Aspen'), resulting in 320 polygons being selected. Rather than simply exporting the selected records to a new table, we will use a bit of a trick here to have ArcGIS order the polygons by size. To do this, use Summarize on the HECTARES field (and be sure to summarize on selected records only).

Attributes of Sum_ROMO_veg

OID	COMMON_MAP	Count	Average	Sum_H	Pcnt
0	Blue Spruce	95	2.1	200.4	0.12
1	Cliff Face - Bare Soil / Rock	162	41.9	6780.5	3.92
2	Cottonwood	29	1.1	31.1	0.02
3	Disturbance - Dead and Down	108	4.2	449.6	0.26
4	Exposed Soil - Man made	50	4.2	211.1	0.12
5	Glacier	93	1.6	145.1	0.08
6	Herbaceous Upland Alpine > 9600 ft	1268	4.7	5997.9	3.47
7	Herbaceous Upland Alpine Fellfield	685	11.3	7717.9	4.46
8	Herbaceous Upland Montane < 9600 ft	1518	2.5	3721.5	2.15
9	Herbaceous Wetland Cross Zone - Marsh	59	0.5	30.8	0.02
10	Herbaceous Wetland Cross Zone - Wetland	1912	1.5	2822	1.63
11	Herbaceous Wetland SubAlpine / Alpine - Alpin	1373	6.3	8654.4	5
12	Juniper	103	3.5	360.2	0.21
13	Krummholz	3356	1.1	3686.5	2.13
14	Lodgepole Pine - High Elevation > 9500 ft	1039	10.3	10721.	6.2
15	Lodgepole Pine - Low Elevation < 9500 ft	2438	7.3	17751.	10.26
16	Lodgepole Pine - Rock	145	3.3	485.1	0.28
17	Mixed Conifer with Aspen (Douglas-fir)	533	2.1	1139.9	0.66
18	Mixed Conifer with Aspen (Lodgepole Pine)	461	1.6	741.7	0.43
19	Mixed Conifer with Aspen (Ponderosa Pine)	403	2.1	835.9	0.48
20	Mixed Conifer with Aspen (Spruce - Fir)	254	2.1	527.9	0.31
21	Montane Douglas Fir	2279	6.7	15359.	8.88
22	Natural Lakes - Ponds	532	1.9	985.8	0.57
23	Outwash	5	10.7	53.5	0.03
24	Ponderosa Pine Graminoid	1136	4.9	5593.1	3.23
25	Ponderosa Pine Rockland	807	5.9	4797.6	2.77
26	Ponderosa Pine Shrubland	804	6.4	5140.2	2.97
27	Reservoirs - Stock tanks	51	16.5	842.4	0.49
28	Ribbon forests Islands	14	3.2	44.8	0.03
29	Riparian Aspen	320	1.2	370.8	0.21
30	Riparian Lower Montane Mixed Conifer < 8500	136	2.9	397.8	0.23
31	Riparian Upper Montane Mixed Conifer > 8500 f	662	5	3340.9	1.93
32	Rock (Alpine-Upper Subalpine)	559	2.4	1362.4	0.79
33	Rock (Foothill-Lower Subalpine)	2229	0.5	1170.9	0.68
34	Shrub Riparian Cross Zone < 9600 ft	505	2.6	1329.2	0.77
35	Shrub Riparian Cross Zone > 9600 ft	476	3.3	1577.8	0.91
36	Shrub Upland Alpine	727	2.5	1838.5	1.06
37	Shrub Upland Lower Montane - Big Sagebrush	160	2.9	462.3	0.27
38	Shrub Upland Lower Montane - Bitterbrush	64	1.5	94.3	0.05
39	Shrub Upland Lower Montane - Undifferentiate	485	2.7	1291.2	0.75
40	Streams - Rivers	38	2.1	80.5	0.05
41	SubAlpine Limber Pine	513	5.2	2681.2	1.55
42	SubAlpine Mixed Conifer	4515	9.4	42244	24.42
43	Talus	1564	4.4	6824.1	3.94
44	Unvegetated Surface	144	7.4	1070.6	0.62
45	Upper Montane Aspen	1349	0.8	1016.9	0.59

Record: |◄ ◄ [0] ► ►| Show: All | Selected   Records (0 ▼

Assuming that the values in the HECTARES field are unique, then the values in Count should all be 1. I added another field ("ROrder", DOUBLE) and calculated it to be:.

([OID] + 1) / 320.

The cool thing about this table is that it is ordered by polygon size and the ROrder field allows deciles to be identified in the distribution. For example, the smallest 10% (1st decile) of riparian aspen patches is shown at right.

Attributes of Sum_RiparianAspen

OID	HECTARES	Count_HECTARES	ROrder
0	0.020308	1	0.003125
1	0.024261	1	0.00625
2	0.026885	1	0.009375
3	0.029624	1	0.0125
4	0.030248	1	0.015625
5	0.032041	1	0.01875
6	0.03317	1	0.021875
7	0.034477	1	0.025
8	0.035766	1	0.028125
9	0.037707	1	0.03125
10	0.04031	1	0.034375
11	0.046098	1	0.0375
12	0.047107	1	0.040625
13	0.047751	1	0.04375
14	0.049227	1	0.046875
15	0.050873	1	0.05
16	0.05178	1	0.053125
17	0.052045	1	0.05625
18	0.054435	1	0.059375
19	0.058751	1	0.0625
20	0.058945	1	0.065625
21	0.060994	1	0.06875
22	0.063145	1	0.071875
23	0.063188	1	0.075
24	0.063319	1	0.078125
25	0.064116	1	0.08125
26	0.064716	1	0.084375
27	0.066831	1	0.0875
28	0.067126	1	0.090625
29	0.067548	1	0.09375
30	0.071991	1	0.096875
31	0.074916	1	0.1

Record: 0 Show: All lect

This also provides the basis for a powerful way to visualize distributions called a Cumulative Distribution Function (CDF), which is complementary to a histogram. This allows patches to be identified on the basis of their relative importance or rank within some overall distribution. This CDF plot shows that most of the patches are quite small: half of them are less than 0.45 ha in size, while the top 10% (0.9 proportion) are larger than 2.6 ha. It also, importantly, shows that the distribution of patch area is a highly skewed distribution (i.e. not normally distributed). Consequently, basic descriptive statistics such as average can be misleading (i.e. average of 1.2 ha is in the 75% percentile of this distribution).

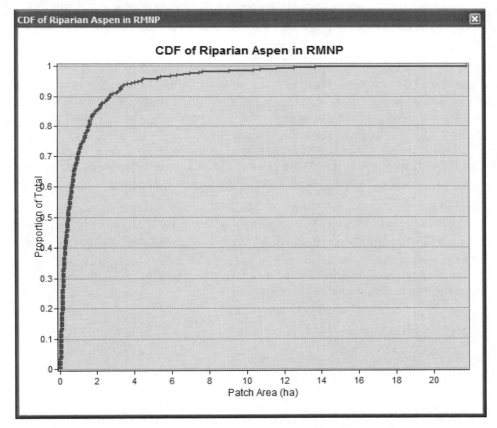

8.3 Measurement

Many ways have been developed to measure different aspects about geographic features that are represented on a map. Below are some of the more commonly used methods.

8.3.1 Number

A basic way to measure a map is to simply count the number of features. This can be obtained easily using either the *statistics* or *summarize* tools. Note that the number of selected features in a layer is displayed in the status bar (lower-left) of ArcMap, and in the lower-left hand portion of an attribute table.

8.3.2 Area

Before the age of electronic mapping, there were two basic methods to measure *area* from a map. The first was to estimate the area by placing a sheet of plastic containing a grid of dots on top of a map and counting the number of dots found in a polygon of interest.[2] A second method was to trace the boundary of a polygon using a mechanical device called a *planimeter*. These methods were tedious, time consuming, and error prone.[3] In fact, the Canadian Land Inventory (what is recognized as the first GIS) was justified by a cost-benefit analysis that showed that it was more cost effective to compute the area of a land resource unit electronically, even with 1965 computer technology![4]

The standard method to compute area in GIS is based on finding triangles or trapezoids using the vertices of a polygon. For example, to compute the area of a simple polygon (assuming a plane), sum the product of the vertex vectors.[5] An alternative method is to sum trapezia formed by every segment of a polygon and the baseline through the origin.[6] The following is used to compute the area (A) using triangles, and assumes that the polygon vertices (x,y) are in clockwise order:

$$A = \frac{1}{2} \sum_{i=1}^{n-1} (x_i y_{i+1}) minus (y_i x_{i+1})$$

---

2. Wood, W.F. 1954. The dot planimeter: a new way to measure area. *Professional Geographer* 6:12-14.
3. For example, see: Frolov, Y.S. and D.H. Maling. 1969. The accuracy of area measurement by point counting techniques. *Cartographic Journal* 6:21-35.
4. Longley, P.A., M.F. Goodchild, D.J. Maguire, and D.W. Rhind. 2002. *Geographic Information Systems and Science*. Wiley & Sons.
5. Worboys, M.F. 1995. *GIS: A Computing Perspective*. Taylor & Francis. Page 214.
6. Jones, C.B. 1997. *Geographical Information Systems and Computer Cartography*. Longman. Page 65.

Within ArcMap, feature area can be calculated using a short equation in the Field Calculator (see Chapter 6). For raster data, the area of a zone in a GRID (A_z) can be computed by:

$$A_z = c \times r^2$$

where c is the number of cells in the count field and r is the cell resolution (width of a cell). The area units are the same as the coordinate system units (a.k.a. map units). It is wise to set the field name to specify the units (e.g., "hectares" rather than "area").

8.3.3 Length

A central characteristic of a linear feature is its *length* (and perimeter for areal features). Length is computed by summing the length of each straight-line segment calculated using the Pythagorean theorem. Because line segments are not always able to capture the small turns and wiggles of real-world linear features (e.g., a road or trail), map-based measurement of length underestimates "true" length slightly. Typically, the finer the scale of the map, the less underestimation is involved. In addition, length is typically thought of in two-dimensional space, where the third dimension, topographic variation, is ignored.

Estimation of length or perimeter using raster datasets is subject to artifacts that can cause severe underestimation and overestimation. If a very coarse resolution GRID is used to represent a sinuous linear feature (e.g., a winding road up a hillside), then the length can be significantly underestimated. On the other hand, orientation artifacts can cause significant problems, so that a linear feature aligned at 45° to the GRID can overestimate length by up to 41%.[7]

8.3.4 Shape

Shape is often measured for areal features to distinguish those features that are long and skinny from those with a compact or round shape.

8.3.4.1 Compactness index

Although the perimeter (P) to area (A) ratio can be used, it is more common and useful to measure shape by comparing a polygon to a normal form, usually a circle (but occasionally a square, especially for raster data). The equation to compute the compactness index (S_c) for a circle is:[8]

7. Theobald, D.M. 2000. Correcting linear and perimeter measurement errors in raster-based data. *Cartography and Geographic Information Science* 27(2): 111-116.
8. Patton, D.R. 1975. A diversity index for quantifying habitat 'edge'. *Wildlife Society Bulletin* 3:171-173.

$$S_c = \frac{P}{2\sqrt{\pi A}}$$

Values of S_c range from 1 (compact) to greater than 1 (less compact, more distended).

Computing compactness (relative to a circle)

1. In ArcMap, open Field Calculator dialog.
2. Check Advanced box and in the pre-logic box enter:

   Dim dblArea as Double
   Dim dblLength as Double
   Dim dblC as Double
   Dim pArea as IArea
   Dim pCurve As ICurve
   Set pArea = [shape]
   dblArea = pArea.area
   Set pCurve = [Shape]
   dblPerimeter = pCurve.Length
   dblC = dblPerimeter / (3.544908 * sqr (dblArea))

3. In the field expression box, enter:

   dblC

4. Click OK.

8.3.4.2 Zonal geometry

For raster-based features, basic aspects about the shape of zones can be obtained through the Zonal functions. In addition to area and perimeter, the *ZonalGeometry* function computes thickness and a number of parameters based on fitting an ellipse to each zone. *Thickness* is the radius (in cells) of the largest circle that can be fit wholly within a zone. The *major* and *minor* axes of the best-approximating ellipse are dimensioned so that the ellipse area equals the zone area, and the *orientation* specifies the angle between the axes. The ellipse is placed at the *x,y centroid*.

8.3.4.3 Sinuosity

Although less common, the sinuosity (S_s) of a linear feature (a.k.a. "wiggliness") represented as a polyline is measured as the ratio of the straight-line distance from the start to the end of a line (L_e), divided by the full (meandering) length of a line (L_f):

$$S_s = \frac{L_e}{L_f}$$

Values of S_s run from 0 (very sinuous) to 1 (straight).

Computing sinuosity

1. In ArcMap, open Field Calculator dialog.
2. Check Advanced box and in the pre-logic box enter:

```
Dim dblLe as Double
Dim dblLf as Double
Dim dblS as Double
Dim pCurve As Icurve
Dim pFPoint As IPoint
Dim pTPoint As IPoint
Set pCurve = [Shape]
Set pFPoint = pCurve.FromPoint
Set pTPoint = pCurve.ToPoint
dblLe = Sqr((pFPoint.x - pTPoint.x) ^ 2 + (pFPoint.Y - pTPoint.Y) ^ 2)
dblLf = pCurve.Length
dblS = dblLe/dblLf
```

3. In the field expression box, enter:

```
dblS
```

4. Click **OK**.

8.3.5 Fragmentation

A wide variety of fragmentation indices have been developed, including simple metrics such as the number of patches (though this is really only meaningful if the patches are defined functionally). More useful measures have been developed, particularly in the landscape ecology field, that evaluate fragmentation based on the *landscape composition* or *landscape structure* (a.k.a. *configuration*) of patches. A number of stand alone and hybrid GIS programs have been developed to compute these indices as well. For example, the classic *FRAGSTATS* program provides description of a variety of landscape metrics.[9] However, a number of basic metrics can be easily computed in GIS. Also, an ArcGIS

---

9. McGarigal, K., and B. J. Marks. 1995. *FRAGSTATS: spatial pattern analysis program for quantifying landscape structure*. USDA For. Serv. Gen. Tech. Rep. PNW-351. Available at: http://www.umass.edu/landeco/research/fragstats/fragstats.html

toolbox has been developed called *LCaP* (*Landscape Connectivity and Pattern*) that can compute a variety of functional connectivity and landscape pattern metrics using ModelBuilder.[10]

8.3.5.1 Fragmentation index

Fragmentation (*p*) of a map can be calculated as the ratio of the number of contiguous map regions *(m)*, or the number of polygons that would result after classifying and dissolving the boundaries between same-valued neighboring polygons, to the number of original polygons *(n)*:[11]

$$p = \frac{m \ minus \ 1}{n \ minus 1} \qquad .$$

This *fragmentation index* ranges from 1, complete fragmentation (where *m=n*), to 0, completely connected (where *m=0*). For raster data, *m* equals the number of regions (the number of records in the attribute table after using *RegionGroup* function), while *n* equals the number of cells in the raster.[12] As an example, consider the land cover pattern shown in Figure 8.1. Site A has a *p* of 0.059 = (473-1)/(7979-1), while Site B has a *p* of 0.009 =(74-1)/(7979-1) and indeed, Site B looks more connected than Site A. Note that this requires that some classification and dissolving occurs. Otherwise, *m* and *n* are the same with a polygon dataset.

---

10. Theobald, D.M. 2007. LCaP v1.0: Landscape Connectivity and Pattern tools for ArcGIS. Colorado State University, Fort Collins, CO. www.nrel.colostate.edu/'davet/lcap

11. Chou, Y.H. 1997. *Exploring spatial analysis in GIS.* Onword Press. Note that this was originally proposed by Monmonier, M.S. 1974. Measures of pattern complexity for choroplethic maps. *The American Cartographer* 1(2): 159-169.

12. This does not necessarily equal the number of rows times columns, but can be found by summing the Count field.

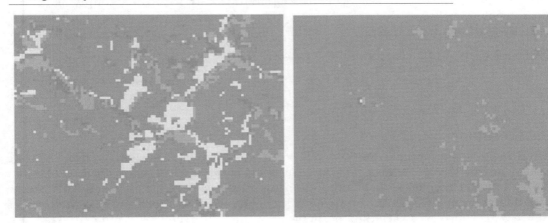

8.3.5.2 Relative size of the largest patch

Another measure of fragmentation is the *relative size of the largest patch metric* (RS_i).[13] RS_i is the ratio of the area of the largest patch (a_i) to the area of all the patches of the same class as the largest patch (A_i):[14]

$$RS_i = \frac{a_i}{p_i \times A_i}$$

The area of a_i can be found by using the Statistics tool on the area (feature based) or count field (GRID based). RS_i for a connected landscape approaches a value of 1.0, while fragmented landscape approach 0.0. For the example landscapes, the RS_i for Site A = 0.705 = (4368/6192) and for Site B = 0.999 = (7589/7594).

8.3.5.3 GISFrag

The GISFrag metric computes fragmentation by computing the average distance from the nearest patch and accounts for the configuration of patches.[15] This metric assumes a binary landscape (e.g., habitat/non-habitat), and is computed by finding the straight-line

---

13. Turner, M.G., R.H. Gardner, and R.V. O'Neill. 2001. *Landscape Ecology in Theory and Practice*. Springer.

14. For a polygon feature type, select the features of the appropriate class, then sum the areas. For a raster representation, this can be found from the zonal attribute table in the count field.

15. Ripple, W.J., G.A. Bradshaw, and T.A. Spies. 1991. Measuring forest landscape patterns in the Cascade Range of Oregon, USA. *Biological Conservation* 57: 73-88.

distance away from patches. Smaller values (>0) indicate less fragmented landscapes and larger values indicate higher levels of fragmentation. GISFrag is simply the mean distance value (including the 0s in the cells that represent the patches), and is calculated in the Raster Calculator using:

[GISFrag] = EucDistance(con([study] == 42, 1))

where 42 is the value representing habitat. Assessing the fragmentation of the coniferous vegetation on the study sites, GISFrag for Site A = 8.74 and for Site B = 1.33, indicating that Site A is more fragmented than Site B.

8.3.5.4 Landscape signature

Both the shape and configuration of patches in a landscape can be examined by measuring how the proportion of a landscape that is occupied by patches changes when patches are enlarged (buffering out) and shrunk (buffering in) across a range of scales. This can be computed by calculating both the straight-line distance away from and into the patches (Figure 8.2). These areas are then normalized to the total study area and expressed as a cumulative distribution function.[16] Notice that the proportion of "habitat" is found at the intersection with 0 (~85%). The shape of the curve with positive values indicates the configuration of the patches, while negative values indicate the number, shape, and size of the patches. Note that this method can also incorporate cost weighted distances and continuous valued (0.0 to 1.0) data as well.

---

16. It is probably easiest to do this in a spreadsheet like Microsoft Excel.

FIGURE 8.2. Landscape signature for Site A using coniferous forest as patches. The top graph shows the cumulative distribution function of the proportion of study area. The bottom map shows within-patch areas in green, outside patches in blue. (Download color figures from www.consplan.com)..

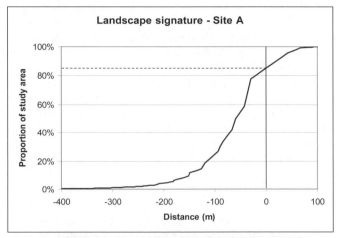

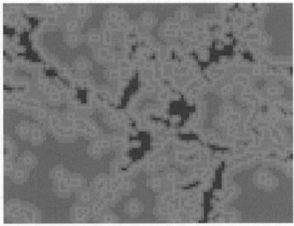

The landscape signature raster can be computed using the following, where [patch] contains 0s and 1s:

[g1] = int(EucDistance ([patch] == 1, 1)) * 1)

[g2] = int(EucDistance (con([patch] == 0, 1)) * -1)

[patch_sig] = [g1] + [g2]

8.3.6 Distance

There are a number of different methods for computing distances between zero-dimensional objects (points), and a couple of these are discussed below. However, some assumptions need to be made when calculating distances between line or polygon features. Often the centroids of linear and areal features are used when calculating distances, but distances can also be computed from the nearest part of a feature or the average distance from all parts of a feature. When creating distance surfaces from linear and polygon features, the closest edge-to-edge distance (not centroid to centroid) is computed. The differences between the centroid and other measurement methods is more important as the ratio of the length or area of a feature to the distance between features increases. For example, if the distance between polygons is an order of magnitude or more than the thickness of a polygon, then approximating the polygon with the centroid will cause minimal bias.

8.3.6.1 Spherical

Calculating distance using geographic coordinates requires using spherical geometry, and the formula to calculate *spherical distance* (D_s) uses the Law of Cosines:

$$D_s = R\cos 1[\sin\phi_1 \sin\phi_2 + \cos\phi_1 \cos\phi_2 \cos(\lambda_1 minus\lambda_2)]$$

where R is radius of a spheroid (typically 6,370,997 m is used), ϕ (phi) is latitude, λ (lambda) is longitude. It is not recommended to use this formula to calculate distances shorter than about 2 km, however, because it is pushing the lower limit of precision that a computer computes inverse cosine values. Also, at higher latitudes (toward the poles), the length of a degree of longitude decreases. At the equator, one degree of longitude is 111.321 km, at 60° latitude it decreases to 55.802 km, and at the poles it is 0.0 km. Because distance (and area) changes with latitude, it is recommended to compute area using projected (not geographical) coordinates.

8.3.6.2 Euclidean

The most common way to calculate the *Euclidean* or straight-line distance (D_E) between two points (x_1, y_1 and x_2, y_2) uses the Pythagorean theorem:

$$D_E = \sqrt{(x_2 minus x_1)^2 + (y_2 minus y_1)^2} \quad .$$

To interactively measure the distance between two features (or locations) on a map, use the *Measure Distance* tool (⟷).

To measure the distance between a given feature and another feature in the same layer, unfortunately, is not easy to do using the standard interface of ArcGIS (with ArcView license) without a custom program. Onr way of computing the distances from a single feature to all other features in a layer is to create a distance surface in raster with just the feature of interest, and then to "overlay" the other features on the distance surface. Note that the precision of the distance values is controlled by the cell size of the raster. Also, the *direction* from a feature to all other features could be computed in this fashion by using the option to create the direction raster when creating the distance surface.

With an ArcInfo license, three tools are available to compute distances between features. First, the *Near tool* calculates the distance between each feature in the Input Features layer to the nearest features in another layer, within a defined search radius. Feature types for both the input and near feature layers can be point, polyline, polygon, or multipoint. For each record in the Input Features layer, values are filled in for the closest feature in a series of fields, including: FID, minimum distance (in map units), x-coordinate, y-coordinate, and angle (0° east, 90° north, 180° (-180°) west, and -90 south). If no feature is found within the search distance, a value of -1 is assigned. A second tool, *Generate Near Table*, is similar to Near, but generates a new output table with FIDs for both the input feature and near feature. Also, there is an option to create a table that contains additional records for all of the near features within the defined search radius or the nearest *k* features, where *k* is user defined. A third tool is the *Point Distance tool* in the Proximity group of tools in ArcToolbox (requires ArcInfo license), which will compute the distances between points in the input feature layer and points in the near feature layers.

Distance from a feature to all other features in a layer

1. Select the feature of interest from a layer.

2. Create a distance surface from the feature of interest by selecting, from the Spatial Analyst toolbar, **Distance -> Straight Line**.

3. Clear the selected feature of interest.

4. Select **Zonal Statistics** from the Spatial Analyst toolbar.

5. Set the original layer as the Zone dataset (and choose an appropriate field).

6. Set the distance surface raster just created as the Value raster.

7. Set the chart statistic to **Mean**.

8. Specify the output table and click **OK**.

9. Join the resulting table back to the original layer's attribute table using the Zone Field.

8.3.6.3 Constrained distance

The Manhattan metric distance[17] between two points x_1,y_1 and x_2,y_2 on a plane assumes that movement is constrained to allow only orthogonal movement (e.g., the road network, assuming it is oriented with the coordinate system). It is computed using:

$$D_M = |x_2 - x_1| + |y_2 - y_1|$$

8.3.6.4 Weighted distance

In addition to Euclidean and constrained distances, recall from Chapter 7 that another approach to computing distance is to recognize that there may be geographic conditions that affect how far a particular location is from another, from a functional perspective. *Cost-weighted distance* incorporates such factors that influence movement across a surface. Cost-weighted distance computes distance in terms of cost units and accumulates these units at locations away from features of interest.

8.3.7 Pattern

Geographic features can be characterized by their pattern or degree of dispersion: *regular, random,* and *clustered* patterns. There are numerous statistics and metrics that quantify the spatial pattern or arrangement of features. However, many of these require

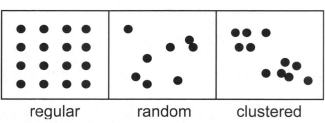

regular   random   clustered

specialized programs to run, though increasingly these are built as user-defined extensions to ArcGIS software.[18] Rather than providing a comprehensive review, below I describe some of the more common statistics that are useful and relatively straightforward to implement in the standard ArcGIS interface.

8.3.7.1 Mean center

The most common way to quantify a feature theme is to simply count the number of features. But themes with the same number of features can differ substantially in their spatial pattern. Another common way to differentiate patterns is to quantify the mean geographic center of *x,y* points:

---

17. So called because of driving on orthogonal streets.
18. Lee, J. and D.W.S. Wong. 2001. *Statistical Analysis with ArcView GIS*. John Wiley & Sons. 192 pgs. (Information is online at: http://www.wiley.com/products/subject/geography/gis/lee/). Note: this is for ArcView v3.X.

$$\bar{x} = \sum_{i=1}^{n} w_i x_i / \sum_{i=1}^{n} w_i, \ \bar{y} = \sum_{i=1}^{n} w_i y_i / \sum_{i=1}^{n} w_i.$$

For example, the US Census Bureau has tracked the center of population since 1790 (Figure 8.3).

FIGURE 8.3. The western march of the US population center from 1790 to 1990.[19]

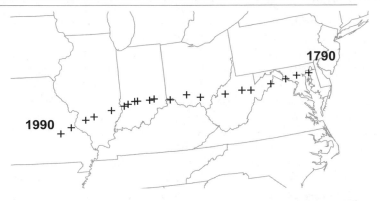

Computing the mean center of a distribution

ArcToolbox -> Spatial Statistics Tools -> Measuring Geographic Distributions -> **Mean Center**.

8.3.7.2 Nearest neighbor

The *nearest neighbor* index (N) measures the degree of spatial dispersion of features based on the minimum distance between individual (point and line) features. A scattered distribution has a greater average distance, while a clustered distribution has a smaller average distance. This index is computed by averaging all the distances from a point to its nearest neighbor:[20]

$$N = \left(\sum_{i=1}^{n} d_i \right) / n$$

---

19. Data from US Census Bureau: http://www.census.gov/population/censusdata/popctr.pdf
20. Chou, Y.H. 1997. *Exploring Spatial Analysis in Geographic Information Systems.* Sante Fe: New Mexico: Onword Press.

where d_i is the distance from location i to its nearest neighbor.

<table>
<tr><td>Computing the nearest neighbor</td></tr>
<tr><td>ArcToolbox -> Spatial Statistics Tools -> Analyzing Patterns -> Average Nearest Neighbor.</td></tr>
</table>

8.3.7.3 Quadrat analysis

Quadrat analysis is a common technique that can be used to detect non-randomness in spatial distributions. This technique requires that *quadrats*, usually squares, are superimposed over the points of interest. Then, the number of points that fall within each quadrat are counted. Finally, the observed number of points per quadrat (i.e. the average number of points per quadrat) are compared with the number of points that would be expected if the points were randomly distributed (the variance).[21] To create a listing of the quadrat classes and their frequency, convert the point feature dataset to a raster. However, because only one feature per cell is recognized when using simple feature-to-raster conversion, you will need to use a function that counts the number of points in a cell. The Neighborhood Statistic dialog can be parameterized to use a single-cell neighborhood to count the number of features. The attribute table of the resulting GRID lists the frequency of class counts (note that there is no 0 class).

<table>
<tr><td colspan="1">Creating count frequency table</td></tr>
<tr><td>

1. Create a field (e.g., COUNT) in the feature attribute table with the value of 1. (use LongInt type).

2. Select **Neighborhood Statistics...** from the from the Spatial Analyst toolbar.

3. Set the input data layer to be the point layer of interest.

4. Set the field input to be the newly created Count field.

5. Set the statistic type to be **Sum**.

6. Set the Neighborhood type to **Rectangle**.

7. Set both the height and width to 1 (to count just the features within a single cell).

8. Set the output cell size and raster name.

9. Click **OK**.

</td></tr>
</table>

21. Muehrcke, P.C. and J.O. Muehrcke, 1992. *Maps Use: Reading, analysis, and interpretation*. Madison, Wisconsin: JP Publications.

One difficulty with this method is that the results are especially dependent on the quadrat size—different quadrats will produce different results. One suggestion for the optimal quadrat size[22] sets the cell size (width) (r) to:

$$r = \sqrt{A/n}$$

where A is the study area and n is the number of points in the study area. However, because the results are dependent on the cell size, it would be useful to examine how the results change with a range of cell sizes, and in this way the *scale* of the process represented by the point distribution could be examined.

8.3.7.4 Autocorrelation

Recall that the First Law of Geography states that near things are more related than distant things.[23] To test this law and make use of this information, a number of methods have been developed to directly measure *autocorrelation*, including joint counts, Moran's I and Geary's c. These techniques have been implemented in the *Geostatistical Analyst* extension[24] as well as in the Spatial Statistics toolbox.

Computing spatial autocorrelation

ArcToolbox -> Spatial Statistics Tools -> Analyzing Patterns -> **Spatial Autocorrelation (Moran's I)**.

8.4 Proximity analysis

There are numerous situations that require knowing the distances between features. This "distance from" notion is entrenched in laws and prescribed in regulations, for example, all neighbors within 1000 feet of a proposed zoning change must be notified, and a drug-free zone is typically established around schools. Buffering is the basis for *proximity analysis* and creates a buffer feature that is a polygon feature type. Although most often you will want to create a new layer that represents buffered features, particularly if the layer will be used in an overlay operation (e.g., clip or union) with another layer. But if the buffer

---

22. Greig-Smith, P. 1952. The use of random and contiguous quadrats in the study of the structure of plant communities. *Annals of Botany* 16: 312.
23. Tobler, W. 1970. A computer movie simulating urban growth in the Detroit region. *Economic Geography* 46(2):234-240.
24. See: Johnston, K., J. M. ver Hoef, K. Krivoruchko, and N. Lucas. 2001. *Using ArcGIS Geostatistical Analyst*. ESRI Press.

layer will simply be used to select features from another layer, recall from Chapter 5 that a *buffered selection* can be done using the *Select by location* interface.

8.4.1 Buffering

Point, line, and polygon features can all be *buffered* by expanding outward in all directions a defined distance from a feature. Typically buffer analysis uses a single, equidistant zone around a feature. Multiple zones can also be created to examine how the results of an analysis might change with a range of distances. The buffer distance might also vary with an attribute of the feature. So, for example, points that represent warehouses might be buffered further than points representing houses. Or, the buffer distance could vary with direction (e.g., in response to differences in wind strength at the edge of a forest) or with the characteristics of a polygon's edge (e.g., exposure is greater at a grassland-forest edge compared to a shrubland-forest edge).

The *Buffer tool* can be used to create buffers around the selected features of a feature layer. First, you'll need to select the layer of interest and choose whether to use all the features or just the selected ones. Note that the number of selected and total features is displayed in the dialog.

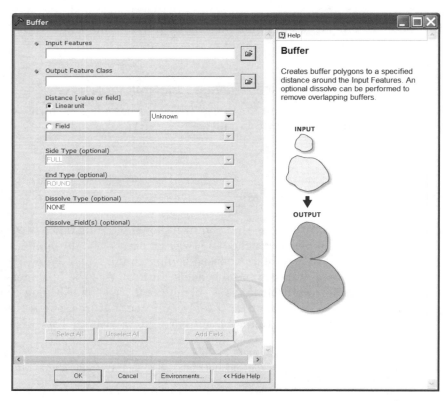

There are three ways buffer distances can be defined. *At a specified distance* allows you to set a distance that is applied to all selected features in the layer. This is the default. *At a distance from an attribute field* allows you to set the buffer distances based on the value in the field you specify. This allows you, for example, to change the buffer distance based on some feature attribute. *As multiple rings* allows you to create multiple rings at a defined, uniform increment. Notice that at the bottom of the dialog the distance units can be changed.

When your datasets are in projected coordinate systems, the buffering tool uses Euclidean (or 2D Cartesian) formulas to compute distance. However, if you are buffering point features that are distributed broadly north-to-south (i.e. latitude), then the resulting buffers might suffer from too much distortion. In this case, it is advisable to use *geodesic buffering*, which is performed on point or multi-point features that are in geographic coordinates.

You can also specify a number of characteristics about the output from the buffering operation. You can choose to dissolve barriers between buffers (or not). Dissolving barriers removes the polygon boundaries if two polygons overlap. This enforces buffer polygons to be embedded in a two-dimensional plane. Not dissolving barriers allows the buffer polygons that overlap to remain intact. If the features to be buffered are polygons, then you have the choice of buffering them so that the resulting buffer polygon is both inside and outside, outside only, inside only, or outside only with the core included (see Figure8.4). Note that a fifth option shrinks a polygon boundary, and is accomplished by entering a *negative buffer* value (e.g., using -200 in the *at a specified distance* option) using the *outside only with the core included* option. Lastly, specify how the buffers are to be saved. The default is to create them in a new layer. They can also be saved as graphics in the data frame or added to an existing editable layer.

Computing proximity using buffers
ArcToolbox -> Analysis -> Proximity -> **Buffer**.

Although buffers are typically created on feature datasets, the concept also applies (and in some ways is easier to implement) to raster datasets. That is, buffers can be created using distance surfaces by specifying a maximum distance when calculating the Straight Line distance, or in the Raster Calculator using:

EucDistance ([lakes], #, #, 400)

Multi-rings of equal distances can also be created easily by dividing (using modulo division) a distance surface by the interval distance (e.g., 200 m):

[DS] = int (EucDistance([lakes]))

con([DS] == 0, 0, (int([DS] / 200) * 200))

FIGURE 8.4. Different buffer types that can be created using the Buffer tool on a polygon feature (top left): inside and outside (top center); only outside (top right); only inside (bottom left); outside and include inside (bottom center); and outside and include inside with a negative value (bottom right). The resulting buffer polygon is shown in grey and the original polygon is a black ring.

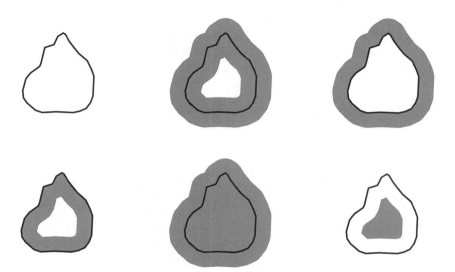

8.4.2 Variable buffers

Although frequently buffer zones are specified using a straight-line distance (e.g., 300-foot buffer zone), the concept of a *variable buffer* whose width changes in response to geographic variation is very attractive.[25] For example, riparian zones are often modeled in GIS by simply buffering stream lines a certain distance (perhaps using different distances for each stream order), and this is a useful—but a first—approximation. In reality, the width of both the stream and flood channel typically changes in response to bedrock geology and the dynamics of stream flow. As a result, it would be useful to represent buffers that vary in response to these changing channel characteristics. Recall the recent discussion about creating buffers using distance surfaces? A natural extension of this approach is to create variable buffers using weighted surfaces. That is, rather than assuming straight-line distance away from stream lines, a cost-weighted surface that represents the valley geomorphology could be used, based on the slope of the adjacent

---

25. This is also called effective distance. See: Berry, J.1993. *Beyond mapping: Concepts, algorithms, and issues in GIS.* Wiley & Sons.

GIS Concepts and ArcGIS Methods

valley walls. Riparian zones are more likely to be found in areas that gently grade away from the stream channel as opposed to narrowly incised valleys (Figure 8.5).

FIGURE 8.5. A variable-buffer computed around a stream using cost-weighted distance (shown in teal). Fixed-width buffer is shown in red for comparison. (Download color figures from www.consplan.com).

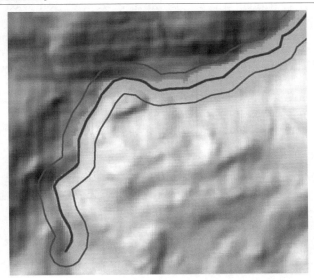

Creating a variable buffer

1. Create a cost-weighted distance surface based on the continuously varying factor that influences the buffer width (e.g., slope classes).

2. Select Distance -> Cost weighted... from the from the Spatial Analyst toolbar.

3. Set the cost raster to be the cost weighted distance surface (e.g., slope classes).

4. Set the maximum distance to be the buffer width.

5. Specify the output raster name.

6. Click OK.

8.4.3 Neighborhoods

Neighborhood analysis finds features that are adjacent to one another (usually polygon features). You will need to identify features that are adjacent to a particular feature.

Finding the directly adjacent neighbors is typically accomplished on polygon features (but is not limited to polygons) such as counties. It can be easily accomplished using a "what is adjacent?" query (see Chapter 5). This analysis can be extended to find second- and third-order (and so on) neighbors by using the selected neighborhood features as the selected set. Another type of neighborhood analysis identifies nearby features that are within some defined distance. For instance, a typical planning application is to identify potentially affected neighbors who are within 500 feet of a home whose owner is proposing a zoning change. A third type of neighborhood analysis identifies features that are adjacent but that have particular attributes. For example, it might be important to identify patches of coniferous forest that are adjacent to urban areas because fire protection efforts might need to be focused there in the event of a forest fire. In this case, you will need to select the urban patches that are adjacent to coniferous forest patches from a map of land cover types. Finally, *zones of influence* neighborhoods could also be created, as we did in Chapter 7. These are more formally called Thiessen Polygons (aka called proximity zones).

Computing Thiessen polygons

ArcToolbox -> Analysis Tools -> Proximity -> **Create Thiessen Polygons** (ArcINFO only).
ArcToolbox -> Spatial Analyst Tools -> Distance -> **Cost Allocation**

8.5 Transformations

There are many GIS operations that transform a feature of a particular type to another type: from and to point, line, polygon, and raster (see Table 8.1). This contrasts with a *projection*, which changes the coordinates of the vertices used to represent features, but the features themselves remain represented by the same feature type. Because many of these *transformations* are not typical tasks, only the relatively common ones are covered below. Also, many of these transformations are not easy to accomplish in standard ArcGIS, although a number of user-created extensions and programs are available to do them. (Note that conversion to raster data is also considered a transformation, but is handled in Chapter 7.)

TABLE 8.1. Common transformations.[a]

From Type	To Point	To Line	To Polygon	Raster
Point	Interpolation Merge Sample	Interpolation	Buffer Convex hull Interpolation Thiessen polygon	Conversion
Line	Nodes Vertices	Generalize	Buffer	Conversion
Polygon	Centroid Label center Vertices	Medial-axis	Buffer Dissolve Eliminate Generalize Sample	Conversion: center, dominant area, or priority method
Raster	Conversion	Conversion	Conversion	Resample Aggregation

a. Adapted from: Bonham-Carter, G.F. 1996. *Geographic Information Systems for Geoscientists: Modelling with GIS*. Ontario, Canada: Pergamon Press.

8.5.1 Feature center and centroid

A typical transformation applied to polygons (and to a lesser extent points and polylines) is to find the *center* of a feature. There are four types of feature centers: simple, center of gravity, weighted centroid, and label. The *simple centroid,* or *geographic centroid,* is the center of the geographic extent of a feature, usually found at the center of the smallest rectangle that encloses (minimum bounding rectangle) the geographic feature(s) of interest. The *center-of-gravity centroid* (a.k.a. true centroid) is the "balance point" of a feature. For irregularly shaped features, the center-of-gravity centroid is often a different location than the simple center. For points, the centroid is located at the average x and average y values. For triangles, the center-of-gravity centroid is equivalent to the mean center of the three vertices. Note that the average x and average y of the vertices of a polygon only *approximates* the center-of-gravity centroid.[26] The center-of-gravity centroid is calculated most commonly using the trapezoidal method, which reduces a polygon to a

---

26. Jones, C.B. 1997. *Geographical Information Systems and Computer Cartography*. Longman. Page 66.

series of overlapping triangles for which the center is found. The *weighted centroid* is generally applied to a series of points that have some values associated with them. For example, the center of US population can be calculated (Figure 8.5).[27] Finally, the *label center* is a point that approximates the centroid, but is guaranteed to fall inside a polygon, which is a useful property for labeling purposes.

ArcGIS provides a variety of ways to compute feature centers (Figure 8.6). To transform features to a point feature to capture the centers is a two-step process. First, the x and y coordinates of the center type of choice are computed in fields in the feature attribute table. Next, a new point feature dataset is created from the x,y coordinates in the original feature attribute table. This can be done using the *Add X,Y Data* tool. A second way is to use the Field calculator to calculate either the true centroid (.Centroid) and label center (.LabelCenter).

FIGURE 8.6. Various feature centers, including simple (center of minimum bounding rectangle), centroid, zonal centroid, and label.

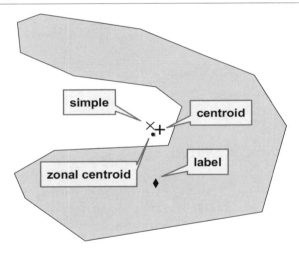

27. Clarke, K. 1990. *Analytical and computer cartography*. Englewood Cliffs, N.J.: Prentice Hall. Page 154.

8.5.2 Dissolve

An important operation to simplify line and polygon features is to *dissolve* the shared boundary (or point) between adjacent features with similar attributes. For example, to simplify a land use/cover map that has major and minor categories into major categories, the boundaries of polygons that are adjacent and have the same major land use categories could be removed. The

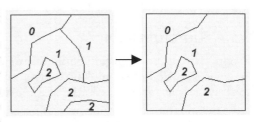

boundary between the upper-right polygon with a value of 1 and the adjacent polygon with the same value is dissolved, and the boundary between the lower-right polygon with a value of 2 and its adjacent polygon is dissolved.

Dissolve replaces multiple features with a single feature by removing unwanted nodes between lines or boundaries between polygons. The output theme contains the shape and the dissolve fields, and fields that contain the average, sum, minimum, maximum, variance, and/or standard deviation of the aggregated features can be added. The primary way to dissolve features in ArcGIS is through the Dissolve tool. Note, however, that this method dissolves all features that have the same attribute into a single feature, regardless of whether the features are adjacent or not (i.e. a single feature with disjoint multiple parts). The polygon and line features appear to be the same, but the attribute table has only one entry per unique feature value. This can be a powerful way to represent feature data (indeed, it mimics zones in a GRID!).[28] A second way to dissolve features, and one that does not result in disjoint multi-part features, is use the *Dissolve* tool). Again, this requires the input feature dataset to be a coverage.

Dissolving features on a common field
ArcToolbox -> Data Management Tools -> Generalization -> **Dissolve**.

8.5.3 Eliminate

The *eliminate* operation removes unwanted lines and polygons from a feature theme. This operation is useful when your feature dataset has numerous small polygons (a.k.a. sliver polygons) that are artifacts of digitizing and that may cloud subsequent analysis. Elimination of these artifacts can be accomplished using the *Eliminate tool* in ArcToolbox, which merges selected polygons with neighboring polygons that have the largest shared

---

28. Just as in ArcView v3.x, dissolving features without creating disjoint multi-part features requires the use of an additional VBA program called *Explode*. This can be acquired from ESRI ArcObjects online: http://arcon-line.esri.com/arcobjectsonline/.

border between them or that have the largest area. Unfortunately, there is no easy way in ArcGIS (with an ArcView license) to emulate this functionality.[29]

8.5.4 Generalization

Frequently, linear and polygonal features need to be simplified by reducing the number of vertices that depict them. The eternal question has been: which points should be removed so that the essential character of a feature remains intact? Over the years, cartographers have developed numerous ways to preserve the caricature of a line.[30] An easy method is to remove every n^{th} vertex, but this creates very poor results and is not recommended.[31] One of the most enduring methods is the *Douglas-Peucker* algorithm,[32] and this is used in several places in ArcGIS (e.g., conversion of raster to features). Because generalization can move (or remove) vertices, topology can be corrupted. This is particularly true when generalizing the boundaries of polygons.

ArcGIS provides a variety of generalization tools. The *Aggregate Polygons* tool combines polygons that are within a specified distance of one another into new polygons. Also, the minimum area of an aggregated polygon that is to be retained can be specified. The *Collapse Dual Lines to Centerline* tool can be used to derive centerlines from double-line features, such as road boundaries or a wide river. The *Eliminate tool* merges selected polygons with neighbors that have either the largest area or the longest shared border. This is a useful tool to eliminate sliver polygons. The *Simplify Building tool* is a specific tool that works on polygons that represent the boundary or footprint of a building, while maintaining its shape and size. The *Simplify Line tool* generalizes a line by removing small, un-wanted bends while retaining its essential shape. The *Simplify Polygon* tool generalizes polygons in a similar fashion. Both of the simplify tools have a method to handle topological errors. The *Smooth Line tool* uses either a polynomial approximation or

---

29. One method would be to convert the feature dataset to raster, create regions, identify the regions that are to be eliminated, and then use the Nibble function, then convert back to feature. A very fine resolution GRID would be required, however.

30. Buttenfield, B.P. and R.B. McMaster. 1991. *Map Generalization: Making Rules for Knowledge Representation* (eds). London: Longman.

31. Weibel, R. 1997. Generalization of spatial data: principles and selected algorithms. In: *Algorithmic foundations of geographic information systems*. Berlin: Springer

32. Douglas, D.H. and T.K. Peucker. 1973. Algorithms for the reduction of the number of points required to represent a digitized line or its caricature. *Canadian Cartographer* 10:110-122.

Bezier interpolation to smooth a line to improve its aesthetic quality. All generalization tools require an ArcInfo license (except for Dissolve).

Generalizing linear and polygonal features

ArcToolbox -> Data Management Tools -> Generalization -> **Aggregate Polygons, Collapse Dual Lines to Centerline, Dissolve, Eliminate, Simplify Building, Simplify Line, Simplify Polygon, Smooth.**

8.5.5 Resampling

Resampling is needed when two raster datasets of different cell size are combined or overlaid, or if two raster datasets with the same cell size are not aligned.
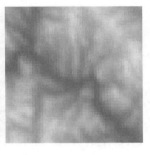

Resampling is automatically performed when using GRIDs with different cell sizes, and ArcGIS identifies the cell that has its center closest to the center of the output cell. The *nearest neighbor* method (left above) is most appropriate for discrete (nominal) data (e.g., land use classes). The *majority method* determines the value based on the most frequent occurrence of a value in the filter window. It is also used with nominal data and gives a smoother result than the nearest neighbor method. For continuous data, the *bilinear interpolation* method (center above) is recommended, which uses the weighted distance average of the four nearest input cells. The *cubic convolution* method (right above) is similar to the bilinear, but uses the 16 nearest cells and produces the smoothest output.

Resampling rasters

ArcToolbox -> Data Management Tools -> Raster -> **Resample**.

Resampling is also used during display of rasters in ArcMap, and nearest neighbor is the default method. Using this method, the cell boundaries are clearly visible (left). When representing a continuous variable (e.g., elevation), it may make sense to  change the display methodology to show a smoother surface by changing the resampling method to bilinear (right) or cubic convolution.

8.6 Chapter review

- *Geoprocessing* is a broad framework in ArcGIS to apply an operation with a tool to manipulate GIS datasets.

- The History toolbox automatically logs the processing steps, inputs, and messages to document your work.

- A wide variety of basic landscape metrics can be easily computed in GIS, and a toolbox has been developed called *LCaP* to compute a variety of functional connectivity and landscape pattern metrics using ModelBuilder.

- Buffering is the basis for *proximity analysis*, which can be conducted with either vector or raster datasets.

- When resampling nominal (class) data, use nearest neighbor (or majority neighbor) methods. For quantitative data, use bilinear or cubic convolution.

9   *Dual-layer analysis*

The ability to overlay and compare two or more maps is one of the most powerful analytical features found in a GIS. There are three broad classes of analysis that involve two (or more) maps. The first is *selection*, where the selected features of one layer are used to select features of another layer. *Select by location* was covered in the chapter on spatial queries (Chapter 5) so it will not be discussed further in this chapter. A second type of analysis is *overlay*, where a new layer is generated by performing an overlay operation on two input layers. This type of analysis is probably the premier example of GIS analysis and is discussed in detail below. Related to overlay analysis are spatial join operations, which join the attributes of one feature layer to another based on spatial relationships between features in different layers. More complex models that combine layers are described in the next chapter.

9.1 Overlay analysis

The idea of conducting an analysis by overlaying two or more maps has no doubt been around for some time. During the American Revolution, General George Washington employed a French cartographer who used hinged overlays to examine the location of Washington's troops in relationship to General Cornwallis' troops.[1] Another example is Dr. John Snow's use of overlay mapping to investigate the cause of cholera, pioneering the field of epidemiology. Dr. Snow superimposed a map of cholera deaths in central London in relation to water pumps, thereby determining the Broad Street pump was the likely source of the 1854 outbreak.[2] An early use of overlays to analyze landscapes was Warren Manning's study of the town of Billerica, Massachusetts in 1912.[3] And perhaps the most widely recognized example of work using overlay analysis is Ian McHarg's classic book *Design with Nature.*[4]

Today, computer technology enables overlay analysis to be conducted rapidly for large study areas that consider many input factors. To enable layers to be overlaid reliably, they first must be georeferenced so that feature geometry is coincident. Note that although layers may appear to line up properly in the display, due to the approximations made by on-the-fly projection, the layers should be in the same coordinate system for the most accurate results.

There are a variety of overlay operations available, and a useful way to organize the possible overlay combinations is to examine which operations can be employed given two input layer types (e.g., point, line, polygon features and raster) (Table 9.1). There are three ways layers can be overlaid, and these can be differentiated based on how the features and attributes are modified (or not) as a result of the overlay process.

1. Wikle, T.A. 1991. Computers, maps, and geographic information systems. *National Forum* (Summer): 37-39.
2. Gilbert, E.W. 1958. Pioneer maps of health and disease in England. *Geographical Journal* 124: 172-183.
3. Steinitz, C., P. Parker, and L. Jordan. 1976. Hand-drawn overlays: Their history and prospective uses. *Landscape Architecture* 56(4):146-157.
4. McHarg, I. 1969. *Design with Nature.* Doubleday/Natural History Press: New York, NY.

TABLE 9.1. Common overlay analyses involving two layers.

From type	On Point	On Line	On/in Polygon	Raster
Point	Merge	Cut lines	Clip/Erase	
Line		Merge	Clip/Erase Intersect Union	
Polygon	Clip/Erase	Clip/Erase	Clip/Erase Intersect Merge Union	
Raster				Combine Map Algebra

First, some overlay operations change the feature geometry of one layer on the basis of another layer, but the attributes of the first layer are not modified. For example, a polygon feature dataset that represents public lands could be used to *clip* or remove the portions of land cover polygons that overlap public lands. Note that an attribute that is based on a feature's geometry (e.g., area, length, compactness, etc.) needs to be re-calculated because the feature geometry has changed. Second, some overlay operations simply append the attributes of one layer based on another. For example, the attributes of a polygon feature dataset (e.g., land cover types) could be joined to the attribute table of a point feature dataset (e.g., soil sample locations), solely on the basis of location. This process is called *spatial join*. Third, some operations cause both feature geometry and attributes to be changed in the output layer (e.g., union). Table 9.2 shows a diagram of these various operations.

TABLE 9.2. Examples of clip, intersect, and union overlay types. (Download color figures from www.consplan.com).

Type	Input layers	Output layer
Clip The output layer's attribute table contains only attributes from the input layer		

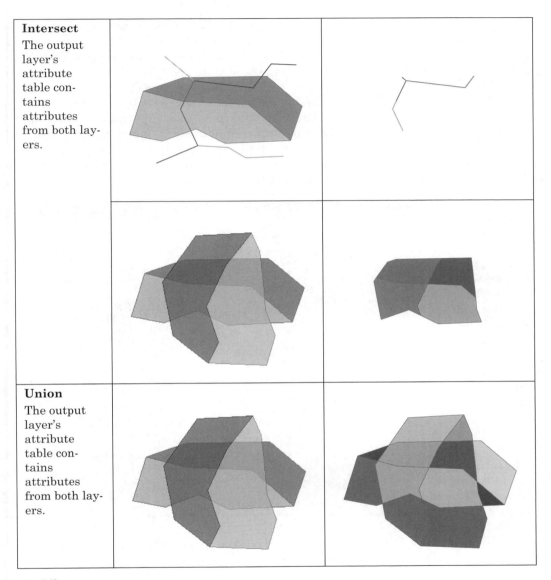

| **Intersect** The output layer's attribute table contains attributes from both layers. | | |
| **Union** The output layer's attribute table contains attributes from both layers. | | |

9.1.1 Clip

The *clip* operation uses one input layer to change the feature geometry of a second layer. This process works like a cookie cutter and creates a new layer by clipping the first layer, called the *input layer*, with a *clip layer* so that features from the input layer that fall outside of the clip layer are cut away or removed. This operation is used to clip portions of layers that fall outside of a study boundary, thus reducing the size of the original dataset. Another common use of clip is in combination with buffering. For example, to find the land cover types that are within 1 km of a stream, the stream layer would first be buffered by 1 km and then used to clip out the features from the land cover layer. Note that although the input layer can be any feature type (e.g., point, line, or polygon), the clip layer must be a polygon feature type. The input features are clipped so that only those features that are located inside the clip layer are exported to the output layer. As a result, an attribute that is based on feature geometry (e.g., area, length, etc.) should be re-calculated. The attributes of the output layer are the same as the input layer (not the clip layer). Clip uses only the selected features from both the input and clip layer.

Although clip retains the features that are inside the clip features (i.e. inclusive), sometimes you may want to remove or *erase* the features that are inside the overlapping portion. However, for most cases (where the spatial extent of both layers is the same), an erase-like operation using clip can be conducted by first selecting the features *outside* the chosen area in the clip layer and then switching the selected feature set in the clip layer. Note that a raster dataset can be clipped as well using the Raster tools in Data Management.

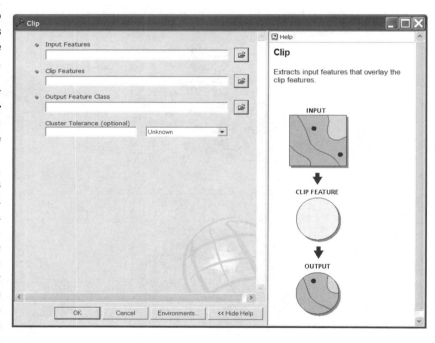

Clipping features
ArcToolbox -> Analysis Tools -> Extract -> **Clip**.

Erasing features
ArcToolbox -> Analysis Tools -> Overlay -> **Erase**.

Clipping raster
ArcToolbox -> Data Management Tools -> Raster -> **Clip**.

9.1.2 Intersect

The *intersect* operation is similar to clip in that they both preserve only those features within the spatial extent common to both layers (and those features that are selected). It is different from clip, however, in two ways. First, intersect computes the geometric intersection of the *input* layer and the *overlay layer*. The resulting features and attributes of both are then added to a new dataset.

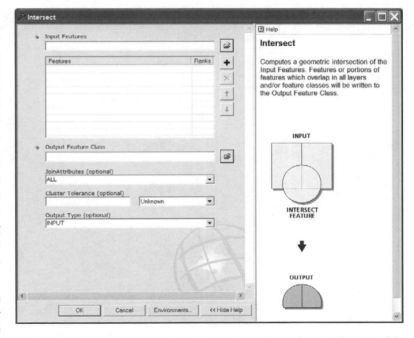

The features of the *input* layer (line or polygon feature type) are intersected with the *overlay* layer (polygon only). The *output* layer's attribute table will contain fields from both layers but will be the same feature type as the *input* layer (line or polygon). Second, all of the polygon boundaries (not just the outside ones) are intersected with the feature geometry of the input layer. In this way, boundaries that cross one another are "cut" at their intersection.

Intersecting features
ArcToolbox -> Analysis Tools -> Overlay -> **Intersect**.

Also, recall that raster datasets also can be combined in such a way that simulates the intersect operation for feature data. The *Combine* function combines two or more raster layers on a cell-by-cell basis and is called in the Raster Calculator using:

Combine ([G1], [G2])

Unique combinations of the input values are given a unique index value, which is assigned to the cells of the output layer. The original value of the input raster dataset is added to the attribute table, one field per input layer.

Combining rasters
ArcToolbox -> Spatial Analyst Tools -> Local -> **Combine**.

9.1.3 Union

Like the intersect operation, *union* creates a new layer by computing the geometric intersection of features from the *input layer* and the *overlay layer*. The resulting features and the attributes from both layers are added to the new dataset. Union differs from intersect by including features found in the spatial extent of either layer, including those features that may not have overlapped the spatial extent of the other layer (Figure 9.1).

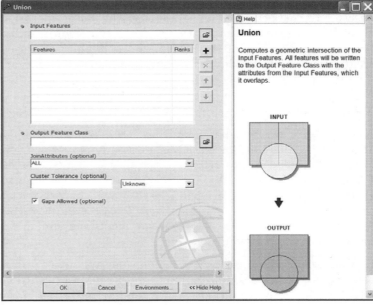

FIGURE 9.1. The difference between intersect and union.

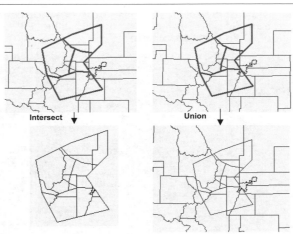

9.1.4 Merge/append

Although merge is not really considered to be one of the primary overlay operations, it is described here because of its popularity. The *merge* operation combines two or more layers of the same feature type into a single layer that contains all the features from all the input layers. The main intent of this function is to merge a series of adjacent layers that were created as a series of tiles (e.g., quadsheets). This operation, however, does not determine if features touch at the boundary or if features cross lines, it simply merges all the features from the input layers into a new layer. That is, merge does not enforce planar topology, so it does not break features into smaller features if a crossing is found.

A common use of the merge operation is to reconcile GPS points that were collected in two different UTM zones, for example. First, the points are separated by zone into separate layers. Next, the points are projected into a single zone, creating a layer for each zone. Finally, merge is used to combine the reprojected points back into a single layer. A secondary use of this function is to merge layers with features that are spatially coincident, so that linear and polygon features may overlap or cross one another. If the features are points, then merging two layers is a simple way of updating a dataset with more recent information.

Similar to the Merge tool, the *Append tool* appends multiple input datasets (vector and raster). Unlike the Union tool, append keeps all features intact, so that features that possibly overlap one another are not "planarized" (that is, their geometry does not change during the operation).

FIGURE 9.2. Attention to how adjacent tiles of raster data are mosaic-ed is important. An example of an artifact from Google Earth named the "Baseline Rift" because it follows Baseline Road in Boulder, Colorado (40 latitude).

Merge and append features

ArcToolbox -> Data Management Tools -> General -> **Merge, Append**.

Two or more raster datasets (e.g., G1, G2, and G3) can also be merged together using the *Merge* function in the Raster Calculator:

Merge ([G1], [G2], [G3])

If cells overlap, then the priority is determined by the input order (e.g., first G1, then G2, etc.). For raster datasets that represent continuous data, a second function, *mosaic*, is available that averages overlapping cells to create a smooth transition:

Mosaic ([G1], [G2], [G3])

Mosaic uses a weighted average to smooth the cell values at the edges in the Raster Calculator.[5] As the *Mosaic tool* (note that there is no Merge tool for raster), there are a variety of ways that overlapping areas can be handled.

Mosaic features

ArcToolbox -> Analysis Tools -> Overlay -> **Intersect**.

9.2 Join by location

A special type of overlay analysis is the ability to associate two layers based on the relationships between their feature locations—without modifying feature geometry—to gain access to attribute information. The *join by location* operation (a.k.a. spatial join) uses relationships between the features in two layers to append the attributes of a layer onto a second layer.

---

5. The smoothing is specified by a Hermite Cubic function. See: Franke, R. 1982. Smooth interpolation of scattered data by local thin plate splines. *Computer & Mathematics with Applications* 8(4): 273-281.

This type of join differs from joining attribute tables via a common field in two important ways. First, joining tables assumes a one-to-one or many-to-one relationship, whereas spatial join provides the means to deal with a one-to-many join. That is, imagine we wanted to know about the cities (points) that are found within a particular county, for example: How many cities are there? What is their average population? What is the largest city's population? In this example, there is one county, but many cities. One-to-many relationships can be handled by either summarizing the *many* aspect (e.g., cities) through some statistic (e.g., average, min, max, etc.) or by selecting only the closest one (or if there are ties, the first one processed is selected). In the latter case, we are using distance as a selection criteria and so a *distance field* is added to the table. A second way spatial join differs is that it creates a new layer with the attributes appended

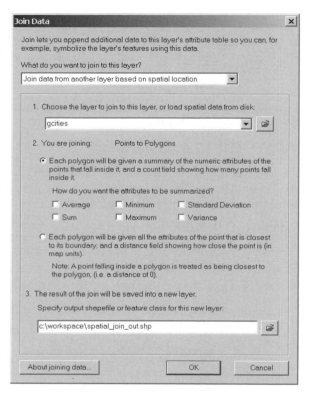

to the new table, rather than being temporarily joined through a dynamic link between two tables. Note that spatial join works on all the features in both layers, not the selected set.

There are many types of relationships or spatial association between features—recall from Chapter 1 the list of *spatial relations*: equivalent, partially equivalent (i.e. overlap), contained, adjacent, or disjoint. The spatial join interface in ArcMap implements only the more common types of relations, though there still is an impressive variety available (Table 9.3). There are three ways to group these methods that cut across feature types:

those that find features that are inside a polygon, features that intersect, and the nearest feature.

TABLE 9.3. **Spatial join methods organized by feature type.**

From type	To point	To line	To polygon
Point	Summarize (closest) Closest (w/distance)	Summarize (intersected or closest) Closest (w/distance)	Summarize (fall inside) Closest (w/distance, if inside=0)
Line	Summarize (intersects) Closest (w/distance)	Summarize (intersected) Part of	Summarize (intersect) Closest (w/distance, if inside=0)
Polygon	Falls inside Closest to (w/distance, if inside = 0)	Summarize (intersected) Completely inside Closest (w/distance)	Summarize (intersect) Completely inside

9.2.1 Nearest feature

The nearest feature method adds a distance field to the attribute table. For example, if you wanted to answer the question: "Which city is closest to each summit (hill or mountain)?" then the city layer is joined by location to a summit layer, and we can see that Boulder Mountain is about 8 km (straight-line distance) to the city of Boulder, Colorado (right). Note that if a feature falls on or inside another feature, the distance will be 0. If two or more features have the same distance, the first feature processed will be used to join the attribute data. The

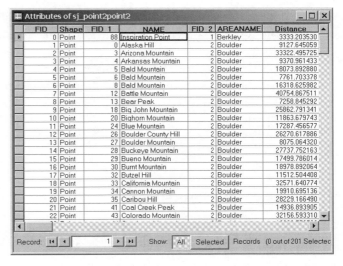

nearest or closest feature can be determined for all but the polygon-to-polygon spatial join.

9.2.2 Intersecting a feature

Another way to examine the relationship between two features is to examine if they intersect. For example, if you wanted to determine the average traffic volume along a stretch of highway, then a layer with point events that have the traffic count could be joined to a layer (line feature) representing the stretch of highway of interest. For each feature (e.g., highways), spatial join finds those features that intersect it. Then the selected features are summarized to provide the average traffic volume, for example.

9.2.3 Inside a polygon

Perhaps the most common use of spatial join is to find features that fall within a polygon feature. Two of the more common GIS operations are *point in polygon* and *line in polygon* operations. For example, joining by location would be used if you wanted to determine the number of mountains over 3,000 m located in each county of Colorado. If a feature falls within more than one feature (e.g., Lake Tahoe falls in five counties), then the first feature to be processed is used.

Joining by location

ArcToolbox -> Analysis Tools -> Overlay -> **Spatial Join.**

- OR -

1. In ArcMap, right-click on the desired feature layer that another layer's attributes are to be joined to, and select Joins and relates -> Join....

2. At the top drop-down box, select *join data from another layer based on spatial location*.

3. Select the layer to join to this layer.

4. Select the type of join, to either summarize (top) or choose closest (bottom).

5. Specify the output filename and location.

6. Click OK.

9.3 Chapter review

- Datasets in layers that are overlaid should be in the same projected coordinate system (and not in geographic coordinates) for the most accurate results.

- The common overlay operations are: clip, erase, intersect, and union.

- A spatial join associates two layers based on the relationships between their feature locations—without modifying feature geometry—to gain access to attribute information.

10 *Spatial modeling and geoprocessing*

In this chapter I synthesize what we have learned in the proceeding chapters within the context of building spatial models using *Geoprocessing*. Modeling as a process has been likened to "peeling back the layers of an onion," where a problem is explored iteratively, typically building on previous models and incorporating additional assumptions or exploring other details. But parsimony should reign when modeling: it is far too easy to get carried away building more and more complicated (not complex!) models. So, the question is typically raised: how do you know when you have the right model?

It is wise to approach modeling from the perspective that "all models are wrong, but some are useful."[1] Just as the cartographers' mantra in designing maps (what is the purpose of the map?), it all hinges on a clear understanding and statement of the purpose of a model. The Geoprocessing tools provided in ArcGIS enable you to easily build models. But remember, just because you *can* doesn't mean you *should*.

Below some basic modeling concepts and ways to represent models will be described. This is followed by a detailed illustration of iterative modeling using an example of modeling accessibility. The basics of the

---

1. G.E. Box.

ModelBuilder are described, followed by a primer of Python and how to write scripts that access ArcGIS.

10.1 Modeling concepts

Why use and build a model? Because a model assists you in thinking about conceptual issues -- about what factors are important, about what assumptions are being made. Too often (especially in GIS), the tendency is to get bogged down in some obscure detail (or in the syntax), that is, not seeing the forest for the trees. Building a model also (typically) forces you to generate an explicit representation of your logical thought process. This is useful to be clear when sharing with others what your model does and how it works. It is also extremely valuable as a way to self-document your work, so that in a few days, weeks, months or even years you can come back to your work and be rapidly productive. This also allows you to leverage your own work. If you've built a model once, why build it again?

Often a number of maps need to be manipulated and processed to answer a question. Even with seemingly simple models, the logic or work flow can get quite confusing, so that it quickly becomes hard to remember which layer was used to do what when! In a full-fledged *suitability analysis*, the logic can become quite involved indeed. Various means to conceptualize and document the logical flow of a model have been developed, but perhaps the most enduring has been the *flow chart*, which is described below. There are an infinite number of ways to combine various maps to conduct an analysis, but typically these fall within a couple of types: binary, arithmetic, and weighted arithmetic.We'll examine these approaches first, and then dive into a description of how to build models in the ModelBuilder application.

10.1.1 Flow charts

Diagrams have long been used to depict the flow of logic or steps followed in an analysis. Flow charts are important not only to communicate an idea, but also in that the very act of drawing and diagramming helps us to think about a problem.[2] An early example (1962) of using a flow chart to depict an overlay analysis is Alexander and Mannheim's procedural tree diagram that describes the logical framework and explicit weighting used in their analysis of highway routing.[3]

---

2. Edwards, B. 1979. *Drawing on the Right Side of the Brain: a course in enhancing creativity and artistic confidence*. Los Angles: J. P. Tarcher.
3. Alexander, C. and M.L. Manheim.1962. *The Use of Diagrams in Highway Route Location*. Civil Engineering Systems Laboratory, Massachusetts Institute of Technology. Research Report R62-3.

Although modeling is often an unorganized, ad-hoc process, it is best to think of it as consisting of three stages (Table 10.1). First, in the *development stage* a conceptual model is developed that represents the basic structure and assumptions of a particular model. This helps you to create a road map so that you can remain focused and not "lose the forest for the trees." Second, the conceptual model is formalized during the *implementation stage*. At this point it is time to roll up your sleeves and begin to use ArcGIS to implement the conceptual model. Third, the *use stage* occurs when the model is used, either immediately after creating it or perhaps by another person.[4] However, modeling is best seen as an iterative process, where the understanding of a problem is gained by conceptualizing a system, implementing a model, and exploring the behavior of the model under different assumptions. Ideally, these stages of modeling can be integrated with a flow chart that provides, as Joe Berry has written in his *Beyond Mapping* column: "...a succinct expression of a model's logic and an iterative mechanism to execute the model under various interpretations."[5]

A simple flow chart technique to diagram GIS models represents a *dataset* (e.g., an existing map layer) with a rectangle, a *derived dataset* (e.g., new map layer) created in the model with a smoothed rectangle, and a *function* (e.g., process or operation) with an oval. *Models* or components of models are represented by a circle. The *data flow* between these objects is represented by *connectors* (arrows) between data and function objects. Although a number of different flow charting software programs can be used, a simple alternative is to use *AutoShapes* in Microsoft Excel or PowerPoint.

TABLE 10.1. **Stages in diagramming a flowchart. Note that these are represented as linear steps, but ideally modeling is an iterative process.**

Stage	Comments
I. Conceptualize	1. Start at the end—identify the finished map layer or product and place a data object on the right of the diagram.
	2. Identify the main datasets needed to create the desired product. Place additional source data objects on the left side of the diagram.
	3. Insert main processes needed to create datasets.
	4. Connect data objects to processes with connectors.

4. Theobald, D.M. 1998. A visual programming environment for spatial modeling: The ArcView Spatial Modeler extension. *Proceedings of the ESRI User Conference '98*, San Diego, CA. http://gis.esri.com/library/userconf/proc98/PROCEED/TO150/PAP1010/P101.HTM.

5. Berry, J. 1993. Moving toward a humane GIS. *GeoWorld*. Pg. 22.

TABLE 10.1. **Stages in diagramming a flowchart. Note that these are represented as linear steps, but ideally modeling is an iterative process.**

II. Implement	1. Start at the beginning—add the necessary source datasets to an ArcMap document.
	2. Create each derivative dataset using the specified process. Often there will be details that need to be worked out to accomplish the function.
	3. Make sure that the details needed to implement a process are recorded and that the flowchart is updated to reflect major changes.
III. Use	1. Examine the flowchart—does it describe the essential characteristics of the model? Separate questions or concerns about the factors considered and assumptions used from basic understanding of the model.
	2. Identify the factors and parameters that are most influential in the model.
	3. Update the flowchart based on feedback about the diagram and through experience of using the model.

An early effort to develop a diagram-based interface that provided dynamic modeling abilities within a spatial framework was the Environmental Modeling Language written in the Extend program (Figure 10.1).[6] Within commercial GIS, flowchart diagrams have been used sparingly, most notably ERDAS's IMAGINE Model Maker. Clark Lab's Idrisi32 Macro Modeler provides a diagram-based modeling environment that allows dynamic modeling. For ESRI GIS products, the *Spatial Modeler* extension for ArcView v3.x GIS was an early suggestion of how a model-building environment might function within the ArcView v3.x GIS environment.[7] And of course ESRI has fully developed the *Model Builder* application within the Geoprocessing framework of ArcGIS. Later in this chapter the Model Builder application for ArcGIS is described in detail. But first, let's investigate two main types of models: boolean and arithmetic.

6. Theobald, D.M. and M. Gross. 1994. EML: A modeling environment for exploring landscape dynamics. *Computers, Environmental, and Urban Systems* 18(3): 193-204. This is an old-time screen snapshot (literally a photo of the CRT monitor)!

7. Theobald, D.M. 1998. A visual programming environment for spatial modeling: The ArcView Spatial Modeler extension. *Proceedings of the ESRI User Conference '98*, San Diego, CA. http://gis.esri.com/library/userconf/proc98/PROCEED/TO150/PAP1010/P101.HTM.

FIGURE 10.1. A dynamic model flowchart describing a fire spread model using the Environmental Modeling Language.

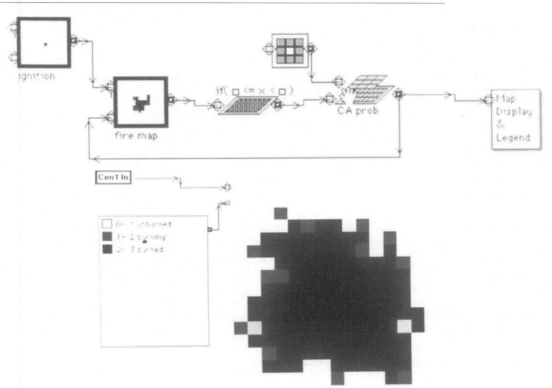

10.1.2 Boolean model

Oftentimes suitability models are expressed using Boolean logic. That is, a number of factors are considered, where each factor can be expressed in terms of *Boolean logic* and converted into a binary map. Boolean models are attractive because they are simple, and it is easy to convert laws or regulations that are expressed in terms of a condition to a binary map. Each of the factors are mapped as yes/no, binary maps, and in the end, the location that satisfies all the conditions comes through. Note that typically a Boolean model is created using raster datasets, where GRID values are 0 or 1 or NoData or 1. However, a Boolean model can also be created using feature datasets, where the logical constraints are implemented through a series of clips or a series of unions with a final attribute query after all layers are combined.

The formula to compute a Boolean model (M_B) is expressed as:

$$M_B = \prod_{i=1}^{m} X_i$$

where pi (Π) denotes that the values X_i in the m input maps (or factors) should be multiplied together.

For example, imagine that a suitable location for a new landfill needs to be found near your town. Typically, a number of factors are considered—for simplicity we'll just consider three here: permeability of surficial geology, proximity to town, and critical wildlife habitat (Figure 10.2). Note, however, that this method does not differentiate the relative quality of different locations that meet the initial criteria. The sensitivity of the model to a given assumption can be tested by bracketing a parameter—that is, specifying a slightly lower and higher value (e.g., distance from town > 2 km, >5 km, and >10km)—and re-running the model with the different parameters. A *sensitivity analysis* is helpful to understand how variable the results are given different assumptions. If the results vary to a large degree with different values of a particular parameter, then perhaps more resources (i.e., time, money, effort) should be spent to redefine the estimate of the parameter.

FIGURE 10.2. Flowchart of a Boolean logic model identifying suitable landfill sites. Three layers of evidence are considered.

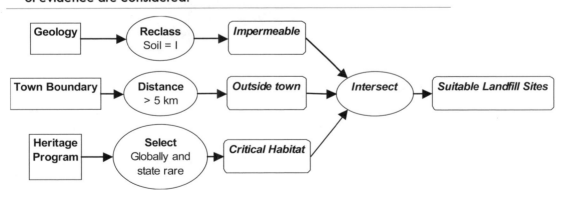

One of the more powerful aspects of using Map Algebra is the ease with which models can be created. For instance, the suitable landfill site model above could be expressed as a series of expressions:

[imperm] = con([geology] == 1, 1, 0)

[out_town] = con (EucDistance([town_bnd]) > 5000, 1, 0)

[critical_hab] = con ([heritage] > 2, 1, 0)

[suitable] = ([imperm] * [out_town] * [critical_hab])

10.1.3 Arithmetic model

A popular method of combining a number of inputs is to score each factor (represented by a layer) and then total the scores. This general model is called the *indexed model* (a.k.a. indexed or arithmetic overlay). The indexed model (M_I) is expressed as:

$$M_I = \sum_{i=1}^{m} X_i$$

where X_i contains the values (in a map). Note that the various factors should have values with similar ranges, otherwise the relative importance between factors becomes difficult to distinguish from the relative importance within a factor. That is, if the Factor *A* values range from 0 to 10 and Factor *B* values range from 0 to 20, then the output is biased strongly towards Factor *B*. The indexed model is based on two important assumptions. First, the additional value of a factor is assumed to increase linearly. That is, the increase in value stepping from 0 to 1 is the same as going from 4 to 5. Second, no interaction between factors is assumed; that is, two factors should not be highly correlated. If there is strong correlation, then locations that are represented by those factors may have an overly strong bias.

Weighted sum (arithmetic model)
ArcToolbox -> Spatial Analyst Tools -> Overlay -> **Weighted Sum**.

Let's examine how an example GIS application can be characterized as an arithmetic model. Scientists at the Wilderness Society mapped *wildness* in the coterminous United States based on the degree of freedom and naturalness.[8] Factors that contribute to freedom are opportunities for solitude, the remoteness of land from mechanical devices, and the degree to which natural processes are left uncontrolled by humans (e.g., no fire suppression). Factors that contribute to naturalness include the degree or level of natural

---

8. Aplet, G., J. Thomson, and M. Wilbert. 2000. Indicators of wildness: Using attributes of the land to assess the context of wilderness. In: *Proceedings: Wilderness Science in a Time of Change*. Cole, D.N. and S.F. McCool (eds). U.S. Department of Agriculture, Forest Service, Rocky Mountain Research Station. Also available at: http://www.wilderness.org/wild/network/mapping_wildness.pdf

composition, the absence of artificial human structures (e.g., buildings), and the level of pollution. The flowcharts in Figures 10.3, 10.4, and 10.5 describe the model and its parameters, and the final map of wildness is shown in Figure 10.6.

FIGURE 10.3. Flowchart of *freedom* factors.

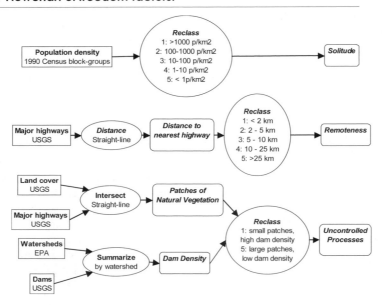

FIGURE 10.4. Flowchart of *naturalness* factors.

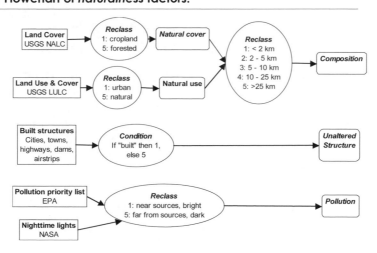

FIGURE 10.5. Flowchart of a wildness model—combining freedom and naturalness (from Figures 10.3 and 10.4).

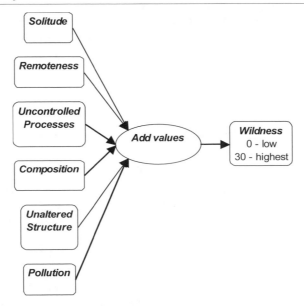

FIGURE 10.6. Final map showing areas of high (blue) and low wildness values (red). (Download color figures from www.consplan.com).

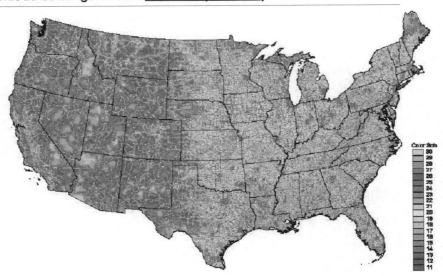

10.1.4 Weighted arithmetic model

An extension of the arithmetic model is to weight the relative importance of each factor to reflect the importance placed on each factor by decision makers. This general model is called the *weighted arithmetic model (WA)* (a.k.a. weighted linear combination).[9] The WA model (M_W) is expressed as:

$$M_W = \sum_{i=1}^{\cdots} w_i X_i$$

where X_i contains the values (in a map) and w_i is the weight for factor (map) i. Note that the weights must be normalized so that they sum to 1. The values mapped in each factor should also be normalized, preferably so they range from 0.0 to 1.0 (or 0 to 100).

Again, let's examine an application that has used the weighted arithmetic model approach. A common task in natural resource management is to inventory and prioritize lands based on biological significance and risk of development. The goal of the Lower Gunnison River Basin Conservation Lands Inventory project (completed in 2001) was to identify the portions of the riparian corridor that are valuable for preservation and/or suitable along the Lower Gunnison River and its near tributaries.[10] Four primary factors or conservation criteria were identified: riparian habitat condition, development pressure, level of surrounding protection, and agricultural land. Various GIS data layers were used to represent these factors (Figure 10.7).[11] This type of problem is considered to be a multicriteria decisionmaking problem[12] and the challenge is to combine multiple factors, including biological significance, threats by development, and land-owner willingness into a single indicator.

In addition, weights were determined through interviews of stakeholders. Stakeholders were interviewed individually to determine their individual weightings, and those were averaged to produce final weights. A useful technique to develop the weights is through a pairwise comparison of the criteria using the *Analytic Hierarchy Process*.[13] Decisionmakers examine pairwise comparisons of all factors and then use a simple mathematical formula to compute the weights. Not only does the process result in weights

9. Malczewski, J. 1999. *GIS and multicriteria decision analysis*. John Wiley & Sons.
10. Molacek, R. 2001. *Lower Gunnison River Basin Conservation Lands Inventory*. Report prepared by Delta Soil Conservation District, Delta, Colorado.
11. Theobald, D.M. 2001. *Documentation of methods to produce factor maps for the Lower Gunnison Basin Conservation Lands Inventory*. Report for the Delta Soil Conservation District, Colorado. 24 August. 4 pages.
12. Carver, S.J. 1991. Integrating multi-criteria evaluation with geographical information systems. *International Journal of Geographical Information Systems* 5(3): 321-339.
13. Saaty, T.L. 1977. A scaling method for priorities in hierarchical structures. *Journal of Mathematical Psychology* 15: 234-291.

GIS Concepts and ArcGIS Methods

that reflect the expert opinions of decisionmakers, it helps to identify potential factors that are important that were not considered, and potential factors that were thought to be important but were not. Stakeholders were presented with a series of maps showing each factor and then were asked to estimate the relative importance of each pair of factors by filling out a simple score sheet. The weights were then computed from a matrix of values and a consistency indicator was generated to determine the probability that the matrix ratings were randomly generated.[14] This is useful to identify the degree of agreement and dissension among stakeholders. The weights were as follows: riparian habitat condition = 0.25; development pressure = 0.33; level of surrounding protection = 0.17; and prime agricultural lands = 0.25. Note also that weights were developed by biologists to create the riparian habitat condition map.

Weighted overlay (weighted arithmetic model)
ArcToolbox -> Spatial Analyst Tools -> Overlay -> **Weighted Sum**.

FIGURE 10.7. **Flowchart of a conservation prioritization model for the Lower Gunnison Basin.**

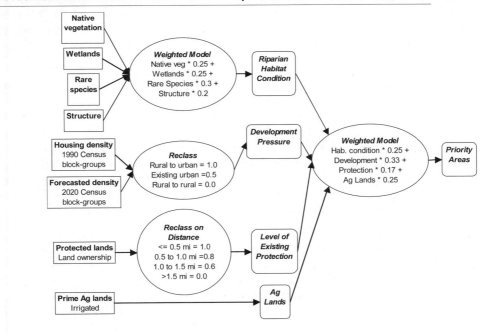

---

14. There are numerous software decision support packages that implement AHP, including: Criterium® Decision Plus®, available as a student version through www.infoharvest.com.

10.2 Evolution of user interfaces in GIS

I began this book with a brief discussion of the evolution of GIS interfaces, from command-line to GUI-based, and here I will end it by returning to that topic. As we have seen, a number of innovations have been developed with ArcGIS, notable among these are the close integration of ArcGIS with Internet mapping and mapping services and the seamless support for metadata—both innovations will likely change the way GIS data is developed and shared. Yet the way we go about *doing* GIS has remained more or less the same over the past two or three decades. Recently, though there have been significant ways in which this has been improved.

GUI-based interfaces are powerful ways to interact with GIS data and functionality, in particular they allow us to see the data we are working with and manipulate it readily. No wonder the artist in us all is immensely satisfied with the immediate visual stimulation and gratification provided by GUI interfaces in ArcGIS. However, the careful, practical scientist in us all is left grimacing at the lack of documentation of the process. That is, GUI interfaces are notoriously poor at capturing the steps taken to create a map and conduct an analysis in an automated fashion. As a result, creating a map or conducting an analysis once is fun, but doing it twice or more is a chore. And we all have experienced (or will!) that painful realization, when revisiting a map or model a month or two later, that we should have kept better notes about what we did.

So, what does process documentation have to do with modeling and flowcharts? A lot! Typically, modeling is considered to be a purposeful exercise, as I portrayed in the three modeling stages discussed earlier, where the logical framework of a model is carefully constructed. In addition, one might consider the ad hoc tinkering with a GUI as a model, albeit a messy one. In fact, after trimming away the dead-ends and irrelevant steps of a GUI-based work session, what is left at the end of process is the beginnings of a model that can be formalized for repetitive use.[15] The next step in interface design is to simply formalize this model through a flowchart. In this way, a flowchart could be constructed either purposefully through a flowchart interface (e.g., the Model Builder extension), or automatically generated by ArcGIS as one is working through the GUI interface.

Another important advancement of GIS modeling is minimizing the distinction between *doing* GIS from *using* the results of GIS. That is, today a model is constructed and analysis is done typically at a separate time and place from where the information will be used. A vast unrealized opportunity exists to situate GIS analysis directly within the decisionmaking context for which it is needed. Recent interactive whiteboard technology—so called "smart boards"—has developed to enable GIS use in public participatory

---

15. Steadfast command-line users of workstation ArcInfo have long had this ability through *watch* files.

situations. Again, flowcharts will likely be central to actively engaging a whole new set of users of GIS. This will free GIS analysis from the confines of the office, allowing excursions into the board rooms, hearing rooms, and into the great outdoors.

10.3 ModelBuilder

The *ModelBuilder* window is an interface that allows you to string a number of processes together to create a model. There are four general mechanical or implementational steps in creating a model in ModelBuilder: creating a new model, adding tools, saving a model, and running it.

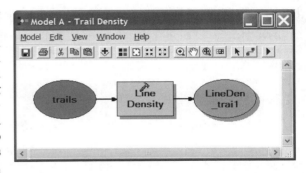

First, create a new model. Because models are tied so closely to ArcToolbox, it is in the ArcToolbox window where a new model is created. Recall (from Chapter 1) that models are stored within toolboxes. To create a new toolbox, bring up the ArcToolbox window, then right-click on the root level "ArcToolbox" and select "New Toolbox." Rename it to something meaningful, perhaps "Z_MyModels".[16] Next, right-click on your new toolbox and select New --> Model. This should bring up the ModelBuilder window (at right). Note that there are menus and toolbars above the model diagram or model display portion of the model.

Second, tools or processes are added to the model display window to construct a model. A model process contains three parts:

- the input variable(s),
- the tool itself, and
- the derived or output variables or datasets.

Note that two or more processes are linked together by using the output of one tool as an input to another tool. An *input variable* is used to represent geographic data, such as a data layer that exists as a layer in ArcMap. A *value* is used to represent non-geographic data, such as scalar values that may set the cell size of a raster or cluster tolerance. To

---

16. It is helpful to keep the system tools separate from your tools, and because tools are sorted alphabetically, starting your tool with a "Z" will place them at the bottom.

capture outputs, a *derived data* element represents output geographic data created by a tool. Other, non-geographic, data that are output from a tool are known as *derived values*. In the example model above (Model A), *trails* is an input variable, *Line Density* is a tool, and *LinesDen_trail* is derived data.

The easiest way to add a tool to your model is to locate the desired tool in the ArcToolbox window, then drag and drop it into the model. Open a tool by double-clicking on the tool. Next, specify the input datasets and/or values that are needed, and the output dataset (or value) name as well. (One quirky thing to watch out for: sometimes when parameterizing a tool requiring two or more inputs, a derived data element will be drawn directly and exactly on top of another.)

Third, save your model by clicking Model --> Save. Models are saved within a specific toolbox file (*.tbx). You can find the file location by right-clicking on a model, then select Properties, Source tab.

Fourth, run your model. Click on the Model menu and select Run (or Run Entire Model). The *Run Entire Model* menu item forces ModelBuilder to run all processes within the model. The other option, *Run*, simply runs processes that have data that have been changed or updated, and so runs only the processes that are needed to generate the final output. Also note that you can run an individual process by right-clicking on a tool.

10.3.1 Modeling accessibility -- an illustration of iterative modeling

Imagine, if you will, that your task is to conduct a spatial analysis to better understand the influence of park visitors on the resources of a park. A typical way to visualize the effects of park visitation is the trail network (Figure 10.8).

We'll work through a series of steps or iterations of logic. At each step, we'll consider other models that we have already built and grab tools or process as needed. Often we'll just start another step by copying (and pasting) the model representing the previous step. Building up a model iteratively is a useful way to work because we can build on previous work, we keep track of our logic, we can backtrack in case we do not like the approach we took, and because we can automatically document our work. Also note that in this example a number of tools from raster-based analysis will be used, especially cost-weighted distance tools. Please refer back to the previous chapters for a more detailed discussion.

FIGURE 10.8. The Bear Lake corridor in Rocky Mountain National Park, Colorado, USA. The roads (solid black line), trails (dashed black line), and hydrology (blue lines) are displayed over a hillshade. (Note: Longs Peak is in the lower-right corner. (Download color figures from www.consplan.com).

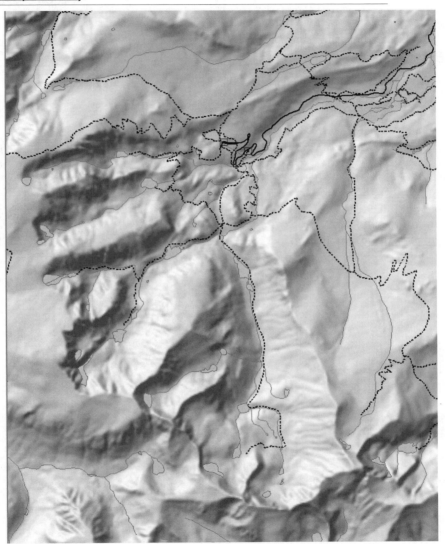

There are a couple of ways that trails are used to develop a measure of influence. One way is to compute the trail density using a moving window with a given radius, such as 1 km. **Model A** shows a single process, in which the *Line Density* tool (from Spatial Analyst) is used to compute the density from the input layer *trails*.

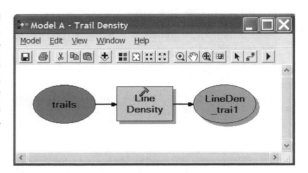

This initial model identifies locations with high average density of trails (dark purple at right), but does not differentiate locations that are further away from trail heads. Also, because the results are driven largely by the search radius, one must be careful to explicitly state, and provide a rationale for, the search radius.

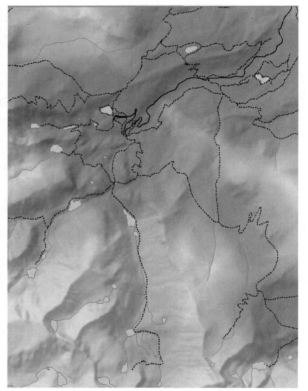

Another common way is to compute the distance from roads and/or distance from trails. Here we could either generate multiple buffers at incremental distances (e.g., 100, 200, 300, 500, 1000 m, etc.). Instead, **Model B** shows a single-process model using the *Euclidean Distance* tool that allows us to model surfaces using raster datasets. The resulting raster (EucDisttrail1) has, for every cell, the straight line distance back to the nearest trail. Note that the optional Output Direction raster was not computed.

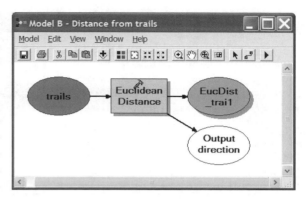

Here, areas in red are short distances, yellow is further away. Again, this gets at part of what we are wanting to measure, but does not distinguish the context of a trail or road. That is, all parts or segments of a trail are the same -- no matter if a portion is directly adjacent to a trailhead (typically with lots of people) or far away from a trailhead (less people). We need to think about the source from which people emanate -- the parking lots and trailheads.

So, a next step is to differentiate parts of trails that are close to the trailhead from those that are far away. Again, we'll use the Euclidean distance tool, but this time we'll compute distance from *trailheads*. To create **Model C**, we'll copy our previous model (Model B), then paste to create a new one and call it "Model C - Distance from trailheads". We simply need to change the input file to *trailheads* and change the output file name to *EucDist_ths*.

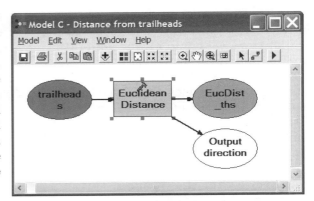

Now we can see the distance increasing away (red to yellow to blue) from the trailheads (shown by green circles). This is getting better, but does not differentiate where a trail is or is not.

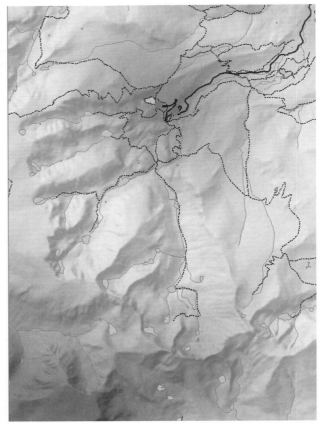

Our next step is to constrain computation of distance from trailheads to stay *along* the trails. Here, we'll use a tool called *Cost Distance*, which computes distance by accumulating "costs" from specified starting locations. Again, we copy Model C, paste it back into the working toolbox, and rename it **"Model D - Dist from trailheads along trails."** Because we want to count distance along trails (and not off trail), we'll first convert trails to a raster with cell values of 1 (using the *Feature to Raster* tool and a field in *trails* that contains values of 1). The output *trails_r* is the cost-weight input into the Cost

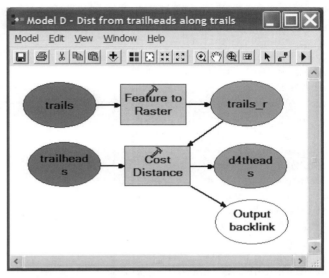

Distance tool. We'll use the trailhead locations as the starting location. The *Cost Distance* tool starts at a trailhead, then accumulates distances using a weight of 1. This will result in the Euclidean distance (because we are using a weight of 1), but it will be computed recognizing the bends and wiggles of the trails. (The tool automatically recognizes the cell size, so our output will be in map units, meters in this case). Be sure that the trailheads are "snapped" to the trails. That is, the trailheads, when converted to raster, need to touch the trails -- otherwise the distances from trailheads will be zero. One other technique (not used in this model) to ensure starting points link to the line work is to first buffer the starting points by some distance.

Because we constrained computation of distance along trails, we see the raster cells depicting distance just along the trails (zoomed in), with increasing distance away from the trailheads (red to orange to yellow). This is valuable because we know, for any location on a trail, the distance back to the closest trailhead.

But, we aren't representing anything about *off-trail* distances. That is, all locations off-trail are the same distance, which doesn't seem to get at what we are trying to measure.

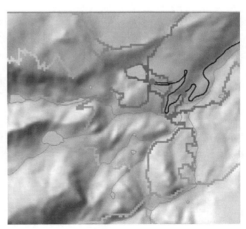

Our next step is to compute the off-trail distance from trails, but this time we'll add the along-trail distance as well. This assumes that to get to a location X that is off-trail (e.g., one of the lakes), a person would hike along the trail to the closest point, then hike off-trail to get to location X. The way that we'll compute the closest along-trail distance is using the *Euclidean Allocation* tool. Here we have added the Euclidean Allocation tool. But because the output of the Euclidean Distance tool is a floating-point raster (with real values), and the allocation tool requires an integer raster as input, we first use the *Int* tool to convert from a floating point to integer raster. To get to any location off-trail we assume that one must first hike along the trail to the closest point, so we add (using the *Plus* tool) the on-trail and off-trail distances to get a final, off-and-on trail distance raster (called *EucD_onofft*).

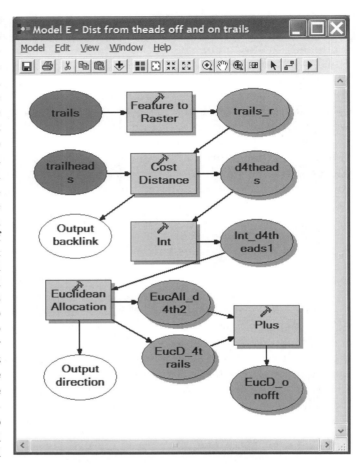

Now this is more like it! We now have, for every location in our study area, the distance back to the nearest trailhead. Note that there are some abrupt differences in distances (shown by non-continuous color gradations, e.g., red to yellow or yellow to blue). These are due to the allocation zones, which simply "grow" from the nearest trail.

This is all well and good and we are making steady progress, but on deeper reflection, you might notice that here we have assumed that a person can walk anywhere off-trail with equal ease. Is this realistic? No...

So, our next step (and this is a big, powerful one!) is to adjust distances by the difficulty of moving across a given stretch (or cell). A primary factor influencing this is *slope*. For example, walking up a steep trail takes more energy and time than a flatter trail. We're computing one-way distance, so whether we are hiking up or down a steep slope does not matter too much at this point. First, *trails_r* is multiplied (using the *Times* tool) times the DEM to return a raster with elevation values found only on the trail (*dem_trails*). Then we use the *Slope* tool to compute the slope at each location along the trail (*slope_trail*). We then compute a function (using a map algebra statement in the *Single Output Map* tool) based on slope (see below). We'll use the equation outlined in Chapter 7 (Section 7.9.1.2) that relates a hiker's average velocity in relation to slope. The average velocity is 5.04 km per hour, for flat ground. We'll simply adjust the cost-weight so that distance travelled is expressed as effective distance, where locations that have steeper slopes require more time -- which we can also express as increased distance. In other words, if a person hiking on a steep slope moves at half the velocity as on a flat section, then it is the same as if he/she was walking twice as far on all flat ground. The *slope_wt* raster is then used as the cost-weights in the *Cost Distance* tool.

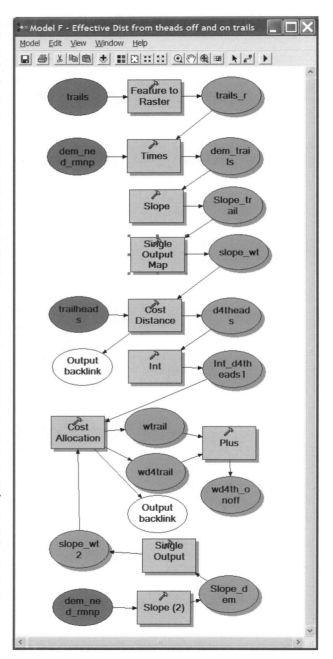

The Map Algebra expression from the Single Output Map tool (in Model F) to compute the effective distance weight based on trail slope is provided below.

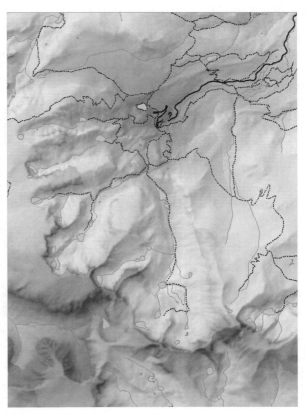

Single Output Map Algebra

Map Algebra expression

5.04 / (6 * exp (-3.5 * abs(tan (slope_trail / 57.29578) + 0.05)))

Now our model measures effective distance in a way that recognizes the difficulty of hiking, relative to slopes. Note that computing slope along a trail requires extracting the elevation along just the trail, then computing slope. Slope computed on a full DEM provides the slope in the direction of the maximum fall line, which typically exceeds the trail slope (because a trail is typically aligned to cut across a slope). Indeed, trails are likely to become heavily eroded if their alignment follows the "fall-line" of a hillside.

The output from this model is looking pretty good. But one more thing (yes, the proverbial "one more thing"): isn't it slower when walking off-trail than on-trail? And are some off-trail areas easier or harder to hike through? Glad you asked: yes. One situation where this definitely is the case is around lakes (we can climb the highest mountains, but we can't walk on water!). That is, our model should be constrained so that we must walk around a lake to get to the other side (see arrows, right). In addition, other land cover types offer different resistance to walking through an area -- for example think about the difference between an open forest or grassland (tundra in our example) vs. thick shrub cover or dense old-growth forest.

Here in **Model G** we'll adjust the cost-weights to account for the difficulty of off-trail hiking (regardless of the slope), based on land cover types (Table 10.2). We incorporate these weights into our model by the *Single Output* tool that takes *nlcd_rmnp* as an input and creates *nlcd_wts*. This is then multiplied times the *slope _wts* to create cost weights that incorporate both slope and cover type.

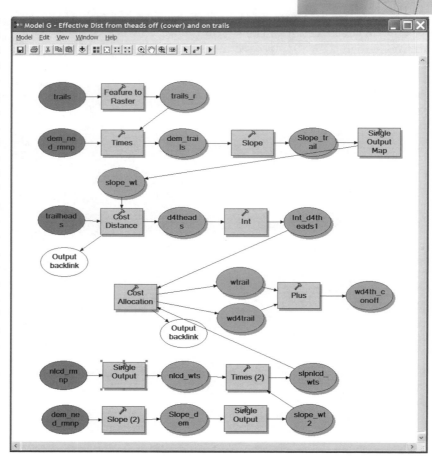

The map algebra expression is used to compute the land cover weights (right). A conditional statement is used here, rather than the

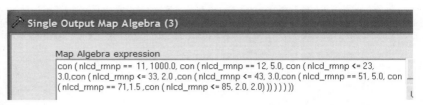

Single Output Map Algebra (3)

Map Algebra expression
con (nlcd_rmnp == 11, 1000.0, con (nlcd_rmnp == 12, 5.0, con (nlcd_rmnp <= 23, 3.0,con (nlcd_rmnp <= 33, 2.0 ,con (nlcd_rmnp <= 43, 3.0,con (nlcd_rmnp == 51, 5.0, con (nlcd_rmnp == 71,1.5 ,con (nlcd_rmnp <= 85, 2.0, 2.0))))))))

Reclassify tool, because the output of Reclassify is an integer raster, so only whole values can be generated (e.g., 1, 2, 3...) but not 1.5.

The effective distances computed by Model G (shown right) are able to distinguish the likely busy location near the trailheads (and roads), the farther-flung areas, as well as incorporate different land cover types (the lakes are now visible as pockets of higher distance). Note that the symbology shown here, and in particular the red colors, makes it look like the distances increased. However, the color scheme has simply stretched because of longer distances, thereby shifting some moderate distance values into the red (short) hue range.

One way to portray these distances a little more simply is to convert the effective distance values into something more meaningful, perhaps the number of minutes it would take to travel to a given place. We can do this by simply dividing the effective distance (in meters) by the number of meters that an average person can travel in a minute assuming flat ground and on trail, which is 84 meters per minute (see Figure 10.9).

To summarize, we've gone from a simple model based on computing density of roads and/or trails, to a more sophisticated representation of what we believe are important aspects of park visitation and possible effects on natural resources. Which of these models is "the best"? Again, this can be judged only within the context of the purpose or goal of a model.

FIGURE 10.9. One-way travel time from trailheads (green circles) in the Bear Lake corridor in Rocky Mountain National Park, Colorado, USA. The roads (solid black line), trails (dashed black line), and hydrology (blue lines). (Download color figures from www.consplan.com).

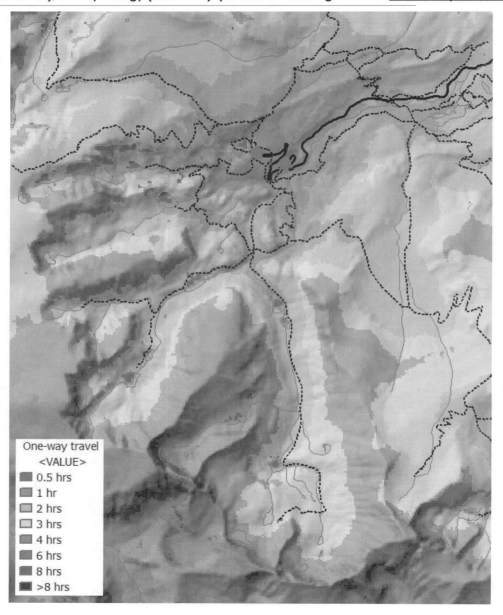

One-way travel
<VALUE>
0.5 hrs
1 hr
2 hrs
3 hrs
4 hrs
6 hrs
8 hrs
>8 hrs

TABLE 10.2. Estimated weights for cost-weights of off-trail travel through land cover types, using National Land Cover Dataset.

Value	Type	Weight
11	Water (lakes, reservoirs)	1000.0
12	Snowfields, glaciers	5.0
21, 22, 23	Urban/built-up (residential, commercial, industrial)	3.0
31, 32, 33	Transitional	2.0
41	Forest - deciduous	3.0
42	Forest - coniferous	3.0
43	Forest - mixed	3.0
51	Shrubland	5.0
61	Orchards	2.0
71	Grasslands	1.5
81, 82, 83, 84, 85	Agricultural	2.0
91, 92	Wetlands	3.0

10.4 Programming scripts using Python

10.4.1 Why use Python?

Python is a scripting language that provides yet another way to construct models. Python has quickly become the primary language to write geoprocessing tools with ArcGIS. Why? For a variety of reasons:

- Python is easy to learn because it based on simple, clear concepts and clean syntax;
- it supports object-oriented programming;
- Python code is readable and so less documentation is needed;
- it is COM compliant and can be easily integrated with other languages (C++, Fortran, Java, etc.);
- it is platform independent; and
- Python is free and has a broad user community (and can be installed with ArcGIS v9).

One of the best ways to learn how to program spatial Geoprocessing with ArcGIS using Python is to simply generate a model (as we did above) with Model Builder, and then export the model to Python. Then you've got someplace to start from that does something with which you are familiar. So, for example, Model A (right), looks like this in Python code (below).

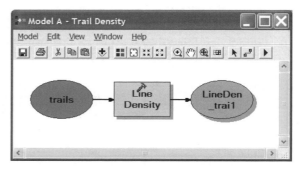

```
# ----------------------------------------------------------------
# model_a.py
# Created on: Sat Jun 25 2005 07:10:51 PM
#   (generated by ArcGIS/ModelBuilder)
# ----------------------------------------------------------------

# Import system modules
import arcgisscripting, string, os

# Create the Geoprocessor object
gp = arcgisscripting.create()

# Check out any necessary licenses
gp.CheckOutExtension("spatial")

# Load required toolboxes...
gp.AddToolbox("C:/Program Files/ArcGIS/ArcToolbox/Toolboxes/Spatial Analyst Tools.tbx")

# Local variables...
LineDen_trail = "C:\\davet\\projects\\RMNP\\ROMO_data\\lineden_trail"
trails = "trails"

# Process: Line Density...
gp.LineDensity_sa(trails, "NONE", LineDen_trail, "C:\\davet\\projects\\RMNP\\ROMO_data\\eucdist_bear1", "1000", "HECTARES")
```

Another excellent resource for learning about scripting is ESRI's document: *ArcGIS v9: Writing Geoprocessing Scripts*. But before we dive right into some of the nitty-gritty details, a brief primer on Python programming basics is in order. Remember that when you begin programming in Python to do a geoprocessing task, you'll need to keep Python syntax, modules, etc. distinct from the peculiarities of the gp object (your gateway to ArcGIS).

10.4.2 Basics of Python programming

There are a variety of programming techniques, variables, and data structures that are important to know about. These are not so different from other programming languages, so if you know BASIC, Fortran, C, or VBA, Python should be a snap to learn. Here I presume that you have installed Python v2.4 and PythonWin (a programming application window), which is provided by the ArcGIS Desktop install program. Note that throughout this section I will provide snippets of Python code (a couple of lines of code, but these does *not* constitute a complete program in and of itself), which will be distinguished by `black`, `Courier` font. Sections of code that were written as a whole, stand-alone program are portrayed with colored text, as in the following script:

```
#import standard library modules
import arcgisscripting, sys, os
print "Hello there!"
```

10.4.2.1 PythonWin

PythonWin is an application that allows you to interact with Python through a command-line window (ArcGIS does not need to be running to access geoprocessing tools!). Start up PythonWin through Start --> All programs --> Python 2.4--> Pythonwin.[17] Note that there is an interactive window that allows you to type much of the following code directly, and see the results. Or, you can create a script file (*.py) and run it from within PythonWin. The steps are to:

1) write your script;

2) save it;

3) check it (click on the check mark on the Standard toolbar); and

4) run it (running guy button).

Later we'll see how to run a Python script from within ArcGIS.

10.4.2.2 Modules

Modules are the way that scripts are organized in Python, similar to libraries in other programming languages. Modules store Python scripts that are somehow related (such as routines to handle strings). To bring a module (and its associated individual scripts, functions, or variables into a program), use the `import` statement. For example, nearly every script that you will write will have the following lines at the beginning of the program:

```
#import standard library modules
import arcgisscripting, sys, os
```

This code imports the arcgisscripting, system, and operating system modules. The `sys` module refers to the Python system, while the `os` module provides access to fundamental functions associated with the operating system, such as filename manipulation tools.

There are many, many other modules available in Python.

---

[17] The version of PythonWin that comes with the installation is Pywin32-207.wind32-py2.4.exe.

10.4.2.3 Peculiarities of Python

Python is fastidious. Python variable names and functions are case-sensitive (so x and X are two different variables). Moreover, the logical structure of a program is specified by indentations, rather than start/end statements (e.g., if... then/endif in VBA). So, you will need to learn to be neat-and-tidy in your scripting -- and soon you'll appreciate the simplicity and ease of scripting in Python.

10.4.2.4 Comments

It is very important to document your code. Comments are one of the best ways to do this (using variables with meaningful names is another). A comment in Python is distinguished by a special character -- a pound sign ("#"). Everything to the right of the # on the same line is a comment. This means that comments can be on their own line, as in:

```
# This is an example of a comment
```

or a comment can be "in-line", such as:

```
apples = 2      # initialize the number of apples
```

10.4.2.5 Variables

There are a variety of types of variables, but the most frequently-used ones are numbers, strings, lists, and dictionaries (Table 10.3). Note that Python does not require you to explicitly identify a variable before it is used (e.g., in VBA one usually must first "dimension" a variable).

Variables names should start with a character (and remember, Python is case sensitive) and contain only alpha-numeric characters. A useful naming convention is to use descriptive variable names (avoid abbreviations) and capitalize the beginning of each word. For example, a variable that stores a list that stores the neighbors of a polygon might be called:

```
lstPolygonNeighbors.
```

Numbers can be assigned to a variable name using the equal sign ("="). For example:

```
lakeAcres = 10
intSqFeetPerAcre = 43560
lakeAcres * intSqFeetPerAcre   #returns 435,600 square feet
```

Note that the divisor operator "/" is an integer divisor if all variables or numbers in an equation are integers. That is, x in the statement below would equal 3, not 3.5.

```
x = 7 / 2
```

If you want real values to be computed, then use:

```
x = 7 / 2.0
```
Strings can also be used to store literal strings. These can be enclose in single or double quotes, but typically double quotes are used so that single quotes can be used within a string to indicate contraction or possesion:

```
strCity = "Winter Park"
strMotto = "Mountain biking fun!"
```
Two strings can be joined together into a single string, or be *concatenated*, by the + operator:

```
strGlued = "Once upon a time" + " " + "in a land far away..."
```
results in:

```
Once upon a time in a land far away...
```
A string can span more than one line by "escaping" it with a back-slash ("\"):

```
strVerse = "I can't seem to face up to the facts. I'm tense \
and nervous and I can't relax."
```
Characters in a string can be accessed through indexes that are offset by square brackets ("[]") rather than parentheses. The first character is indexed by 0. So, strX in the following would be "W":

```
strX = strCity[0]
```
You can also access a range of characters by using a colon, so the following would return "Win".

```
strX = strCity[0:2]
```
Note that common functions in VBA like left() or right() that return all characters to the left or right of a place can be accessed. Getting all characters to the right of the 1st character would result in "inter Park":

```
strX = strCity[1:]
```

10.4.2.6 Common data structures

A *list* is a compound data type that is used to group together a variety of items (strings, numbers, or a mixture). A list is written as a list of comma-separated items between square brackets. For example, a list of states that neighbor California would be:

```
lstCaliforniaNeighbors = ["Arizona", "Nevada", "Oregon"]
```
Getting the first item in a list is the same as getting characters in a string ("Arizona"):

```
strFirstNeighbor = lstCaliforniaNeighbors[0]
```
A list can also contain another list.

A list can be used as a *stack* data structure ("last-in, first-out"). Imagine a stack of fruit-filled pancakes, where the last pancake made and added to the stack is the first one to be eaten. Append() is used to add a new item to the stack, while pop() is used to remove the top item.

```
lstPancake = [ "blueberry", "banana", "raspberry" ]
lstPancake.append( "coconut" )     # new pancake added
x = lstPancake.pop()    # x gets the coconut pancake
```

A list can also be used as a *queue* ("first-in, first-out") data structure. In this case, append() is used again to add new items to the back of a list, but pop(0) retrieves the first item.

A *dictionary* is similar to a list, but it provides a set of unordered key:value pairs. The keys must be unique within a dictionary. Dictionaries are created by using a pair of braces ("{}"), and key:value pairs (items) are separated by commas. To obtain a list of the keys, use keys().

TABLE 10.3. Useful functions for strings and lists. Example variables are: x = 3.1415, strX = "Crested Butte", and lstX = [1, 2, 3, 4, 5, 6]. Note: remember Python is case-sensitive!

Function	Description	Example
append()	Adds or appends an item to the end of the list (to append to a string, use + or concatenate function).	lstX.append(7) >>> 1, 2, 3, 4, 5, 6, 7
Assign value	Assign a value to an individual item of a list	lstX[2] = 10 >>> 1, 2, 10, 4, 5, 6
	Assign values to multiple items (also called a "slice")	lstX[0:2] = [2, 2] >>> 2, 2, 3, 4, 5, 6
count()	Returns the number of times value x occurs in a list or string.	strX.count("t") >>> 3 lstX.count(6) >>> 1
del()	Deletes the value at index x in a list	lstX[1] >>> 1, 3, 4, 5, 6
find()	Returns the position of the first occurrence of value x in a string.	strX.find("e") >>> 3
index()	Returns the index or position in a list whose value is x. This returns an error if the value does not exist in the list. Use find() for strings.	lstX.index(1) >>> 0 strX.index("d") >>> 6

TABLE 10.3. Useful functions for strings and lists. Example variables are: x = 3.1415, strX = "Crested Butte", and lstX = [1, 2, 3, 4, 5, 6]. Note: remember Python is case-sensitive!

Function	Description	Example

insert()	Insert an item into a list. Can use "slice" syntax or insert() function.	lstX[1:1] = [8, 8]
		>>> 1, 8, 8, 2, 3, 4, 5, 6
		lstX.insert(0, 0)
		>>> 0, 1, 2, 3, 4, 5, 6

Left	Return the first x number of characters in a string or items in a list	strX[:5] >>> 'Crest' lstX[:3] >>> 1, 2, 3
len()	Returns the length or number of items in a list or string	len(strX) >>> 13 len(lstX) >>> 6
pop()	Returns and removes an item at a given index, or last index if none specified.	lstX.pop(0) >>> 1 lstX.pop() >>> 6

remove()	Remove items from a list -- can use "slice" syntax or remove() function. Removes the first item from the list whose value is x. This returns an error if no such item exists. Use count() to see if or how many occurences of x there are in a list.	lstX[0:2] = []
		>>> 3, 4, 5, 6
		lstX.remove(1)
		>>> 2, 3, 4, 5, 6

replace()	Replaces a target string with a new string.	strX.replace("Crested", "Snowy") >>> "Snowy Butte"
reverse()	Reverses the elements of a list, keeping them in place.	lstX.reverse() >>> 6, 5, 4, 3, 2, 1
Right	Return the last x number of characters in a string or items from a list.	strX[-5:] >>> 'Butte' lstX[-2:] >>> 5, 6
sort()	Sorts the items of a list, in place, ascending.	lstX.sort() >>> 1, 2, 3, 4, 5, 6
split()	Splits a string into a list based on a separator string.	strX.split(" ") >>> ['Crested', 'Butte']

TABLE 10.3. Useful functions for strings and lists. Example variables are: x = 3.1415, strX = "Crested Butte", and lstX = [1, 2, 3, 4, 5, 6]. Note: remember Python is case-sensitive!

Function	Description	Example
escape sequences	There are a variety of escape sequences or special characters that can be generated in a string, and commonly used ones are listed here.	\n >>> newline \\ >>> backslash \n >>> linefeed \r >>> carriage return \t >>> tab
random functions	The random module provides access to a number of useful functions that access a pseudo-random number generator. Need to import random before calling these functions.	random() >>> uniform random value between 0,1.0 seed(x) >>> initializes the random seed value to x shuffle(x) >>> randomly shuffles or permutes list x

10.4.2.7 Conditional statements (if/then/else)

An important statement is called a *conditional statement* that uses Boolean logic to control program flow. Essentially, it implements "if *X* occurs, then do *Y*". Note that there are no matching end statements -- rather indentation and the colons (":") control the blocks of logic. And yes, *elif* is not a typo -- rather it stands for "else if".

For example, the following snippet would help decide flow based on whether x was negative, zero, or positive:

```
if x < 0:
     print "Negative"
elif x == 0:
     print "Zero"
else:
     print "Positive"
```

10.4.2.8 Looping

Loops are powerful structures within a program to do repetative tasks. Combined with conditional statements, loops are very common in programs.

There are a variety of ways to loop, but the most commonly-used loop statements are for and while. *For* iterates over the items of any list (or string), in the order the items appear. *While* loops as long as a condition is true. This statement typically requires three steps: 1) initialize a variable; 2) test the condition of the variable; and 3) increment the variable. (Don't forget this last step, otherwise you'll be stuck in an infinite loop). Here are a couple of examples to show you how loops work.

```
# looping example1
lstX = [ 1, 2, 3]
for x in lstX:
    print x
```

This generates the following list:

```
1
2
3
```

Again, the keywords *for*, *in*, and the colon (":") are required, and indentation controls the structure. That is, all lines of code that are indented will be included in the loop, while those that are outside of the indentation are not. For example:

```
# looping example2
lstX = [1, 2, 3]
for x in lstX:
    print x
    print "Go!"
```

This generates the following output:

```
1
Go!
2
Go!
3
Go!
```

But if a statement is out of the indentation structure, it is *not* included in the loop:

```
# looping example3
lstX = [1, 2, 3]
for x in lstX:
```

```
    print x
print "Go!"
```

This results in the following output (note that it is good practice to provide a line between groups of lines of code:

```
1
2
3
Go!
```

The following program uses a while statement to generate the same output ("1 2 3 Go!"):

```
# looping example4
x = 1
while x < 4:
    print x
    x = x + 1


print "Go!"
```

Note that the while loop executes as long as the condition is true. Any non-zero integer value is true, while zero and negative values are false. The *break* statement breaks out of the smallest enclosing for or while loop. The *continue* statement bypasses the rest of the statements in a loop and continues with the next iteration.

10.4.2.9 Short examples

Here are a couple of short examples of Python code to demonstrate some of the basics about lists, dictionaries, and for loops.[18]

```
# example to demonstrate lists, dictionaries, and loops
lstNodes = [ 1, 2, 3, 4, 5, 6 ]
dctNeighbors = { 1: [2, 4, 5], 2: [1, 4, 5], 3: [5, 6], 4: [1,
2, 5], 5: [1, 2, 3, 4], 6: [3] }
print "A list of the Neighbors for each Node:"
for x in lstNodes:
    print x, dctNeighbors[x]
```

---

18. The adjacency lists are a based on an example from: Anselin, L. and O. Smirnov. 1996. Efficient algorithms for constructing proper higher order spatial lag operators. *Journal of Regional Science* 36(1): 67-89.

This script generates the following output:

```
A list of the Neighbors for each Node:
1 [2, 4, 5]
2 [1, 4, 5]
3 [5, 6]
4 [1, 2, 5]
5 [1, 2, 3, 4]
6 [3]
```

The script below generates a list of 1st and 2nd order neighbors.

```
# example to find 1st and 2nd order neighbors
1stNodes = [ 1, 2, 3, 4, 5, 6 ]
dctNeighbors = { 1: [2, 4, 5], 2: [1, 4, 5], 3: [5, 6], 4: [1,
2, 5], 5: [1, 2, 3, 4], 6: [3] }

for x in 1stNodes:
    print "1st order of " + str(x) + ": " + str(dctNeighbors[x])
    # find 2nd order neighbors
    z = []
    for y in dctNeighbors[x]:
            print "\t2nd order of " + str(y) + ": " +
str(dctNeighbors[y])
```

The output is:

```
1st order of 1: [2, 4, 5]
    2nd order of 2: [1, 4, 5]
    2nd order of 4: [1, 2, 5]
    2nd order of 5: [1, 2, 3, 4]
1st order of 2: [1, 4, 5]
    2nd order of 1: [2, 4, 5]
    2nd order of 4: [1, 2, 5]
    2nd order of 5: [1, 2, 3, 4]
```

```
1st order of 3: [5, 6]
    2nd order of 5: [1, 2, 3, 4]
    2nd order of 6: [3]
1st order of 4: [1, 2, 5]
    2nd order of 1: [2, 4, 5]
    2nd order of 2: [1, 4, 5]
    2nd order of 5: [1, 2, 3, 4]
1st order of 5: [1, 2, 3, 4]
    2nd order of 1: [2, 4, 5]
    2nd order of 2: [1, 4, 5]
    2nd order of 3: [5, 6]
    2nd order of 4: [1, 2, 5]
1st order of 6: [3]
    2nd order of 3: [5, 6]
```

10.4.3 Arguments

An important way that you can communicate with a Python script is through script *arguments* (or sometimes known as parameters). This allows you to pass in input parameters, such as a shapefile to do some geoprocessing on, or output parameters that details where to save an output file. Arguments are usually assigned to local variables at the beginning of a script, using the variable sys.argv[] list. Note that all arguments are passed in as strings -- so you may need to do some type conversion if other variable types are needed. For example, if you want to pass in an integer, then the argument (e.g., "2") is converted to an integer (note that argv[0] is reserved for the script name itself):

```
# example to demonstrate passing an argument in
strNode = sys.argv[1]
xNode = int(strNode)
lstNodes = [ 1, 2, 3, 4, 5, 6 ]
dctNeighbors = { 1: [2, 4, 5], 2: [1, 4, 5], 3: [5, 6], 4: [1,
2, 5], 5: [1, 2, 3, 4], 6: [3] }
print "Neighbors of node " + str( xNode ) + ": " +
str(dctNeighbors[xNode])
```

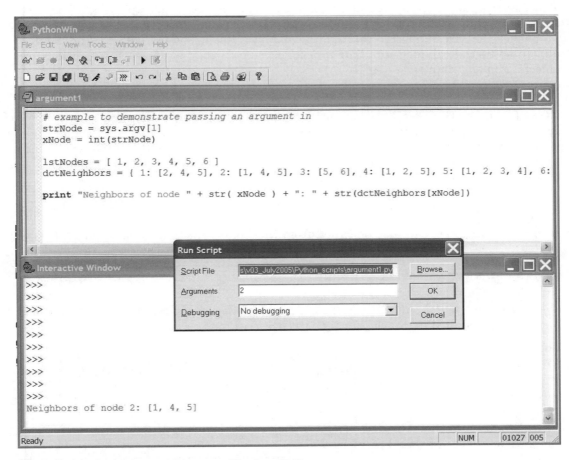

10.4.4 Connecting Python with ArcGIS

And now for the part you have been waiting for -- accessing ArcGIS functionality through a Python script. This "magic" is done by declaring an object called the *geoprocessor* object. So, to declare the geoprocessor object, you'll simply copy the following lines into your script (its the fourth line starting with "gp" that does declares the geoprocessing object:

```
#import standard library modules
import arcgisscripting, sys, os
gp = arcgisscripting.create(9.3)
```

There are two main groups of objects that can be called through "gp": those that access ArcGIS tools directly and are named after a tool (e.g., gp.Clip...); or methods and properties that are supported through the gp object itself. The methods and properties of gp can be further divided into four types: describe objects, enumeration objects, cursor objects, and environment settings.

10.4.4.1 Tools

Every tool in ArcGIS (listed in section 10.4) can be called from Python direction using the gp object. A helpful way to understand what the code should look like is to: 1) identify the desired tool in ArcToolbox; 2) open the tool; 3) click on the Help button (right side); and 4) examine the Scripting syntax section (and Script example) at the bottom (see below). For example, to call the Select tool, you could call it from Python using:

```
gp.select_analysis("wells.shp", "gas.shp",'"WELL_TYP" =
\'GAS\'')
```

Also note that a tool can also be called from the Command Line (with slightly different syntax):

```
select_analysis wells.shp wells_Gas.shp "WELL_TYP" = 'GAS'
```

Another useful document is the Quick Reference Guide (*Geoprocessing_Quick_Ref_Gde.pdf*) that comes with the digital documenation library (most likely installed in c:\esri_library\ArcGIS_Desktop\...).

To streamline incorporating ArcGIS tools within Python scripts, I have written a Python script[19] called *Tool2Gp.py*. This allows you to enter the name (or part of, it supports a wildcard search) of a tool to search for, then provides the Usage (a concise

description of all parameters of a tool) and a Python-ready string that can be copied and pasted into a script.[20] For example, a search based on an input argument of "select_analysis"produces the following in the Interactive Window of PythonWin:

```
Tool2Gp: *select_analysis*
### Usage: Select_analysis <in_features> <out_feature_class>
{where_clause}
```

---

19. Thanks to J. Norman for helping brainstorm how this script could be improved.
20. This, and other scripts from this text, are available electronically from: www.consplan.com.

```
Gp.Select_analysis( "in_features", "out_feature_class",
"where_clause")
### Usage: TableSelect_analysis <in_table> <out_table>
{where_clause}
Gp.TableSelect_analysis(  "in_table",  "out_table",
"where_clause")
```

Note that two tools were found with the search string, and for each tool found, two lines are produced. The first line that is commented out (with "###") shows the full usage to help you recall what parameters are needed. The second line ("Gp.Select....") can be triple-clicked, copied, and then pasted into a *.py script window. You'll need to then set the parameters to tie into the rest of your code. Note that the parameters are already enclosed with double-quotes (which is required by Python).

Also, default parameters are assumed and inserted into the code when there are optional arguments (of course you can change these by editing the text):

```
Tool2Gp: *buffer_analysis*
### Usage: Buffer_analysis <in_features> <out_feature_class>
<buffer_distance_or_field> {FULL | LEFT | RIGHT} {ROUND | FLAT}
{NONE | ALL | LIST} {dissolve_field;dissolve_field...}
Gp.Buffer_analysis( "in_features", "out_feature_class",
"buffer_distance_or_field", "FULL", "ROUND", "NONE",
"dissolve_field;dissolve_field...")
```

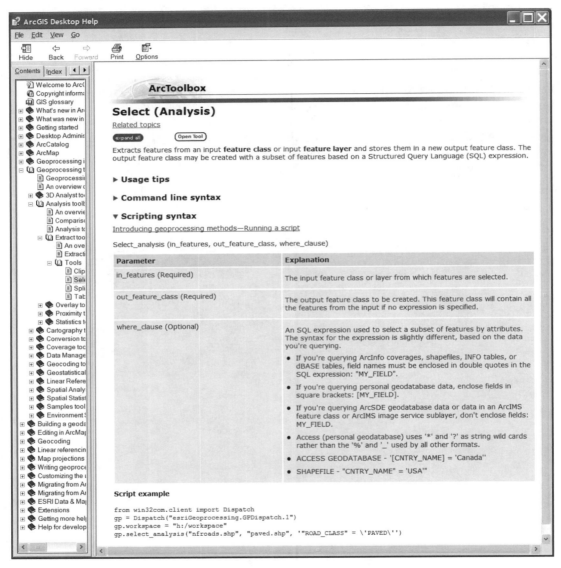

10.4.4.2 Listing and describing objects (enumerations)

The describe objects provide descriptive properties about a dataset (spatial or tabular), and different dataset types have different properties. Accessing these properties allows you to change the logic of a program based on different properties, such as doing different processing on point vs. polyline vs. polygon feature types. This is a two-step process. First, you will need to obtain a dataset that you are interested in, and this is often done by selecting from a list of datasets. pp recognizes the following different dataset types: feature class, coverage feature class, layer, tableView, datasets, relationship class, table, and workspace. Once you've found the dataset of interest, you can access properties that describe it.

There are a variety of enumerations (sequences or arrays of pp objects) that are used to generate a list of these objects (see Table 10.4): *datasets, feature classes, raster datasets, tables, and workspaces*. Lists of fields and indexes for a particular table can also be generated. These lists or enumerations are stored as an *array*, and there are a number of functions for arrays (Table 10.5). Note that parameters for these functions are optional, and support using wildcards ("*") for the first optional input.

For example, to get a list of all the polygon feature classes in a particular workspace, you could use the following code. Note seven important steps that are common to enumerations:

1) set the workspace;

2) get the enumeration;

3) reset the enumeration to the beginning;

4) get the first object;

5) enter a while loop, until the objects in the sequence are done;

6) do something with the object; and

7) get the next in the sequence (otherwise you'll be stuck in an infinite loop).

```
# Import modules
import arcgisscripting, sys, os
gp = arcgisscripting.create(9.3)
# List all feature classes in workspace
gp.Workspace= "c:/temp/data.mdb"   #1st
fcs = gp.ListFeatureClasses("*","polygon") #2st
#list them out to user
fcs.Reset()       #3nd - must reset to start at the first object
fc = fcs.Next() #4rd - get the first object
while fc:         #5th - enter loop
```

```
print fc.Name #6th - do something with it
fc = fcs.Next()  #7th - get the next in sequence
```

TABLE 10.4. List enumerations of datasets and objects. Typically the workspace must be defined before using any of the list methods (e.g.,: gp.Workspace ("c:/temp"))

Dataset type	Properties
ListDatasets()	Lists the datasets in the current workspace. ListDatasets({nameWildcard}, {datasetType}). E.g., Gp.ListDatasets ("d*", "All"). Possible dataset types are: *All, CAD, Coverage, Feature, RasterCatalog, TIN, Topology, VPF*
ListEnviron-ments	Lists the environment variables available. ListEnvironments({nameWild-card}). E.g., Gp.ListEnvironments("").
ListFeature-Classes	Lists the feature classes in a workspace. ListFeatureClasses({nameWild-card}, {featureType}). E.g., Gp.ListFeatureClasses ("*", "Polygon"). Possible feature types are: *All, Arc, Label, Line, Node, Point, Polygon, Region, Route*
ListFields	Lists the fields for a specified table. ListFields (<path/name>, {nameWild-card}, {fieldType}). E.g., Gp.ListFields ("c:/temp/roads.dbf", "*", "Integer"). Field types are: *All, Blob, Date, Double, Geometry, Integer, OID, Single, SmallInteger, String*
ListIndexes	Lists the fields that are indexed for a specified table. ListIndexes (<path/name>, {nameWildcard}). E.g., Gp.ListIndexes ("c:/temp/roads.dbf", "*").
ListRasters	Lists the raster datasets in the specified workspace. ListRasters({nameWildcard}, {rasterType}). E.g., Gp.ListRasters("*", "GRID"). Possible raster types are: *All, ADRG, BIL, BIP, BSQ, BMP, CADRG, CIB, ERS, GIF, GIS, GRID, IMG, JPEG, LAN, NITF, PNG, RAW, SID, SDE, STACK, TIFF*
ListTables	Lists the tables in the current workspace. ListTables(<nameWildcard>, <tableType>). E.g., Gp.ListTables ("d*", "All"). Possible dataset types are: *All, dBASE, INFO*
ListToolboxes	Lists the toolboxes in a workspace. ListToolboxes({nameWildcard}). E.g., Gp.ListToolboxes ("FLoWS").
ListTools	Lists the tools in a workspace. ListTools({nameWildcard}). E.g., Gp.List-Tools ("Create*").
ListWorkspaces	Lists the workspaces available in the current workspace. ListWork-spaces(<nameWildcard>, <workspaceType>). E.g., Gp.ListWorkspaces ("d*", "All"). Possible workspace types are: *All, Access, Coverage, SDE, Shapefile*

TABLE 10.5. Functions for the various enumeration objects. Get the array from some list operation (e.g., fc = gp.List..., then intC = fc.Count

Function	Description
Array	**Add**(k) - adds an object *k* to array at the end of the list.
	Count - returns the number of objects in the array.
	GetObject(i) - gets the object at a specified index *i*.
	Insert(i, k) - insert object *k* at index *i*.
	Next() - returns the next object in array, usually used at the bottom of a while loop.
	Remove(i) - remove object at index i from array.
	RemoveAll() - remove all objects from array.
	Reset() - resets the arary to the first object.

The properties that can be accessed and described depend on the dataset type, and are listed in Tables 10.6 and 10.7.

TABLE 10.6. Describe objects and properties associated with each dataset type. Note that these properties are accessed from desc.<property>, where desc = Gp.Describe (<inDataSet>).

Dataset type	Properties
Coverage	**Tolerances.Dangle**
	Tolerances.Edit -
	Tolerances.Fuzzy -
	Tolerances.Grain -
	Tolerances.NodeSnap -
	Tolerances.Snap -
	Tolerances.TicMatch -
	Tolerances.Weed -
Coverage feature class	**Extent** - The xmin, ymin, xmax, ymax of minimum enclosing rectangle.
	FeatureClassType - The feature type: *point, arc, polygon, annotation, file, label, link, node, region, route, tic*
	Fields - List of the fields.
	HasFAT -Boolean indicator of existence of feature attribute table.
	HasOID - Boolean indicator of an OID (object ID) field.
	Indexes - list of the indexed fields.
	OIDFieldName - The name of the OID field.
	Topology - State of topology: *exists, nonapplicable, preliminary, unknown*

TABLE 10.6. Describe objects and properties associated with each dataset type. Note that these properties are accessed from desc.<property>, where desc = Gp.Describe (<inDataSet>).

Dataset type	Properties
Dataset	DatasetType - *coverage, featuredataset, featureclass, table, relationship-class, rasterdataset, rasterband, rastercatalog, any, caddrawing, container, geo, planargraph, geometricNetwork, topology, text, tin, tool, toolbox* Extent - The xmin, ymin, xmax, ymax of minimum enclosing rectangle. SpatialReference -
Feature class	**FeatureType** - The type of feature (one of the following constants: *simple, simple_junction, simple_edge, complex_junction, complex_edge, annotation, coverage_annotation, dimension*). **HasM** - Boolean value if feature class has M (measured) values. **HasZ** - Boolean value if feature class has Z (elevational) values. **HasSpatialIndex** - Boolean value if spatial index has been built. **RelationshipClassNames** - A list of the names (";" delimited) of associated relationships. **ShapeFieldName** -The name of the shape field. **ShapeType** -The type of the shape (feature): *point, multipoint, polyline, polygon, null, line, circulararc, ellipticarc, bezier3curve, path, ring, enve-lope, any, bag, multiPatch, triangleStrip, triangleFan, ray sphere*. **SpatialReference** - The spatial reference object that stores coordinate system information. **TopologyName** -Name of the topology of this feature class.
Layer	**FeatureClass** - The source location of the feature class associated with the layer. Note this is a temporary file stored in memory, and generated during an ArcMap session. **FIDSet** -a list (";" delimited) of record numbers (integers) **FieldInfo** - **WhereClause** - The definition query used to define the layer (SQL where clause). **NameString** - The name of the layer.

TABLE 10.6. Describe objects and properties associated with each dataset type. Note that these properties are accessed from desc.<property>, where desc = Gp.Describe (<inDataSet>).

Dataset type	Properties
Raster band	**Height** - Number of rows. **IsInteger** - Boolean of integer data (1) or float (0) **MeanCellHeight** - Height of cell in map units. **MeanCellWidth** - Width of cell in map units. **NoDataValue** - The value of that represents NoData. **PixelType** - F32 (floating point 32-bit) **PrimaryField** - **TableType** - Indexed **Width** - Number of columns.
Raster catalog	**Dataset Properties** - see Dataset Properties above. **RasterFieldName** - the name of the raster field. **Table Properties** - see Table below.
Raster dataset	**BandCount** - Number of bands in raster dataset. **CompressionType** - None, etc.... **Format** - GRID, IMG or TIFF. **Permanent** - Boolean true or false. **SensorType** -
Relationship class	**IsVersioned** - Boolean for version type. **Fields** - see Fields above.
Table	**Fields** - See Fields above. **HasOID** - Boolean if OID exists. **Indexes** - List of indexes. **OIDFIeldName** - The name of the OID field.
TableView	**Table** - See Table above. **FIDSet** - **FieldInfo** - See FieldInfo. **WhereClause** - **NameString** -
Workspace	**ConnectionString** - **Domains** - **WorkspaceFactoryProgID** - **WorkspaceType** -

TABLE 10.7. Additional describe objects and properties.

Type	Properties
Field (from enumeration of Fields)	**Name** - The name of the field. **AliasName** - The aliased name of a field **Domain** - **IsEditable** - Boolean describing editable state. **HasIndex** - Boolean of existence of index. **IsNullable** - Boolean of nullable. **IsUnique** - Boolean of unqiue field. **Length** - Length of text field. **Type** - Type of data. **Scale** - Places to the right of the decimal for real values. **Precision** - Places to the left of the decimal for real values.
Geometry[a]	**Type** - Null, point, multipoint, line, circulararc, ellipticarc, bezier3curve, path, polyline, ring, polygon, envelope, any, bag, multiPatch, triangleStrip triangleFan, ray, sphere **Extent** - xMin; yMin; xMax; yMax. **Centroid** - Returns the true centroid if within or on the feature, otherwise a label point is returned **TrueCentroid** - Returns the center of gravity for a feature. **LabelPoint** - The point where the label is located, which is always within or on the feature. **FirstPoint** - first coordinate of the feature. **LastPoint** - the last coordinate off the feature. **Area** - the area of the polygon **Length** - length of the linear feature (or perimeter for polygons). **IsMultipart** - true if multipart feature. **PartCount** - the number of geometry parts for a feature. **HullRectangle** - the coordinates for the convex hull rectangle. **GetPart** (i) - returns an array of points for a part of geometry.
Index	**Name** - name of the index. **IsAscending** - Boolean sorting in ascending order. **IsUnique** - Boolean if unique index. **Fields** - Fields object for this index.

TABLE 10.7. Additional describe objects and properties.

Type	Properties
Point	**X** - the horizontal location. **Y** - the vertical location **Z** - the evlevation. **M** - the measure value. **ID** - a long integer providing unique identification

TABLE 10.7. Additional describe objects and properties.

Type	Properties
SpatialReference	**Type** - *Unknown, projected, geographic* **Name** -The name of the projection. **Abbreviation, Remarks** - **FactoryCode** - The factory code of the spatial reference **HasMPrecision, HasXYPrecision, HasZPrecision** - Boolean if data stores coordinates as integers **FalseOriginAndUnits** - falseX; falseY; Units. **MFalseOriginAndUnits** - falseM; Units **ZFalseOriginAndUnits** - falseZ; Units **Domain, MDomain, ZDomain** - xmin;ymin;xmax;ymax **Usage** - Notes on common usage of projection **CentralMeridian** - Origin of x coordinates in decimal degrees. **CentralMeridianInDegrees** - Origin of x coordinates in degrees, minutes, seconds. **LongitudeOfOrigin** - Origin of y coordinates in decimal degrees **LatitudeOf1st** - Latitude of first point of a projected coordinate system. **LatitudeOf2nd** - Latitude of second point of a projected coordinate system. **FalseEasting, FalseNorthing** - **CentralParallel** - Defines the origin of the y coordinates. **StandardParallel1** - Defines latitude where scale is 1:1 for conic projections. **StandardParallel2** - Defines latitude where scale is 1:1 for conic projections. **LongitudeOf1st** - Longitude of the first point of a projected coordinate system. **LongitudeOf2nd** - Longitude of second point of a projected coordinate system. **ScaleFactor** - A value applied to center point of map projection. **Azimuth** -Defines the center line of a projection. **Classification** - The classification type of a projection. **SemiMajorAxis** - The longer or major radius of an ellipsoid. **SemiMinorAxis** -The shorter or minor radius of an ellipsoid. **Flattening** - The percentage difference between major and minor axes. **Longitude** - The left longitude bounding a 360 degree range. **RadiansperUnit** -The radians per angular unit.

a. Also see the help for Geoprocessing --> Reading geometries.

A *cursor* is an object that is used to access rows in tables, or to insert new rows into tables. There are three types of cursor objects, each tailored to a particular task. Each of these cursors generate an enumeration of row objects that are contained in an array (Table 10.8). Cursors support navigation but only in a forward direction, you cannot back up.

The *search cursor* is a basic cursor object: it simply returns the rows that have meet a particular condition, specified by a "where clause" or SQL expression (similiar to the Select by Attributes dialog). This allows you to find, for example, all the lakes in a feature class that are larger than a specific size (i.e. described in an "area" field). The other two cursors also use the same search string, but allow you additional functions to change a table. The *insert cursor* is used to insert new rows into a table (or feature class). This is typically used to add new features and associated attributes into a table. The *update cursor* allows you to update (or change) an attribute's value.

```
# Import modules
import arcgisscripting, sys, os
gp = arcgisscripting.create(9.3)
gp.Workspace = "c:/temp/fraser_forest"
# Get fields
fields  =  gp.ListFields  ( "c:/temp/fraser_forest/
waterbodies.shp")
fields.Reset()
field = fields.Next()
# Get rows
rows  =  gp.SearchCursor  ("c:/temp/fraser_forest/
waterbodies.shp")
#list them out to user
row = rows.Next()
while row:
    print str( row.GetValue ( field.Name ) )
    row = rows.Next()
```

TABLE 10.8. **Cursor types and methods.**

Cursor type	Properties
SearchCursor	Retreives the next object in the array. SearchCursor(<dataset>, {where-Clause}). E.g., rows = Gp.**SearchCursor**("c:\temp\roads.shp"). **Reset** - rows.Reset() **Next** - row = rows.Next() - gets the next row
InsertCursor	Can be used to insert an object in the array. InsertCursor(<dataset>, {whereClause}). E.g., rows = Gp.**InsertCursor**("c:\temp\roads.shp") **Reset** - rows.Reset() **NewRow** - newRow = rows.NewRow() **InsertRow**() - rows.InsertRow(newRow)
UpdateCursor	Can be used to insert an object in the array. InsertCursor(<dataset>, {whereClause}). E.g., rows = Gp.UpdateCursor("c:\temp\roads.shp"). **Reset**() - rows.Reset() **Next**() - row = rows.Next() **UpdateRow**() - rows.UpdateRow(row) **DeleteRow**() - rows.DeleteRow(row)

10.4.5 Debugging tips

The basic *debugging* recipe is one part logic and one part intuition. The strategy is to systematically eliminate possible problems, by developing a series of ways to test if a certain assumption is true or not. It also relies on intuition (and experience), because there are typically a large number of possible things that could go wrong, but some are more likely than others. If you find yourself losing your cool in the heat of the battle with a bug, stop guessing, step away from your computer, and construct a quick list of things to check. Then, order your checklist (ascending) by the things that are most likely to happen.

Easier said than done, so here is a general checklist of things that you might want to use:

1. Determine if the error is due to a pure Python statement or if it occurs when calling a GpDispatch object.

2. If it is a Python error, check consistency of variable names (remember, Python is case-sensitive)

3. If it is a GpDispatch error:

3a. Run the tool manually in the Command Line window with the parameters you are trying to use. The Command Line dialog provides additional error messages that might give you a better clue as to what is causing the problem.

3b. If you believe the dispatch object is acting improperly, at least resort you could quit ArcCatalog and ArcMap applications and run your script from Python.

3c. Create a model in ModelBuilder with the desired tool, then export the tool to Python and examine the code.

10.5 Ten ways to improve your ArcGIS experience

I end this book with 10 suggestions that will (hopefully!) increase your productivity and allow you to have more fun using ArcGIS.

1. Manage your "folder connections" (or short-cuts) that specify where your spatial data are located. Create a folder connection for each major project in which you are involved, and delete ones that point to old or suspended projects. You can do this from either ArcCatalog or in the Add Data dialog in ArcMap.

2. A corollary to the first tip is to load your most-frequently-used datasets onto local computer drives for faster performance.

3. Save your ArcMap document frequently. At important steps along the way (perhaps after each major modification) save a copy of your document that is time-stamped (e.g., "MyMDX_20050704"). This provides you a sequence of archives of your past work. Use: File --> Save a copy...

4. Turn off the *Field Calculator* warning message (that warns you every single time of changing values in a table outside of an edit session). To do this: Tools --> Options... Tables tab, check off the "Show warning when calculating field values outside edit session".

5. Change the *warning threshold* that triggers the warning message when using the Select All/Switch Selection buttons. To do this: Selection --> Options, set the value in the Warning Threshold portion (at bottom) to be a really big number (e.g., 999,999).

6. Specify the file formats you wish to see in the Add Data dialog. For raster data, select the formats that you commonly use (probably GRID and IMG), and turn off the ones seldom used (probably GIF, TIFF, BMP, etc.). To do this: Tools --> Options, Raster tab, File formats button...

7. Because there is no "undo" when changing the symbology of a legend, get in the habit of first saving a layer file before you modify an existing one. Another option is to copy the layer (right-click, copy) and then paste a new layer into the data frame.

8. Create a most-frequently-used toolbox that contains a copy of each tool that you use frequently. While the tool approach is powerful, it can be annoying to have to search through hundreds of tools to find your old trusty Phillips-head screwdriver.

9. Build a model to both run and document your spatial analysis.

10. When processing with large datasets, first create a very small (e.g., 5-10% of full extent) dataset to test out your processing/model. Make sure it works as a "proof-of-concept" on the small dataset, then go for the whole enchilada. (Yes, that's a good way to end just about anything, even a textbook).

Symbols

Numerics

A

Mech, L. 272
merge 209, 374
merge features 206
merge slivers 209
Merge tool 209
meta-data 28, 271
metadata view 26
Miller, R.I. 90
minimum bounding rectangles 59
minimum mapping unit 85, 298
minor axis 342
Mitchell, A. 113
model 30
ModelBuilder 30, 382, 391
modeling process 381
models 381
Modify Feature 205
modules 407
Molacek, R. 388
Monmonier, M. 344
Morehouse, S. 52
Morton order 305
mosaic 375
Muehrcke, P. 93, 95, 113, 352
Multi to Single Part tool 206
multi-part 40
multi-variate 143

N

NAD27 88
NAD83 88
National Land Cover Dataset 295
natural breaks 124
Natural Neighbor 289
Near 349
nearest neighbor 351, 363
neatline 152
neighborhood 256
Neighborhood functions 307
neighborhood functions 256
neighborhood shapes 257

neighborhood statistics 259
neighborhood, defined 256
Nelson, C. 274
netCDF 241
Network Analyst 33
network data model 54
network edges 48
network junctions 48
New Text tool 148
NoData 63, 238
nodes 213
nominal data 68
normalized 388
normalizing 119
north arrow 152
northing 95
number format 72
number formatting 72

O

O'Neill, R. 345
O'Sullivan, D. 288
object class 47
object model 36
object-oriented data structure 38
oblate spheroid 87
oblique perspective 146
Ochis, H. 278
ODYSSEY 12
Oimoen, S. 274
Olson, J. 134
on-the-fly 103
on-the-fly, raster 103
orientation 139, 342
Ormsby, T. 42
orthographic 92
orthographic perspective 146
overlap 208
overlay 371
overlay graph 165
overshoot 195

toolset 30
topological association 197
topological data structure 38, 49
topology 38, 44, 49
Topology Edit tool 205, 218
Topology toolbar 218
touch the boundary of 184
Tracking Analyst 33
transformations 358
transparency 141, 277
Trend tool 290
Triangulated Irregular Networks 56
Turner, M. 345
Tyler, D. 274

U
undershoot 195
union 373
union features 206
Unique Values 246
unique values 117
universe polygon 54
Unwin, D. 288
update 429
update cursor 429
updating 374
usage 301
use stage 381
user component 104
USGS National Hydrography Dataset 54
UTM 94

V
validation 212
value 138
Value Attribute Table 64, 243
van Dam, A. 297
van Wagtendonk, J. 268
vat.adf 242
vertical datums 88
vertices 39, 213

viewshed 281
visible layers 175
visualization framework 113
Voisard, A. 59
Voronoi polygons 265

W
w001001.adf 242
w001001x.adf 242
WAAS 106
Wade, T. 1
Wagner, D. 308
warning message 431
warning threshold 431
watch 390
Watershed tool 293
Watson, D. 285
WCS Server 22
Weibel, R. 362
weighted arithmetic model 388
weighted centroid 360
weighted linear combination 388
weighted mean 333
weird polygons 201
Wentz, E. 8
WGS84 88
while 413
White, D. 197
Wide Area Augmentation System 106
Wikle, T. 366
Wilbert, M. 385
Windows Explorer 14
wire-frame 146
within a distance of 183
Wizards 30
WMS Server 22
Wong, D. 350
Wood, W. 340
Worboys, M. 37, 45, 340
world file 156, 245
Wright, J. 136

X

Z